THERMOPHYSICAL PROPERTIES
OF MATTER AND SUBSTANCES

TT 72-52001

Gosudarstvennaya Sluzhba Standartnykh i Spravochnykh Dannykh
Seriya : Sborniki "Fizicheskie konstanty i svoistva veshchestv"

State Standards and Reference Data Service
Series : Collection "Physical Constants and Properties of Matter"

thermophysical properties of matter and substances

Volume 2

(Teplofizicheskie svoistva veshchestv i materialov)
Vypusk 2

Editor
V. A. Rabinovich

Komitet standartov, mer i izmeritel'nykh priborov Publishers
Moscow 1970

Translated from Russian

Published for the National Bureau of Standards,
United States Department of Commerce, and the
National Science Foundation, Washington, D. C.
by Amerind Publishing Co. Pvt. Ltd., New Delhi

1974

© 1974 Amerind Publishing Co. Pvt. Ltd., New Delhi

Translated and Published for the National Bureau of Standards,
United States Department of Commerce, pursuant to an agreement
with the National Science Foundation, Washington, D. C.
by Amerind Publishing Co. Pvt. Ltd., 66 Janpath, New Delhi

Translators : Dr. S. P. Pednekar
             Dr. A. S. Deshpande
General Editor : Dr. V. S. Kothekar

Available from the U. S. Department of Commerce
National Technical Information Service
Springfield, Virginia 22151

Printed at Prem Printing Press, Lucknow 226001, India

UDC 541.27

FOREWORD

In recent years, science and technology have experienced a greatly increased need for reference data on the thermophysical properties of substances used in their various states, with requirement for increased data accuracy.

Previous investigations on variation of the thermophysical properties with state, reported in numerous scientific journals, have supplied insufficient data for certain engineering firms requesting information on the thermophysical properties of particular substances. This deficit has perhaps resulted from unsystematic investigation of the thermophysical properties of substances by individual researchers whose efforts were not centrally coordinated.

In such investigations, the chief objectives have generally been to obtain reference data limited to a narrow range of parameters, with no general, overall investigation of the thermophysical properties of the particular substance.

Steam is the only substance whose thermodynamic properties have been studied according to an international program since 1920. The objectives of such programs have been to coordinate the statistical data regarding the thermodynamic properties of water and steam published in different countries. This purpose has been accomplished by tabulation of "skeleton tables", periodically reviewed and ratified by international conferences. These skeleton tables are based on analysis and averaging of experimental and calculated data obtained by investigators of various countries, and represent a framework by which more detailed tables can be obtained by interpolation, usually by equations, for direct application in science and technology. All tables with criteria similar to those of the skeleton tables have "international" status.

The success of this international program has enhanced clarification, among the scientific community, of the general, overall study of the thermophysical properties of liquids and gases. This task has been complicated by the excessive number of pure substances and their mixtures requiring study, and by the occasional inaccuracy of currently existing methods for unified description of these properties. Thus, internationally coordinated investigations would appear to have greater use than individual study of a single substance.

Initiated by the International Union for Theoretical and Applied Chemistry (IUTAC), an international commission was formed in 1964 for compilation of the thermophysical properties of substances of technological importance. The commission decided to organize working groups for the compilation of skeleton tables for a single substance or group of similar substances. Completion of the project was planned within ten years.

In accordance with the structure of the international commission, the Soviet Union organized a national commission for compilation of tables of the thermophysical properties of gases of technological importance. This commission consists of four primary groups whose assigned task is the systematic study of thermophysical properties of the following substances : (1) air and its main components (nitrogen and oxygen) ; (2) hydrogen and monatomic gases (helium, neon, argon, krypton and xenon); (3) hydrocarbons (primarily methane, ethane and ethylene); and (4) carbon dioxide.

Selection of the method of tabulation has been of primary importance in the execution of this program ; thus, a fifth "primary" working group for establishing rational methods for calculation and tabulation of the thermophysical properties was organized. One assigned task of this fifth group was the standardization of publication of experimental data. The group recommended that publications report consistent data and a standard method for determining accuracy, applicable to obtaining both statistical and experimental data on the thermophysical properties of substances. Future programs are planned for investigation of the thermophysical properties of substances such as the alkali metals, freons, halogens and their hydrides, organic heat conductors, and certain binary and multicomponent mixtures.

The study of the thermophysical properties of technologically important gases and liquids is one aspect of the investigations currently undertaken in the Soviet Union according to the Thermophysical Properties of Substances and Materials program of the State Service of Standard and Reference Data (GSSSD ; Gosudarstvennaya Sluzhba Standartnykh i Spravochnykh Dannykh).

A large majority of the papers included in the present collection are the result of investigations conducted in basic organizations of the GSSSD in conformation with the program of the Soviet commission. These studies, however, are only an intermediate link in the investigation program ; the ultimate objective is the international compilation of detailed tables of the thermophysical properties of technologically important substances.

Papers of a qualitative nature with highly approximate data were not selected for inclusion in this collection. However, the present collection contains some experimental and methodological studies, included to instigate further research in this field.

Subsequent publications will attempt greater clarification of both the work of the GSSSD in the field of thermophysics and the activities of the Soviet commission on tabulation of the thermophysical properties of technologically important gases.

V. Sychev

President of the Soviet Commission on
Development of Tables of Thermophysical
Properties of Technologically Important Gases

CONTENTS

Foreword .. ..

I. Air and Its Principal Components

A Method for the Determination of the Thermal Properties of Inadequately Investigated Liquids—*A. A. Vasserman, V. I. Nedostup* and *V. F. Pogorelov* 3

Correlation of Molal Volumes of Nitrogen with Its Thermodynamic Properties—*E. V. Polyakov* and *D. S. Tsiklis* 11

Determination of the Compressibility of a Gas by the Displacement Method—*D. S. Tsiklis* and *E. V. Polyakov* 25

II. Hydrogen and Monatomic Gases

A Single Equation of State for Parahydrogen—*Ya. Z. Kazavchinskii* and *L. S. Serdyuk* 39

Thermodynamic Properties of Parahydrogen up to 1500°K and 5000 bars—*L. S. Serdyuk* 52

Viscosity of Normal Hydrogen Under Rarefaction—*Yu. V. Mamonov* and *S. A. Ulybin* 65

Correction of Experimental Viscosities of Parahydrogen—*V. E. Lyusternik* and *Yu. V. Mamonov* 78

An Equation of State for Helium at Temperature of 20-1500°K and Pressure up to 1000 bars—*V. I. Kudashev* and *V. N. Taran* .. 92

An Equation of State for Liquid and Gaseous Helium—*V. N. Taran* .. 97

Thermodynamic Properties of Neon, Argon, Krypton and Xenon at Saturation Point—*V. A. Rabinovich* and *L. S. Veksler* .. 104

Experimental p-v-T Data for Neon in the Temperature Range of 65-273°K and Pressures upto 250 bars—*E. V. Osnovskii* and *A. I. Moroz* 120

Molal Volumes and Thermodynamic Properties of Argon at Pressures upto 10,000 atm and Temperatures upto 400°C—*E. V. Polyakov* and *D. S. Tsiklis* 130

An Experimental Apparatus for the Determination of Isochoric Specific Heats of Liquids and Gases Over a Wide Range of Parameters—*V. A. Rabinovich* and *O. M. Oleinik-Dzyadik* .. 135

Cryostat for Experimental Determination of Gas Compressibilities at Low Temperatures—*A. I. Moroz, E. V. Onosovskii* and *S. B. Mil'man* 142

Review and Compilation of Data on the Viscosity of Rarefied Gases of the Helium Group—*V. A. Rabinovich* and *V. A. Kryuchkov* .. 150

III. Hydrocarbons and Their Derivatives

Reference Specific Volumes for Methane—*V. A. Zagoruchenko* and *A. M. Zhuravlev* 169

Investigation of the Shape of the Two-Phase Curve for Ethane Near the Critical Point by the Method of Quasistatic Thermograms—*Yu. R. Chashkin, V. A. Smirnov* and *A. V. Voronel'* 178

Measurement of Density of Normal Hexane and Distilled Water at Pressures up to 10,000 kg/cm²—*V. A. Borzunov, V. N. Razumikhin* and *V. A. Stekol'nikov* 187

Enthalpy of Formation of Alkyl Benzenes—*E. A. Smolenskii* and *L. V. Kocharova* 196

Critical and Boiling Temperatures of Benzene and its Fluoroderivatives —*P. A. Kotlyarevskii* and *V. B. Derman* 201

Thermodynamic Functions of Fluorinated Benzene Compounds in Ideal-Gas State—*V. P. Onishchenko* and *V. A. Abovskii* .. 207

Experimental Investigation of Compressibility of Freon-12—*I. I. Perel'shtein* 224

Viscosity of Brominated Freons—*Z. I. Geller, R. K. Nikul'shin* and *N. I. Pyatnitskaya* 235

Experimental Determination of the Coefficient of Thermal Conductivity of Vapors of N-Alkanes, Spirits and Acids—*A. A. Tarzimanov* and *V. E. Mashirov* 240

Experimental Investigation of Thermal Conductivity of Organic Compounds—*G. Kh. Mukhamedzyanov* 254

IV. Carbon Dioxide

Experimental Investigation of the Density of Carbon Dioxide—*V. A. Kirillin, S. A. Ulybin* and *E. P. Zherdev* 273

Thermodynamic Properties of Liquid Carbon Dioxide—*E. A. Golovskii* and *V. A. Tsimarnyi* 283

Thermal Conductivity of Carbon Dioxide in the Near-Critical Region—*P. M. Kessel'man* and *V. R. Kamenetskii* 292

Thermodynamic Properties of Dissociated Carbon Dioxide—*P. M. Kessel'man* and *P. A. Kotlyarevskii* 301

V. Metals and Their Components

Coefficient of Thermal Expansion of Mercury in the Temperature Range 0-350°C—*L. R. Fokin* and *A. T. Yakovlev* 313

Measurement of Thermal Conductivity and Lawrence Number of Conducting Materials in the Solid and Liquid States Over a

Wide Temperature Range—*R. P. Yurchak* and *B. P. Smirnov* .. 321
Orthobaric Densities and Critical Parameters of Series of High-Order
Bromides and Iodides of Groups III and IV Elements of the
Periodic System—*L. A. Nisel'son, T. D. Sokolova* and *R. K. Nikolayev* 332

VI. Mixtures, Solutions and Materials

Coefficient of Diffusion of Vapors in Gases Under Normal Pressure—
A. N. Berezhnoi 347
Measurement of the Molal Volumes of Gaseous Mixtures at High
Pressures—*D. S. Tsiklis, L. R. Linshits* and *I. B. Rodkina* .. 364
Density of Aqueous Solutions of Certain Strong Electrolytes Under
Pressures up to 1200 bar—*A. L. Seifer, V. N. Razumikhin, N. A.
Nevolina* and *V. A. Borzunov* 374
Thermal Conductivity of Some Oriented Plastics Under Compression
and at Temperatures of 180-200°K—*R. I. Zhukova, M. G. Kaganer*
and *N. B. Markelova* 382

I. AIR AND ITS PRINCIPAL COMPONENTS

UDC 541.27

A METHOD FOR THE DETERMINATION OF THE THERMAL PROPERTIES OF INADEQUATELY INVESTIGATED LIQUIDS

A. A. Vasserman, V. I. Nedostup and *V. F. Pogorelov*

Data regarding the pressure, volume, and temperature of liquids is frequently required for calculation of technological processes. Since experimental investigation of the thermal properties of substances in the liquid state is extremely difficult, the density of inadequately investigated liquids should be accurately determined.

The proposed method is based on the use of the law of corresponding states and on data for a well-investigated reference substance. On the basis of these data it is possible to extrapolate, with acceptable accuracy, supercritical isotherms in the high-density region for the substance under study. Experimental values are available for most of the technologically important gases, enabling graphic representation of the isotherms. Further, using the extrapolated data, proper representation of isochore configurations can be plotted and extended to the region of hypocritical temperatures in reference to the properties at saturation level of the substance under study and to the data of the reference substance. The proposed procedure can be illustrated by the example of nitrogen and argon. For nitrogen, the reference substance, experimental data are available on the gaseous and liquid regions upto approximately three critical densities, as well as on the equations of state in relation to these data [1, 2]. Experimental p-v-T data for gaseous argon cover the interval of densities upto 2.1 critical density and are expressed by the equation of state [1]. Liquid argon has been investigated only upto the pressure of 300 bar; however, the experimental data have been extrapolated upto pressures of 500 bar [3]. Assay of the proposed procedure by employing examples of nitrogen and argon will facilitate estimation of the reliability of these data [3].

The effective application of thermodynamic similarity at densities corresponding to those of the liquid was enabled by the selection of reference similarity points on the Boyle curve [4]. The equations of state for nitrogen and argon were, therefore, converted into the coordinates of the compressibility factor z : $\omega = \rho/\rho_0$, $\tau = T/T_0$, using the parameters of the reference similarity points on the Boyle curve at $z_0 = 0.3$. The temperature and density at the similarity points of reference, as determined from experimental data, are : for nitrogen, $T_0 = 131.62°K$, $\rho_0 = 0.4214$ g/cm³ ; for argon, $T_0 = 157.55°K$, $\rho_0 = 0.7149$ g/cm³.

Using the converted equations of state, reduced pressures $\pi = p/p_0$ were calculated for nitrogen and argon on ten isotherms in the interval of reduced parameters $\tau = 1.0$-2.5 and $\omega = 0.1$-1.6. Experimental data are available for the two gases in these intervals. Deviations from the law of corresponding states can be denoted by values of the ratio π_{N_2}/π_{Ar}. From Fig. 1, which displays these values as a function of reduced pressure of nitrogen, it is evident that these differ from unity by 2-8%. At equal π_{N_2}, ratios π_{N_2}/π_{Ar} practically coincide on six isotherms in the interval of $\tau = 1.0$-1.5 and systematically only at higher temperatures.

For plotting the isochore of a liquid, it is sufficient to have data at high densities on a few near-critical isotherms. The effect of temperature on the π_{N_2}/π_{Ar} ratio was, therefore, neglected, and a generalized curve was plotted using data in the interval of $\tau = 1.0$-1.5.

The curve was graphically extrapolated upto $\pi_{N_2} = 30$ in respect to the shape of π_{N_2}/π_{Ar} curves at higher temperatures for which data are available over the entire pressure range. The generalized curve is given by the expression :

$$\frac{\pi_{N_2}}{\pi_{Ar}} = 1 + 1.091 \cdot 10^{-2} \, \pi_{N_2} - 6.229 \cdot 10^{-4} \, \pi_{N_2}^2 +$$

$$\tag{1}$$

$$1.709 \cdot 10^{-5} \, \pi_{N_2}^3 - 1.804 \cdot 10^{-7} \, \pi_{N_2}^4.$$

The values of π for nitrogen were then calculated for six isotherms in the interval of $\tau = 1.0$-1.5 and $\omega = 1.7$-2.0, and values of reduced pressure of gaseous argon for the given density interval were determined from equation (1).

After obtaining the data on compressibility of the gas upto $\omega = 2.0$ by extrapolation of isotherms, the isochores of liquid can be plotted. Thus, the thermal properties of liquid argon were determined for the selected density values on the saturation curve plotted from standardized experimental data [1]. For density $\omega = 2.0$, the solidification curve plotted from reference points [3] was used. The values of the compressibility factor for liquid nitrogen were determined on isochores ω=1.7-2.0. Following this, isochores of nitrogen and argon were plotted together in such a way that the configuration of the isochores were similar, and the change of the ratio for the two elements was consistent in corresponding states depending on the density and temperature (Fig. 2).

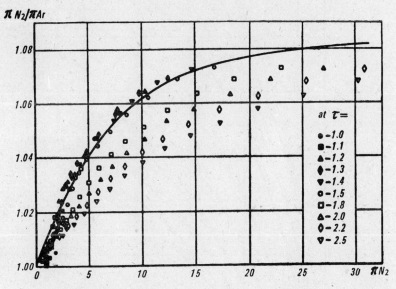

Fig. 1. Ratio between reduced pressures of nitrogen and argon in corresponding states in relation to reduced pressure of nitrogen.

Pressures of liquid argon at 90-150°K were calculated on the basis of the obtained data, and by graphical interpolation on isotherms, density values corresponding to rounded-off pressures were determined and compared with the reference data [3]. Table 1 shows more than half of the calculated values of the density to agree with the reference values within ±0.1%, with a maximum deviation of 0.33%. It must be noted that in the pressure interval of 350-500 bar, for which data were obtained by extrapolation of the isotherms for the liquid [3], the deviations are of the same magnitude as those for the pressure interval investigated experimentally. This fact can be considered as proof of the reliability of the extrapolated values.

The entirely satisfactory agreement between calculated densities of liquid argon [3] have confirmed the reliability of the method and enabled its application to obtaining reference *p-v-T* data for air, which has received little experimental investigation.

The equation of state for air [1] was used to calculate reduced pressures on eight isotherms in the interval of reduced temperatures of τ=1.0905-2.1810 (*T*=150-300°K) and densities of ω=0.1384-1.5221. As in the

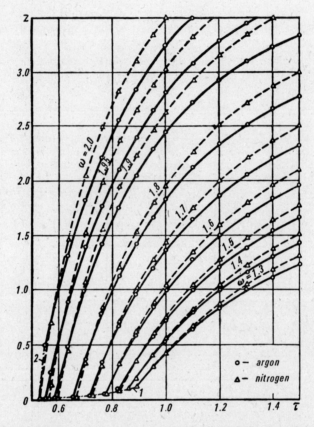

Fig. 2. Isochores of nitrogen and argon in dimensionless coordinates.

earlier case, the reference point of similarity was the point on the Boyle curve corresponding to $z_0 = 0.3$ with the coordinates $T_0 = 137.55°$K and $\rho_0 = 0.4522$ g/cm³. For these values of τ and ω, values of π_{N_2} were determined and ratios of π_{N_2}/π_{air} were computed in the corresponding states.

Fig. 3 shows the indicated ratios as a function of the reduced pressure of nitrogen. It is seen that π_{N_2}/π_B values differ less from unity than the analogous values for nitrogen and argon (Fig. 1), and that in the covered region of change of parameters the values do not exceed 1.021. In the interval of $\tau = 1.0905$-1.4540 ($T = 150$-$200°$K), the ratios are independent of the temperature, but the dependence is observed when the temperature is increased. A common curve was drawn for the given temperature interval and was extrapolated to a pressure of $\pi_{N_2} = 30$. The extrapolation was undertaken in respect to the π_{N_2}/π_{air} relationship on isotherms at $T = 250$ and $300°$K, the data for which covers

Table 1. Comparison of calculated values of the density of liquid argon (second line) with reference data [3] (first line), g/cm^3

p, bar	ρ at T, °K						
	90	100	110	120	130	140	150
20	1.382	1.317	1.247	1.167	—	—	—
	1.380	1.316	1.247	1.166			
40	1.389	1.325	1.258	1.182	1.092	0.967	—
	1.387	1.324	1.257	1.180	1.091	0.968	—
60	1.395	1.333	1.267	1.196	1.113	1.009	—
	1.394	1.332	1.267	1.193	1.112	1.010	—
80	1.400	1.340	1.277	1.208	1.131	1.039	—
	1.400	1.339	1.276	1.206	1.130	1.040	—
100	1.406	1.348	1.285	1.219	1.147	1.064	0.963
	1.406	1.346	1.285	1.217	1.145	1.065	0.963
120	1.411	1.354	1.294	1.230	1.161	1.084	0.995
	1.411	1.353	1.293	1.228	1.160	1.085	0.996
140	1.416	1.361	1.302	1.241	1.174	1.102	1.021
	1.417	1.360	1.301	1.238	1.172	1.102	1.023
170	1.425	1.370	1.315	1.255	1.192	1.125	1.053
	1.425	1.369	1.313	1.252	1.190	1.124	1.054
200	1.432	1.379	1.326	1.269	1.209	1.146	1.079
	1.433	1.378	1.324	1.265	1.206	1.144	1.080
250	—	1.393	1.343	1.289	1.233	1.175	1.116
		1.392	1.340	1.285	1.230	1.173	1.115
300	—	1.406	1.358	1.307	1.255	1.202	1.146
		1.406	1.356	1.304	1.252	1.198	1.144
350	—	1.419	1.372	1.324	1.274	1.223	1.172
		1.419	1.370	1.320	1.271	1.220	1.170
400	—	1.430	1.384	1.338	1.291	1.243	1.195
		1.432	1.384	1.335	1.289	1.241	1.193
450	—	—	1.397	1.352	1.306	1.261	1.215
			1.396	1.350	1.305	1.259	1.213
500	—	—	1.408	1.365	1.321	1.277	1.234
			1.408	1.364	1.320	1.276	1.232
$\delta\rho_{cr}$, %	0.08	0.08	0.11	0.22	0.17	0.16	0.14
$\delta\rho_{max}$, %	0.14	0.15	0.22	0.32	0.25	0.33	—0.20

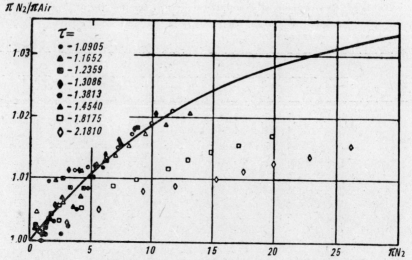

Fig. 3.   Ratios of reduced pressures of nitrogen and air in corresponding states
in relation to reduced pressure of nitrogen.

a large part of the given pressure interval.   The curve is described by the
relationship :

$$\frac{\pi_{N_2}}{\pi_B} = 1 + 2.45 \cdot 10^{-3}\,\pi_{N_2} - 6.75 \cdot 10^{-5}\,\pi_{N_2}{}^2 + 7.5 \cdot 10^{-7}\,\pi_{N_2}{}^3. \qquad (2)$$

Following this, reduced pressures of nitrogen on six isotherms in the
interval $\tau = 1.0905$-1.4540 and $\omega = 1.5913$-1.9372 were calculated and,
using equation (2), values of reduced pressure of gaseous air at densities
corresponding to the densities of the liquid were determined.

The thermal properties of saturation required for plotting isochores
of liquid air were taken from reference [1] and values of density ρ' were
slightly corrected by taking a new reference point on Boyle's curve.   The
configuration of these isochores was determined by applying p-v-T data
for liquid nitrogen.   During plotting of the isochores for air and nitrogen
it was seen that the configuration of like isochores was identical, and that
values of z ratios for both the substances in corresponding states changed
consistently on isotherms and isochores.   The obtained values of the
compressibility factor for air are given in Table 2.

Since deviations from the law of corresponding states were taken
into consideration in the analysis of reference p-v-T data for air, it can be
assumed that errors in the obtained data do not exceed 0.2-0.5% in the
case of densities.   This is confirmed by a comparison of the reference
densities with the few experimental values of density reported by Michels
et al. [5] (Table 3).

Table 2. Reference values of the compressibility factor for air

ρ/ρ_{cr}*	z at T, °K						
	75	80	85	90	95	100	105
2.40	—	—	—	—	—	—	0.142
2.50	—	—	—	—	—	0.179	0.453
2.60	—	—	—	—	0.268	0.573	0.835
2.70	—	—	—	0.403	0.748	1.040	1.288
2.80	—	0.126	0.604	1.002	1.326	1.610	1.860
2.85	—	0.512	0.970	1.344	1.663	1.950	2.177
2.90	0.408	0.938	1.368	1.725	2.038	2.310	2.540
2.95	0.916	1.424	1.804	2.149	2.447	2.710	—

ρ/ρ_{cr}*	z at T, °K						
	110	115	120	125	130	135	140
1.4	—	—	—	—	—	0.2655	0.3315
1.5	—	—	—	—	—	0.2625	0.3339
1.6	—	—	—	—	0.190	0.2694	0.3467
1.7	—	—	—	—	0.201	0.2889	0.3728
1.8	—	—	—	—	0.229	0.3248	0.4156
1.9	—	—	—	0.168	0.278	0.3816	0.4794
2.0	—	—	0.105	0.233	0.354	0.4652	0.5695
2.1	—	—	0.194	0.333	0.462	0.5829	0.6924
2.2	—	0.160	0.322	0.470	0.609	0.7360	0.8543
2.3	0.145	0.339	0.508	0.665	0.807	0.935	1.054
2.4	0.376	0.580	0.756	0.911	1.052	1.184	1.303
2.5	0.692	0.889	1.062	1.220	1.359	1.489	1.606
2.6	1.057	1.258	1.427	1.582	1.725	1.852	1.966
2.7	1.502	1.690	1.861	2.012	2.153	2.275	2.391
2.8	2.072	2.253	2.408	2.546	2.671	2.787	2.897

*ρ_{cr}=critical density.

Table 3. Comparison of reference densities of liquid air with experimental values [5]

T, °K	P bar	ρ, g/cm³		$\delta\rho$, %
		exp	ref	
132.15	37.55	0.3962	0.3980	0.45
—	43.90	0.5088	0.5079	—0.18
130.15	37.10	0.5096	0.5106	0.20
128.15	49.21	0.5886	0.5889	0.05
—	104.6	0.6609	0.6611	0.03
—	206.3	0.7235	0.7223	—0.17
118.15	39.30	0.6684	0.6670	—0.21
—	125.9	0.7309	0.7285	—0.33

Hence, p-v-T data obtained by this procedure are quite reliable and constitute reference points for obtaining the equations of state for inadequately investigated liquids.

References

1. VASSERMAN, A. A., YA. Z. KAZAVCHINSKII and V. A. RABINOVICH. *Teplofizicheskie svoistva vozdukha i ego komponentov (Thermo-physical properties of air and its components).* Nauka, Moscow, 1966.
2. VASSERMAN, A. A. and V. A. RABINOVICH. *IFZh,* **12**, 342, 1967.
3. VASSERMAN, A. A. and V. A. RABINOVICH. *IFZh,* **13**, 190, 1967.
4. KAZAVCHINSKII, YA. Z. DAN SSSR, **161** (5), 1127, 1965.
5. MICHELS, A., T. WASSENAAR, J. M. LEVELT and W. DE GRAAFF. *Appl. Scient. Res.,* **A4**, 381, 1954.

UDC 541.27

CORRELATION OF MOLAL VOLUMES OF NITROGEN WITH ITS THERMODYNAMIC PROPERTIES

E. V. Polyakov and *D. S. Tsiklis*

Measurement of the compressibility of nitrogen upto 10,000 atm and 400°C has been described [1]. For calculating the thermodynamic properties of nitrogen from the molal data it is necessary to ascertain the value of $(\delta v/\delta T)_p$, $(\delta v/\delta p)_T$, and $(\delta^2 v/\delta p^2)_T$. As pressure increases, the curvature of isotherms and isobars (with coordinates v-p and v-T) decreases, and at high pressures it is difficult to determine accurate values of the gas with respect to temperature and pressure.

Deming and Shupe [2-4] suggested correction of Δ and α rather than differentiation of volume functions, on the basis that the lines of $\Delta = f(T)$ and $\alpha = f(T)$ have considerable curvature. This method is convenient at low pressures when the molal volume of the gas and the errors in computation of the derivatives become very small. At higher pressures, Δ and α become comparable in value with the molal volume of the gas and the method recommended by Deming and Shupe no longer applies. In such case, it is more useful to determine the thermodynamic properties of the gas from the equations of state.

Different types of equations were applied for clarification of the data on the compressibility of nitrogen. Rozen [5] has given an approximate equation of state with an accuracy of $\pm 2.2\%$ to describe the compressibility of nitrogen at 0-200°C and 1000-6000 atm.

In Amag units, the equation has the following form :

$$\delta = \frac{pv}{p_0 v_0} = \alpha_0 + \beta_0 \, p + \overline{\mu_p} \frac{T}{273} \, , \tag{1}$$

$$\text{where } \alpha_0 = \frac{A}{p_0 \, v_0} = 0.182 \, ;$$

$$\beta_0 = \frac{B}{p_0 \, v_0} = 1.110 \cdot 10^{-3} \, ;$$

$$\overline{\mu}_p = \frac{C}{R} = 1.229 \, ;$$

where A, B, and C are constants and R is the gas constant.

Molal volumes of nitrogen were calculated from equation (1) for temperatures of 21.5-400°C and pressures of 1,000-10,000 atm. The deviation of the molal volumes calculated from equation (1) from their experimentally determined values, $\Delta v = [(v_{cal} - v_{exp})/v_{exp}] \cdot 100\%$ is 8% at 10,000 atm (Fig. 1).

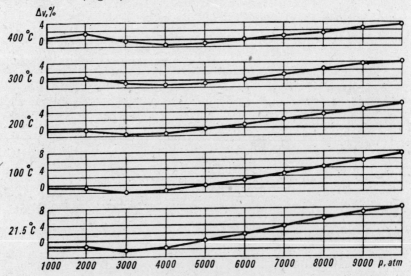

Fig. 1.   Deviation of molal volumes of nitrogen calculated from Rozen's equation from the experimentally determined values.

Rott [6] has reported the following equation for a highly compressed gas :

$$\ln \frac{p - \dfrac{RT}{v}}{A} = C \, \frac{r_m - r}{T} \, , \tag{2}$$

where p = gas pressure, atm; v = volume, cm³/mole; T = temperature; °K; R = the gas constant; $r = \sqrt[3]{v}$; and A, C, and r_m are constants.

Equation (2) has been deduced theoretically. However the mathematical difficulties in this are so great that the author preferred to find out the values of constants A, C and r_m empirically. For nitrogen $A=13,238$, $C=1290.9$ and $r_m=2.84$.

Applying this equation, Rott obtained the equations of state for ammonia (average deviation $\pm0.82\%$) and nitrogen ($\pm0.79\%$) at 3,000-10,000 atm and 50-100°C.

We extrapolated equation (2) to a temperature of 400°C and pressure of 10,000 atm. Calculations showed the deviation of molal volumes of nitrogen calculated from equation (2) from the experimentally determined values to be -2.4% at 10,000 atm (Fig. 2). The deviation increases with increasing temperature and decreasing pressure. Equation (2) gives unsatisfactory agreement with experimental data at 200-400°C and 3,000-7,000 atm.

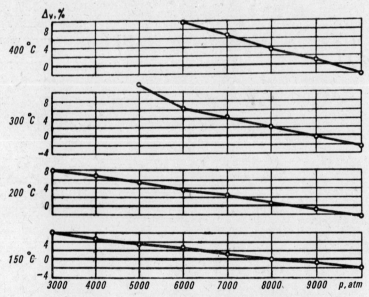

Fig. 2. Deviation of molal volumes of nitrogen calculated from Rott's equation from the experimentally determined values.

In recent investigations, equations obtained by Kazavchinskii's method [7, 8] have been increasingly accepted. The well-known Vasserman equation for nitrogen [9] was obtained by this method :

$$\sigma=\alpha_0+\alpha_1\tau+\beta\Psi+\gamma\varphi\ ;$$
$$\sigma=pv/RT\ ;\ \ \tau=T/T_{cr}\ ;\ \ \omega=\rho/\rho_{cr}\ ;\ \ T_{cr}=126.25°K\ ;$$
$$\rho_{cr}=0.2952\ \text{kg/cm}^3\ ;\ \ R=296.77\ J/(\text{kg}\cdot\text{deg})\ ;$$

$$\alpha_0 = \sum_{n=1}^{9} a_n \omega^n ; \quad \alpha_1 = 1 + \sum_{n=1}^{7} b_n \omega^n ; \quad \beta = \sum_{n=1}^{7} c_n \omega^n ;$$

$$\gamma = \sum_{n=1}^{7} d_n \omega^n ; \quad \Psi = \sum_{n=1}^{5} \frac{e_n}{\tau^n} ; \quad \varphi = \sum_{n=1}^{5} \frac{f_n}{\tau^n}, \tag{3}$$

where a_n, b_n, c_n, d_n, e_n, and f_n are coefficients.

Equation (3) correctly reflects all specific features of the behavior of nitrogen upto 1,000°C and 1,000 bar. Vasserman [9] tested equation (3) at 432 points and found average deviation σ_{av} to be $\pm 0.12\%$.

We extrapolated equation (3) upto pressures of 10,000 atm. Values of σ_{cal} were calculated on a computer and compared with the values of σ_{exp} calculated from experimental data (Fig. 3). Bartlett's experimental data [10] were used for calculating σ_{exp} at 1,000 atm, Benedict's [11] values at 50, 100 and 150°C and pressures upto 6,000 atm, and Tsiklis's [12] values at pressures above 6,000 atm. Our data [1] were used at all remaining temperatures and pressures.

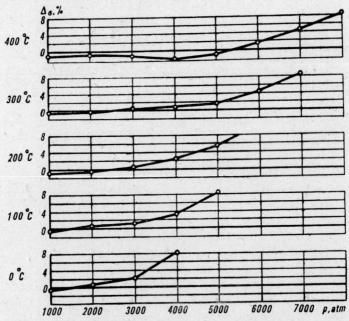

Fig. 3.   Deviation of σ values calculated from therm Vasesan's equation from those values calculated from experimental data.

Calculations showed equation (3) to yield experimental data with an accuracy of 0.1-1.72% for pressures upto 3,000 atm and temperatures of 50-400°C. At temperatures of 300-400°C, the equation can be used with equal success at pressures upto 5,000 atm. At higher pressures, the deviation from the experimental data rapidly increases and reaches 200%.

Thus, the available equations of state for nitrogen do not describe its properties within experimental accuracy at pressures above 6,000 atm and temperatures above 200°C.

Assuming that the properties of highly compressed gases and liquids are similar, we attempted to describe the properties of highly compressed gases by the same equations used for highly compressed liquids. Tsiklis found Tait's [14] equation to describe within experimental accuracy the compressibility of nitrogen at 3,000-10,000 atm and 50-150°C [12] and the compressibility of ammonia at 1,000-10,000 atm and 50-150°C [13].

Tait's equation has the following form for isothermal compressibility [14] :

$$-\left(\frac{\partial v}{\partial p}\right)_{\mathrm{T}} = \frac{C'}{B+p} \tag{4}$$

On integration, this gives :

$$\frac{v-v_0}{v_0} = C \ln \frac{B+p}{B+p_0} \tag{5}$$

where v_0=initial volume, constituting the zero reading; p_0=pressure corresponding to the volume; and v=volume at pressure p.

$$C = \frac{C'}{v_0}$$

where B and C' are constants.

Equation (5) satisfactorily describes the compressibility of liquids [14-20], solids [21] and gases [12-18].

Constant B depends only on temperature [15-21] and C, on the nature of the substance. There are, however, indications that C depends on temperature to some extent [15, 22]. Gibson [19] showed the value of C to be identical for a number of related substances such as benzene, chlorobenzene, bromobenzene, and aniline. The Tait equation has been discussed frequently [23, 24], but the characteristics of constants B and C still remain unclear.

Gibson and Kincaid [25] consider C to be independent of temperature, and the relative independence of C from the nature of the liquid indicates this constant to be possibly related to the repulsive forces. Hence B can be related to the forces of attraction in the liquid. The attraction is balanced by molecular repulsion. With increasing temperature B should decrease and change its sign at the critical point. Actually, it has been shown [13] that B for ammonia changes its sign at about 115°C, near the critical point of ammonia (133°C).

Simha and Hadden [23] consider B to be related to the density of cohesive energy in the liquid.

Atanov [20] showed the value of B at the critical temperature to be thrice the value of the critical pressure and, on this basis, equated B to the internal pressure of the liquid.

A disadvantage of Tait's equation is that it leads to negative volumes at sufficiently high pressures of the order of 10^6 atm [26].

MacDonald and Barlow [27] suggested a modified equation free from this disadvantage :

$$v/v_0 = (1 + n\beta_0 P)^{-\frac{1}{n}} , \qquad (6)$$

where $p = P - p_0$; $n = r - 1$; $r = 1/C$; $\beta_0 = [r(p_0 + B)]^{-1}$; and B and C are constants from equation (5).

Equation (6) describes practically all the Bridgeman data on the compressibility of solids and liquids [28]. The equation was obtained by using other methods [29-31]. However, values of B and C must still be selected for liquids from experimental data. For solids, Gilvarry [32] and Ryabinin [33] obtained identical expressions.

$$n = 2\gamma_{AV} + \frac{1}{3}, \qquad (7)$$

where γ_{AV}=average value of the Gruneizen parameter for the given pressure range.

In connection with the above discussion, the applicability of equations (5) and (6) was studied for describing the data on the compressibility of gases in a wide range of temperatures and pressures.

Values of B were selected from the data of references [1] and [11] and plotted against T (Fig. 4). Values of B calculated in reference [12] for 50, 100 and 150°C respectively show high degree of accuracy on the curve. The value of $C=0.1597$ was taken from the same reference [12]. Standardized values of B for nitrogen at 0-400°C are given below :

t, °C	B, atm	dB/dT, atm/deg
0	—1200	—6.00
25	—1326	—4.19
50	—1420*	—3.60
100	—1576*	—2.87
150	—1714*	—2.35
200	—1818	—1.95
250	—1900	—1.65
300	—1970	—1.41
350	—2036	—1.24
400	—2100	—1.12

*Values of B have been taken from reference [34].

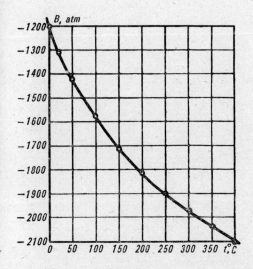

Fig. 4. Dependence of B on temperature.

Table 1. Molal volumes of nitrogen determined from Tait's equation

| | \multicolumn{10}{c}{t, °C} |
| p, atm | \multicolumn{2}{c}{0} | \multicolumn{2}{c}{100} | \multicolumn{2}{c}{200} | \multicolumn{2}{c}{300} | \multicolumn{2}{c}{400} |
	Volume cm³/mole	Deviation %	Volume cm³/mole	Deviation %	Volume cm³/mole	Deviation %	Volume cm³/mole	Deviation %	Volume cm³/mole	Deviation %
3,000	33.42	—	36.79	—	40.00	—	43.13	—	46.33	—
3,500	32.11	—0.06	35.01	—0.23	37.75	—0.42	40.39	—0.61	43.06	—1.03
4,000	31.06	—0.09	33.65	—0.24	36.08	—0.41	38.46	—0.75	40.80	—1.21
4,500	30.19	—0.16	32.54	—0.18	34.77	—0.23	36.94	—0.70	39.07	—1.16
5,000	29.43	—0.34	31.61	+0.03	33.67	—0.03	35.70	—0.61	37.67	—0.92
5,500	28.77	—0.52	30.80	—0.13	32.74	+0.09	34.65	—0.60	36.49	—0.49
6,000	28.18	—0.63	31.10	+0.03	31.93	+0.20	33.73	—0.21	35.48	—0.20
6,500	27.66	—	29.47	+0.07	31.21	+0.32	32.93	—0.06	34.59	+0.03
7,000	27.17	—	28.90	+0.07	30.54	+0.33	32.21	+0.30	33.79	+0.24
7,500	26.73	—	28.38	+0.03	29.97	+0.33	31.55	+0.38	33.07	+0.36
8,000	26.32	—	27.85	0.00	29.43	+0.34	30.96	+0.49	32.42	+0.43
8,500	25.95	—	27.46	+0.14	28.93	+0.28	30.41	+0.43	31.81	+0.44
9,000	25.59	—	27.05	+0.15	28.47	—	29.90	+0.37	31.26	+0.42
9,500	25.26	—	26.67	+0.04	28.04	—	29.43	+0.24	30.74	+0.19
10,000	24.95	—	26.31	0.00	27.64	—	28.98	0.00	30.26	+0.03
10,500	24.65	—	26.01	—	27.26	—	28.57	—	29.80	—
11,000	24.37	—	25.68	—	26.90	—	28.17	—	29.37	—
11,500	21.11	—	25.38	—	26.56	—	27.80	—	28.97	—
12,000	23.86	—	25.09	—	26.24	—	27.45	—	28.59	—

$$\Delta_v = \frac{v_{cal} - v_{exp}}{v_{exp}} \cdot 100\%.$$

Molal values of nitrogen determined from equation (5) for temperatures of 0-400°C and pressures of 3,000-12,000 atm (Table 1) were compared with experimental data (Fig. 5), showing that deviations are random and do not exceed the experimental accuracy.

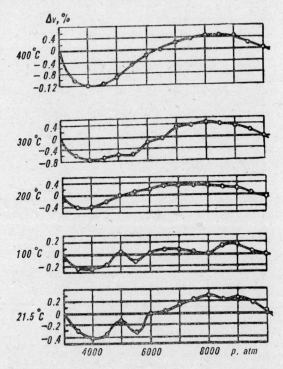

Fig. 5. Deviation of molal volumes of nitrogen determined from the
Tait's equation from experimentally determined values.

Table 2 gives the molal volumes of nitrogen calculated from the modified equation (6). A comparison of the data of Tables 1 and 2 with the experimental values shows equation (5) to describe the data on the compressibility of nitrogen more accurately than equation (6).

The values of some thermodynamic functions of nitrogen can be calculated from Tait's equation and from known thermodynamic relationships.

The following expression was obtained from data for volatility [34] :

$$\ln \frac{f}{f_0} = \frac{v_0}{RT} \{[1+C+C\ln(B+p_0)]p - p_0 - C[(B+p)\ln(B+p) \qquad (8)$$
$$- (B+p_0)\ln(B+p_0)]\},$$

Table 2. Molal volumes of nitrogen calculated from the modified equation of MacDonald and Barlow, cm³/mole*

p, atm	v at t, °C				
	0	100	200	300	400
4,000	31.07	33.62	36.18	38.51	40.88
5,000	29.48	31.67	33.87	35.89	37.94
6,000	28.29	30.26	32.26	34.09	35.96
7,000	27.35	29.17	31.03	32.74	34.49
8,000	26.57	28.30	30.04	31.67	33.33
9,000	25.92	27.55	29.23	30.79	32.38
10,000	25.35	26.92	28.53	30.04	31.58
11,000	24.86	26.37	27.93	29.39	30.88
12,000	24.42	25.88	27.40	28.82	30.28

*Pressure 3,000 atm=the starting point.

where f_0 is the volatility at pressure p_0.

On differentiating equation (5) with respect to T, we obtain :

$$\left(\frac{\partial v}{\partial T}\right)_p = \left(\frac{\partial v_0}{\partial T}\right)_{p_0} \left(1-C\ln\frac{B+p}{B+p_0}\right) - v_0 C \frac{dB}{dT}\left(\frac{1}{B+p} - \frac{1}{B+p_0}\right) \tag{9}$$

On combining equation (9) with the equation for isothermal entropy change, we obtain :

$$S_{p,T}-S_{p0,T} = -\int_{p_0}^{p}\left(\frac{\partial v}{\partial T}\right)_p dp = -\left\{\left[\left(\frac{\partial v_0}{\partial T}\right)_{p_0} + \right.\right.$$

$$\left. v_0 C\frac{dB}{dT}\frac{1}{B+p_0}\right]\int_{p_0}^{p}dp - \left(\frac{\partial v^\circ}{\partial T}\right)_{p_0} C\int_{p_0}^{p}\ln\frac{B+p}{B+p_0} dp - v_0 C\frac{dB}{dT}$$

$$\int_{p_0}^{p}\frac{dp}{B+p}\right\} = \left\{\left[\left(\frac{dv_0}{dT}\right)_{p_0}(1+C) + v_0 C\frac{dB}{dT}\frac{1}{B+p_0}\right](p-p_0) - $$

$$\left(\frac{\partial v_0}{\partial T}\right)_{p_0}C(B+p)\ln\frac{B+p}{B+p_0} - v_0 C\frac{dB}{dT}\ln\frac{B+p}{B+p_0}\right\}. \tag{10}$$

For isothermal enthalpy change, we obtain :

$$H_{p,T} - H_{p_0,T} = \int_{p_0}^{p}\left[v - T\left(\frac{dv}{\partial T}\right)_p\right]dp = v_0\int_{p_0}^{p}dp - v_0C\int_{p_0}^{p}\ln\frac{B+p}{B+p_0}$$

$$dp - T\int_{p_0}^{p}\left(\frac{dv}{dT}\right)_p dp = \left[v_0 - T\left(\frac{dv_0}{dT}\right)_{p_0}\right]\left[(p-p_0)(1+C) - \right.$$

$$\left. C(B+p)\ \ln\frac{B+p}{B+p_0}\right] - T\,v_0\,C\ \frac{dB}{dT}\left[\frac{p-p_0}{B+p_0} - \ln\frac{B+p}{B+p_0}\right]. \quad (11)$$

The values of $\left(\dfrac{\partial v_0}{\partial T}\right)_{p_0}$ and $\dfrac{dB}{Td}$ were determined by graphical differentiation. With $v_0 - T$ coordinates, the isobar of $p_0 = 3{,}000$ atm is represented by a straight line within limits of experimental error. The straight line is represented by the equation :

$$\left(\frac{dv_0}{dT}\right)_{p_0} = 0.0317\ \text{cm}^3\ (\text{mole}\cdot\text{deg}) = \text{const.}$$

The values of dB/dT were standardized with respect to temperature (Fig. 6 and p. 18). Equations (8), (10) and (11) were solved on a computer to obtain the values of

$$f/f_0,\ (S_{p,T} - S_{p_0,T})\ \text{and}\ (H_{p,T} - H_{p_0,T}).$$

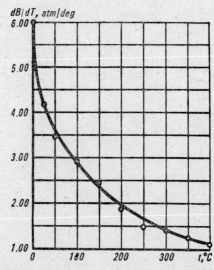

Fig. 6.   Dependence of dB/dT on temperature.

Assuming nitrogen to be at 1 atm and 273.15°K as the standard, we calculated the values of

$$f, (S_{p,\,T} - S^{o}_{273\cdot16}) \text{ and } (H_{p,\,T} - H^{o}_{273\cdot16}).$$

Vol'shakov [35] calculated the values of volatility, entropy, and enthalpy upto 300 atm and 200°C from the data of reference [11]. Tsiklis calculated the volatility of nitrogen at 100°C for pressure of 3,000-10,000 atm. We graphically calculated the volatility, entropy, and enthalpy at temperatures above 200°C from the data reported in references [1, 5]. The values obtained were standardized with respect to temperature.

The results of these calculations are given in Tables 3-5, proving Tait's equation to accurately describe the molal volumes of nitrogen in a wide range of temperature and pressure, as well as the thermodynamic properties of this element. The deviation between the values of $H_{p,T} - H^{o}_{273\cdot16}$°K, given in reference [36] and the values obtained in our calculations do not exceed 2.5% at 10,000 atm and deviation in the values of $S_{p,T} - S^{o}_{273\cdot16}$ is 2.17%.

Table 3.   Volatility of nitrogen

p, atm	$f \cdot 10^{-4}$ at t, °C				
	0	100	200	300	400
3,000	5.45	3.15	2.21	1.71	1.44
3,500	11.32	5.66	3.65	2.66	2.16
4,000	22.89	9.91	5.87	4.05	3.15
4,500	45.33	17.02	9.27	6.05	4.52
5,000	88.16	28.76	14.41	8.89	6.40
5,500	168.8	47.89	22.13	12.93	8.95
6,000	318.6	78.79	33.58	18.60	12.40
6,500	594.0	128.2	50.47	26.51	17.03
7,000	1,095.0	206.7	75.18	37.47	23.21
7,500	1,999.0	330.1	111.1	52.60	31.41
8,000	3,613.0	523.1	163.0	73.35	42.26
8,500	6,474.0	822.7	237.5	101.6	56.52
9,000	11,506.0	1,285	344.0	140.1	75.20
9,500	20,295.0	1,994	495.5	192.0	99.58
10,000	35,540.0	3,075	709.7	262.0	131.2
10,500	61,815.0	4,716	1,011	355.8	172.3
11,000	106,830	7,194	1,435	481.2	225.2
11,500	183,510	10,917	2,026	648.0	293.3
12,000	313,420	16,488	2,843	869.4	380.6

Table 4. Entropy change for nitrogen, cal (mole · deg)

p, atm	$S_{p,T}-S^{\circ}_{273\cdot16}$ at t, °C				
	0	100	200	300	400
3,000	18.05	15.19	13.21	11.59	10.25
3,500	18.40	15.54	13.56	11.94	10.60
4,000	18.70	15.85	13.87	12.24	10.89
4,500	18.96	16.13	14.14	12.52	11.16
5,000	19.20	16.39	14.39	12.77	11.40
5,500	19.41	16.62	14.63	13.00	11.63
6,000	19.61	16.85	14.85	13.22	11.84
6,500	19.79	17.06	15.06	13.43	12.05
7,000	19.96	17.26	15.26	13.63	12.24
7,500	20.12	17.45	15.45	13.82	12.43
8,000	20.27	17.64	15.63	14.01	12.60
8,500	20.41	17.81	15.81	14.19	12.77
9,000	20.54	17.98	15.97	14.36	12.94
9,500	20.67	18.15	16.14	14.52	13.10
10,000	20.78	18.30	16.30	14.68	13.25
10,500	20.90	18.46	16.45	14.84	13.40
11,000	21.00	18.61	16.60	14.99	13.55
11,500	21.11	18.75	16.74	15.14	13.69
12,000	21.20	18.89	16.88	15.28	13.83

Table 5. Enthalpy change for nitrogen, cal/mole

p, atm	$H_{p,T}-H^{o}_{273\cdot16}$ at t, °C				
	0	100	200	300	400
3,000	989	1,897	2,731	3,600	4,460
3,500	1,290	2,200	3,030	3,910	4,770
4,000	1,590	2,500	3,340	4,210	5,070
4,500	1,890	2,800	3,640	4,510	5,380
5,000	2,180	3,090	3,930	4,810	5,680
5,500	2,480	3,380	4,230	5,100	5,970
6,000	2,770	3,660	4,510	5,390	6,260
6,500	3,060	3,950	4,800	5,670	6,550
7,000	3,340	4,220	5,080	5,950	6,840
7,500	3,630	4,500	5,350	6,220	7,120
8,000	3,910	4,770	5,630	6,500	7,400
8,500	4,190	5,040	5,900	6,770	7,670
9,000	4,460	5,310	6,170	7,030	7,940
9,500	4,740	5,570	6,430	7,300	8,210
10,000	5,000	5,840	6,700	7,560	8,470
10,500	5,280	6,100	6,960	7,820	8,730
11,000	5,540	6,350	7,210	8,070	9,000
11,500	5,810	6,610	7,470	8,330	9,250
12,000	6,070	6,860	7,720	8,580	9,510

The small deviations between the values of the thermodynamic functions determined by two different methods indicate that extrapolation on Tait's equation upto pressures of 12,000 kg/cm² may be sufficiently reliable.

REFERENCES

1. TSIKLIS, D. S. and E. V. POLYAKOV. See article in the present collection.
2. DEMING, E. W. and L. E. SHUPE. *Phys. Rev.,* **37,** 638, 1931.
3. DEMING, E. W. and L. E. SHUPE. *Phys. Rev.,* **38,** 2245, 1931.
4. DEMING, E. W. and L. E. SHUPE. *Phys. Rev.,* **40,** 848, 1932.
5. ROZEN, A. M. *Zh. Fiz. Khim.,* **20,** 333, 1946.
6. ROTT, L. A. *Zh. Fiz. Khim.,* **30,** 2827, 1956.
7. KAZAVCHINSKII, YA. Z. *Teploenergetika,* No. 11, 59, 1960.
8. KAZAVCHINSKII, YA. Z. *IZhF,* **7** (6), 129, 1964.
9. VASSERMAN, A. A. *Zh. Fiz. Khim.,* **38,** 2386, 1964.
10. BARTLETT, E. *J. Am. Chem. Soc.,* **50,** 1275, 1928.
11. BENEDICT, M. *J. Am. Chem. Soc.,* **59,** 2233, 1937.
12. TSIKLIS, D. S. *DAN SSSR,* **79,** 289, 1951.
13. TSIKLIS, D. S. *DAN SSSR,* **91,** 889, 1953.
14. TAIT, P. G. *Report on some of the physical properties of water,* 47, 1888.
15. WOHL, A. *Z. Phys. Chem.,* **99,** 234, 1921.
16. CARL, H. *Z. Phys. Chem.,* **101,** 238, 1922.
17. GIBSON, R. E. *J. Am. Chem. Soc.,* **56,** 4, 1934.
18. GIBSON, R. E. *Am. J. Sci.,* **35A,** 49, 1938.
19. GIBSON, R. E. *J. Am. Chem. Soc.,* **57,** 284, 1935.
20. ATANOV, YU. A. *Zh. Fiz. Khim.,* **40,** 1216, 1966.
21. GINELL, R. and T. J. QUIGLEY. *J. Phys. Chem. Solids,* **27,** 1157, 1965.
22. GINELL, R. *J. Chem. Phys.,* **35,** 1776, 1961.
23. SIMHA, R. and S. T. HADDEN. *J. Chem. Phys.,* **25,** 702, 1956.
24. GINELL, R. *J. Chem. Phys.,* **34,** 1249, 2174, 1961.
25. GIBSON, R. E. and J. F. KINCAID. *J. Am. Chem. Soc.,* **60,** 511, 1938.
26. MACDONALD, J. R. *Rev. of Modern Phys.,* **38** (4), 669, 1966.
27. MACDONALD, J. R. and C. A. BARLOW. *J. Chem. Phys.,* **36,** 3062, 1962.
28. MACDONALD, J. R. *J. Chem. Phys.,* **40,** 1792, 1964.
29. GILVARRY, J. J. *J. Appl. Phys.,* **28,** 1253, 1957.
30. GILVARRY, J. J. *Phys. Rev.,* **102,** 331, 1956.
31. COOK, M. A. and L. A. ROGERS. *J. Appl. Phys.,* **34,** 2330, 1963,

32. GILVARRY, J. J.   *Phys. Rev.*, **102,** 325, 1956.
33. RYABININ, YU. N.   *Zh. Theoreticheskoi Fiziki*, **30,** 739, 1960.
34. TSIKLIS, D. S.   *Zh. Fiz. Khim.*, **30,** 1182, 1956.
35. BOL'SHAKOV, P. E.   *Zh. Fiz. Khim.*, **18,** 121, 1944.
36. DIN, F.   *Thermodynamic functions of gases,* Vol. **3,** London, 1961.

UDC 541.11

DETERMINATION OF THE COMPRESSIBILITY OF A GAS BY THE DISPLACEMENT METHOD

D. S. *Tsiklis* and E. V. *Polyakov*

Systematic tabulation of the experimental data on bulk behavior of pure gases and their mixtures at pressures of 10,000-15,000 atm and high temperatures has recently become necessary. The problem has received attention only in a few studies (Table 1).

Table 1. Values of the compressibility of gases above 3000 atm

Gas	Pressure,	Temperature,	Error in measurement,	Reference
	atm	°C	%	
Helium	16,000	30-95	5	[1, 2]
Hydrogen	16,000	30-95	5	[1, 2]
Nitrogen	16,000	30-95	0.5	[1, 2]
	5,800	from −175 to +200	0.25	[3]
	10,000	50-150	0.5	[4]
Ammonia	10,000	50-150	0.5	[5]
Oxygen	10,000	20-400	0.5	[6]
Carbon dioxide	4,000	to 475	0.3	[7]

The present work is an extension of similar studies initiated by one of the present authors [4, 5, 6]. With the exception of references [4, 5], the publications referred to in Table 1 describe methods employing unrelieved high-pressure piezometers. The main disadvantage of these methods is that the pressure gauges deform at high pressures and, especially at high temperatures, the deformation being higher, the gauge is critically important, especially when precise measurements are required.

The thermal deformation can be determined with adequate accuracy using well-known methods. Determination of basic deformation is considerably more difficult. Generally, methods such as those described in references [1, 8] are employed for this purpose. The change in the pressure gauge volume, for instance, is equal to

$$\triangle v_p = \frac{v_0\,p}{E(r_2{}^2 - r_1{}^2)}\,[3(1-2\mu)r_1{}^2 + 2(1+\mu)r_2{}^2], \qquad (1)$$

where $\triangle v_p$=increment in the pressure gauge volume at pressure p; v_0= initial volume; E=Young's modulus; μ=Poisson's coefficient; and r_1 and r_2=inner and outer radii of the pressure gauge.

Equation (1) is, however, only applicable to thin-walled cylinders, with the additional condition that the length of the cylinder exceeds the width. Benedict [3], therefore, recommended the determination of the deformation in pressure gauges in respect to the compressibility of iron rods.

Bilevich, Vereshchagin, and Kalashnikov [9] experimentally tested equation (1) on a pressure gauge with an outer diameter of 16 mm and inner diameter of 8 mm. They observed the experimentally determined volume $\triangle_v$ to exceed the calculated value from equation (1) and the difference between the two volumes to increase with increased pressure (Fig. 1).

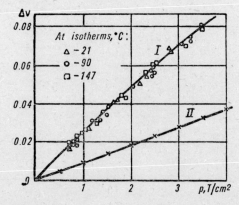

Fig. 1. Comparison of volumes measured experimentally and computed from equation (1).
I—determined experimentally; II—computed from equation (1).

At present, there appears to be no available theory enabling calculation of the baric deformation of the pressure gauge with the required accuracy. Experimental determination of such deformation is complicated by the irregular dimensions of the pressure gauge. In reference [6], for example, the outer diameter of the pressure gauge was reported as 140, the inner diameter as 10 mm, and length as 1000 mm. It is impossible to determine the deformation in such a gauge by the method employed in reference [9].

The objective of the present work is determination of a method requiring no correction for baric and thermal deformations in the gauge during calculation of the gauge compressibility. In such case, irrespective of the magnitudes of pressure and temperature, the accuracy of results will be determined by the accuracy in measuring the pressure, temperature, pressure gauge volume, and amount of gas in the gauge.

Krichevskii recommended that two experiments be conducted under identical pressure and temperature on an apparatus with a constant-volume pressure gauge. In the first experiment, the number of moles of the gas $n_{1p,T}$ contained in the pressure gauge is determined. The second experiment is performed following placement of an insert of known volume in the pressure gauge. Then the number of moles of gas $n_{2p, T}$ in the pressure gauge is determined.

The molal volume of the gas under experimental condtions is expressed by :

$$v_{p, T} = \frac{v_{\text{insert } p, T}}{\Delta n_{p, T}} \tag{2}$$

where $v_{p,T}$ = molal volume of gas at pressure p and temperature T; $v_{\text{insert } p,T}$ = volume of insert at p and T; $\Delta n_{p, T} = n_{1p, T} - n_{2p, T}$ = number of moles of gas displaced by the insert under experimental conditions.

Since the conditions for both experiments are identical, requirements for correction are mutually eliminated for baric and thermal deformations in the pressure gauge as well as the possible errors due to the presence of ballast volumes in the apparatus and nonuniform temperature along the length of the pressure gauge. Furthermore, the tedious job of calibrating the piezometer is rendered unnecessary.

While determining the molal volume of a gas from equation (2), consideration is given only to the effect of change in the volume of the insert on changes in pressure and temperature. Inside the pressure gauge, the insert is subjected to compression from all sides. Therefore, from known compressibility and volume-expansion coefficients of the insert material, it is easy to calculate the volume of the insert under experimental conditions.

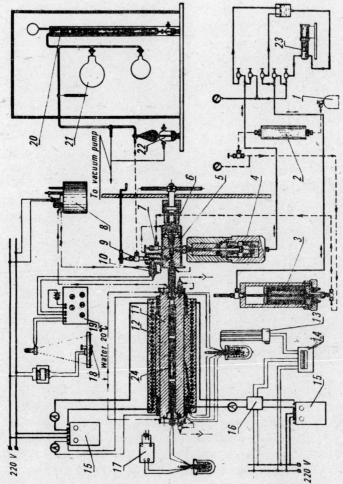

Fig. 2. Schematic diagram of the apparatus for determination of gas compressibility.

1—cylinder; 2—drier; 3—bellows compressor; 4—booster; 5—valve box; 6—press valve; 7—loading valve; 8—ultrathermostat; 9—unloading valve; 10—manganin manometer; 11—high-pressure vessel; 12—electrical furnace with thermal shields; 13—switch; 14—EPV-01 potentiometer; 15—voltage regulator; 16—magnetic starter; 17—PP potentiometer; 18—mirror galvanometer; 19—MTV bridge; 20—mercury manometer; 21—calibrated bulbs; 22—mercury pump; 23—oil pump; 24—metallic insert.

We applied this method to compressibility measurements on argon and nitrogen. The measurements were performed on the apparatus used in reference [6] except with reconstructed blocks of measurements of gas quantity, temperature, and pressure.

The apparatus (see Fig. 2) consists of bellows compressor (3), booster (4), valve box (5) with press valve (6), high-pressure vessel (11), electrically heated furnace with thermal shields (12), and analytical part and manganin manometer (10).

The experiment is performed in the following manner. Gas from cylinder (1) is passed through drier (2) into bellows compressor (3), where it is compressed to a pressure of approximately 1000 atm. At this pressure, the gas passes into the apparatus through valve (7) and fills the channels of booster (4), high-pressure vessel (11), and all channels connected to the constant-volume pressure gauge. The high-pressure vessel is heated to the experimental temperature and the gas pressure in the pressure gauge is measured. Portions of gas are allowed to pass through valve (9) into calibrated bulbs (21). On attaining equilibrium condition in the pressure gauge, the pressure of the remnant gas is measured and portions of the gas are retransferred into the bulbs.

The operation of removal of gas portions is continued until the gas pressure can be measured with the manganin manometer. Following this, without measuring the pressure, the gas is released into the bulbs and the entire amount of residual gas in the gauge is evacuated with mercury pump (22) and is then determined.

The number of moles of a gas in a particular portion is determined from the equation :

$$n = \frac{P_t \left[1 - (\beta - \alpha) \; t\right] \; (v_b + v_t)}{RT}, \qquad (3)$$

where n=number of moles of gas in one portion; P_t=gas pressure at room temperature; $\beta = 0.000182$ deg^{-1} and $\alpha = 0.000008$ deg^{-1} are the coefficients of expansion for mercury and glass respectively; v_b=volume of the calibrated bulbs; v_t=volume of connecting tubes from the calibrated bulbs upto mercury level in the left arm of the manometer; R=gas constant; and T=temperature of the gas in the bulbs.

The total amount of gas in the pressure gauge is determined from the formula :

$$n_{1p,\; T} = \sum_{1}^{k} n, \qquad (4)$$

where k is the number of times the gas is released.

The results of the experiment are plotted by gas pressure in the gauge against the number of moles of the gas (Fig. 3, curve II). The experiment is repeated and the new results are plotted on the same graph. The results are considered satisfactory if the deviation in the number of moles of the gas at the same pressure does not exceed 0.3% in either experiment. The average of the two readings serves as the final result. If the deviation exceeds 0·3% , the experiment is repeated.

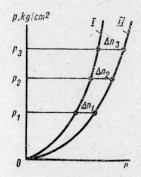

Fig. 3. Method of calculation of displaced gas amount.
I—in the pressure gauge with insert; II—in the pressure gauge without insert.

Following this procedure, the high-pressure vessel is opened to receive a metallic insert of 1Kh18N9T stainless steel of volume $v_0=10.79$ cm^3 at room temperature and atmospheric pressure, determined by H_2O calibration. The required pressure is attained in the pressure gauge and the high-pressure vessel is heated to the temperature of the first experiment. The temperatures of the manganin manometer and the cold region of the pressure gauge are maintained constant at 25°C in all experiments.

Curve I of Fig. 3 is obtained by repeating the procedure in the first experiment. At any pressure $p_1, p_2 \ldots p_m$ the insert displaces Δn_1, $\Delta n_2 \ldots \Delta n_m$ moles of gas from the pressure gauge. The obtained values of $\Delta n_{p,T}$ are substituted in equation (2) and the molal volume of the gas at different pressure and at the given experimental temperature are calculated.

The ratio between volume change in the insert and temperature change was calculated from the well-known equation :

$$v_t = v_0 \, (1+\beta \, t), \qquad (5)$$

where v_t=volume of insert at temperature t; v_0=volume of insert at the temperature of calibration; β=coefficient of volume expansion for the steel [10].

The change in insert volume with pressure is calculated from the Bridgeman equation [8] :

$$-\Delta v = v_0 \, (a \cdot 10^{-7} \, p - b \cdot 10^{-12} \, p^2), \qquad (6)$$

where v_0=initial volume of insert; p=pressure in kg/cm^2 ; a and b= coefficients dependent on properties of the insert material.

Variation in a and b with increasing temperature is negligibly small, as is seen in reference [3].

We could not find the values of a and b for the 1Kh18N9T steel in the literature, and hence have substituted their values for Armco iron, assuming that any difference between the two values would not affect the accuracy of these experiments. Under conditions of experiment (2), the insert volume is :

$$v_{\text{insert}_{p,\,T}} = v_0 \, (1 + \beta t - a \cdot 10^{-7} \, p + b \cdot 10^{-12} \, p^2). \tag{7}$$

The position of the insert inside the high-pressure vessel is accurately determined, necessary due to the temperature irregularity along the height of the high-pressure vessel. Pins and flanges of the high-pressure vessel are water-cooled to avoid leakage. For decreasing the temperature gradient, powerful heaters are placed at the ends of the high-pressure vessel and serve as thermal shields.

Fig. 4 gives the temperature distribution along the height of the high-pressure vessel at 400°C and at atmospheric pressure. The thermal shields ensure uniform temperature over a length of 160 mm at the center of the high pressure vessel (total length of channel= 500 mm). The calibrated insert and thermocouple sheath end are included within this length.

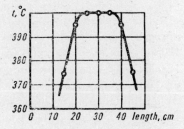

Fig. 4. Temperature distribution along high-pressure vessel at 400°C and atmospheric pressure.

It can be safely assumed that, due to the high density of the medium and convection currents [11], the constant temperature zone will be longer at high pressures and at low temperatures. In order to minimize the effect of the cold zone, ends of the channel of the high-pressure vessel are filled with metallic inserts, the left-hand insert comprising the thermocouple sheath.

Temperature of the gas inside the high-pressure vessel is measured with chromel-alumel thermocouple placed inside the sheath (Fig. 2) and a PP-1 potentiometer. Accuracy of the temperature measurement is ±0.5°C. The temperature outside the high-pressure vessel is measured at three points : at both the ends (temperature of thermal shields) and at the center. The temperatures are measured with EPV–01 potentiometers with an accuracy of ±1.5°C. Coarse temperature control is achieved with the same instrument and the same accuracy.

Fine temperature control is effected within ±0.5°C with the internal thermocouple inside the sheath. Gas pressure inside the pressure gauge is measured with a manganin manometer. Resistance of the manometer is measured with an MTV dc bridge of 0.05 class of a single-bridge circuit. The sensitivity of the circuit is such that the bright spot of the galvanometer is displaced through ten divisions with a resistance variation of 0·01 ohm, ensuring an accuracy of ±20 atm in pressure measurement.

The manometer coil, wound with 0·03 mm diameter manganin wire which has been heat- and pressure-treated [8], is isolated from the experimental gas with pentane-filled bellows. This precaution resulted from our surprising observation that manganin wire previously withstanding direct contact with oxygen pressure to 10,000 atm changed its resistance on contact with nitrogen, possibly due to the absorption of nitrogen at the wire surface.

The manganin manometer was calibrated with reference to the freezing point of mercury at 0°C under pressure [12, 13]. Assuming the resistance of manganin to be linearly dependent on pressure within the error limits of pressure measurement, we observed the baric coefficient of pressure

$$k=2\cdot24\cdot10^{-6}\ \text{cm}^2/\text{kg}.$$

The displacement method was used to measure the compressibility of nitrogen (impurity content upto 0.5%) at 21.5°C (upto 6500 atm pressure), 180°C (upto 5000 atm), 200°C (upto 8000 atm), and 300 and 400°C (upto 10,000 atm). The error in calculation was determined by well-known methods [14, 15], with reference to the error introduced by substituting compressibility values of Armco iron for the values of the 1Kh18N9T steel.

Table 2.   Volume of inserts of different metals at 10,000 atm as calculated from Equation (7)

Metal	a	b	v, cm^3	Deviation, %
Armco iron	5.87	2.10	9.94	—
Chromium	5.19	2.19	9.95	—0.1
Nickel	5.29	2.10	9.95	—0.1
Titanium	7.97	—0.12	9.92	+0.2
Brass	9.207	6.42	9.91	+0.3

The change in volume of inserts (of 10 cm^3) was determined by equation (7) for inserts of Armco iron, nickel, chromium, and titanium (components of 1Kh18N9T steel) and brass. Table 2, which gives the results of these calculations, shows the difference in volume change at high pressures to be under 0.2% for different insert materials (with the exception of brass).

This error was applied for estimating the accuracy of measurement of molal volumes from equation (2).

Table 3. Comparison of averaged molal volumes of nitrogen with data of references [2, 3]

	t, °C										
	21.5			180			200			300	400
	v, cm³			v, cm³			v, cm³			v, cm³	v, cm³
p, atm	Present authors	[2, 3]	Deviation %	Present authors	[2, 3]	Deviation %	Present authors	[2]	Deviation %	Present authors	Present authors
1500	41.93	41.83	+0.24	51.60	51.90	−0.58	53.33	53.22	+0.21	59.47	65.67
2000	38.20	38.28	−0.21	45.70	45.86	−0.35	46.90	46.88	+0.04	51.35	56.00
2500	35.92	35.94	−0.06	42.10	42.05	+0.10	43.00	42.87	+0.30	46.56	50.44
3000	34.23	34.24	−0.03	39.41	39.33	+0.20	40.07	40.04	+0.07	43.13	46.33
3500	32.91	—	—	37.36	37.34	+0.10	37.91	37.92	+0.03	40.66	43.51
4000	31.82	31.75	+0.22	35.73	35.66	−0.20	36.23	36.26	−0.08	38.75	41.30
4500	30.87	—	—	34.40	34.44	−0.10	34.85	34.94	−0.26	37.20	39.53
5000	30.00	29.95	+0.17	33.32	33.34	−0.06	33.68	33.76	−0.24	35.92	38.02
5500	29.36	—	—				32.71	32.76	−0.15	34.86	36.67
6000	28.65	28.56	+0.31				31.86	31.87	−0.03	33.80	35.55
6500	28.09	Δ av ±0.18			Δ av ±0.21		31.11	Δ av ±0.14		32.95	34.58
7000							30.44			32.11	33.71
7500							29.87			31.43	32.95
8000							29.34			30.81	32.28
8500										30.28	31.67
9000										29.79	31.13
9500										29.36	30.68
10,000										29.98	30.25

The error in measurement of the number of moles of gas (Δn_p, $_T$) was observed to decrease with increasing pressure, and to contribute to the error in measurement of molal volume at 10,000 atm by $0 \cdot 2\%$.

The error in pressure measurement is determined by the accuracy of the secondary instrument and the accuracy in maintaining the temperature of the manganin coil ($25 \pm 0 \cdot 5°C$). Self-heating accounts for a few tenths of a degree. Apart from the effect of these factors, the accuracy of pressure measurement is ± 20 atm. This value is assumed as the mean-square error in pressure measurement.

The mean-square error in temperature determination is assumed to be $\pm 0.5°C$. Hence, the relative mean-square experimental error at 10,000 atm and 400°C is $0 \cdot 3\%$ ($1 \cdot 4\%$ at 1500 atm).

The accuracy of the results obtained can be increased, especially at low pressures, by averaging them on *pv-p* isotherms. From averaged values of *pv*, averaged values of molal volumes of gas are obtained by reverse calculation (see Table 3). Table 3 shows the disparity between the results obtained in the present work and those from works [2, 3] to be accidental. The maximum disparity at equal pressures does not exceed $0 \cdot 35\%$. The pressure of 1500 atm is the exception, when the disparity increases to $0 \cdot 6\%$; the average disparity is below 0.21%.

The authors are indebted to I. P. Krichevskii for suggesting the problem and for his advice and attention.

REFERENCES

1. BRIDGEMAN, P. W. *Proc. Nat. Acad. Sci.*, **9**, 341, 1923.
2. DIN, F. *Thermodynamic functions of gases*, Vol. **3**, London, 1961.
3. BENEDICT, M. *J. Am. Chem. Soc.*, **59**, 2233, 1937.
4. TSIKLIS, D. S. *DAN SSSR*, **79**, 289, 1951.
5. TSIKLIS, D. S. *DAN SSSR*, **91**, 889, 1953.
6. TSIKLIS, D. S. and A. I. KULIKOVA. *Zh. Fiz. Khim.*, **39**, 1752, 1965.
7. JUZA, J., V. KMONICEK, and O. SIFNER. *Physica*, **31**, 1735, 1965.
8. BRIDGEMAN, P. W. *Fizika vysokikh davlenii (High-pressure physics)*. ONTI, Moscow-Leningrad, 1935.
9. BILEVICH, A. V., L. F. VERESHCHAGIN and YA. A. KALASHNIKOV. *PTÉ*, No. 3, 146, 1961.
10. LIBERMAN, L. YA. and M. I. PEISIKHIS. *Spravochnik po svoistvam stalei primanyacmykh v kotlofurbostroenii (Handbook on properties of steels used in boiler and turbine construction)*. Moscow–Leningrad, 1958.
11. VERESHCHAGIN, L. F. and Y. A. KALASHNIKOV. *Zh. Teoreticheskoi Fiziki*, **25**, 1458, 1955.

12· TSIKLIS, D. S. *Zh. Teoret, Fiz.*, **15**, 960, 1945.
13· ZHOKHOVSKII, M. K. *Izmeritel'naya Tekhnika*, No. 3, 1955.
14· ZAIDEL', A. N. *Elementarnye otsenki oshibok izmereniya (Elementary evaluation of experimental errors)*. Nauka, Moscow-Leningrad, 1965.
15· NALIMOV, V. V. *Primenenie matematischeskoi statistiki pri analize veshchestra (Use of mathematical statistics in analysis of a substance)*. Fizmatgiz, Moscow, 1960.

II. HYDROGEN AND MONATOMIC GASES

UDC 541.27

A SINGLE EQUATION OF STATE FOR PARAHYDROGEN

Ya. Z. Kazavchinskii and *L. S. Serdyuk*

Analysis of experimental thermal data

At present, there is only one known work [1] on the measurement of p-v-T properties of parahydrogen in a wide range of parameters : temperature range 15-100°K, maximum pressure 350 kg/cm², maximum reduced density $\omega = \rho/\rho_{cr} = 2.8$. The authors of reference [1] considered the error in their measurements to be below 0.1%.

Hoge and Lassister [2] measured thermal properties of parahydrogen on three near-critical isotherms (32.88, 33.04, and 33.28°K).

There are no data on p-v-T properties of parahydrogen above 100°K. These properties can be determined by applying the data for normal hydrogen under analogous conditions. Fig. 1 shows the relationship between the difference in compressibility factors $\Delta z = z_{p\text{-}H_2}, - z_{n\text{-}H_2}$, and density at identical temperatures, with Δz 3% at the critical temperature and diminishing with increasing temperature. Starting from 75°K, the difference does not exceed the experimental error.

The most accurate p-v-T measurements on normal hydrogen were undertaken by Michels and colleagues [3] in 1959. The measurements cover the range of 98.15-423.15°K with a maximum reduced density of $\omega = 2.76$ on isotherms at 273.15 and 298.15°K, of $\omega = 2.5$ on isotherms above 298.15°K, and $\omega = 1.8$ on isotherms below 273.15°K.

Johnston and White [4] have given averaged results of measurements of thermal properties of normal hydrogen within 20-300°K and pressures within 300 bars, corresponding to a maximum reduced density of $\omega = 1.3$ on the 100°K isotherm and $\omega = 0.5$ on the 300°K isotherm. The deviation of these data from the results of work [3] with respect to pressure and within

100-300°K averages 0.1% and does not exceed 0.2%. Furthermore, as is shown by Fig. 1, the data of reference [4] agree closely with the measurements on parahydrogen [1] over some temperature range below 100°K.

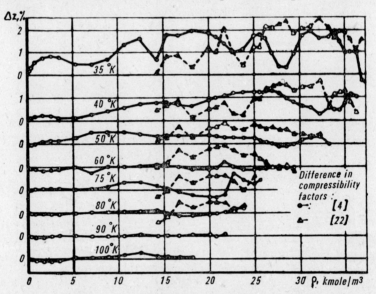

Fig. 1.　Difference in compressibility factors $P\text{-}^{H_2}$ and $n\text{-}^{H_2}$ at equal temperatures and densities.

The $p\text{-}v\text{-}T$ properties given in references [5, 6, 7] relate to earlier investigations and, as was mentioned in reference [8], are less accurate than those of references [3, 4].

Therefore, the more reliable available data served as the reference data for obtaining an equation of state for parahydrogen : data for temperatures below 100°K [1] and for temperatures above 100°K [3, 4]. Fig. 2 shows the range of parameters on $w\text{-}T$ coordinates in various investigations, and the limits of applicability of the equations of state formulated by the different authors. There are no $p\text{-}v\text{-}T$ data for the unhatched region, and the equation of state given in the present work guarantees reliable interpolation and extrapolation, and is the only source of information regarding the behavior of the substance within this range. Supplementary experimental investigations at temperatures of 50-300°K and pressures of 1000-3000 bars are recommended for assaying the equation of state.

Equation of state

In accordance with the van der Waals concept of the continuous transition of gas into liquid, more recent investigations [9] on obtaining an equation of state may provide a single, overall equation of state which offers a

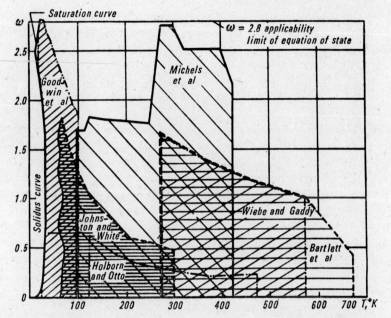

Fig. 2. Experimental *p-v-T* data used for obtaining a single equation of state.

singular adjustment of the *p-v-T* data over the entire single-phase region and which simplifies and improves the calculation of calorific properties.

The method employed in the present work directly applies the experimental data without differentiating the reference data into groups.

According to reference [9], the equation of state has the form :

$$z = \alpha_0 + \alpha_1 \vartheta + \beta \Psi + \gamma \varphi + \ldots, \tag{1}$$

where α_0, α_1, β, $\gamma \ldots$ = elementary functions of reduced density ω; Ψ, $\varphi \ldots$ = elementary functions dependent on inverse reduced temperature $\vartheta = \dfrac{T_{cr}}{T}$.

In reference [8] it was seen from experimental data that for temperatures above the Boyle temperature, which is about 110°K for hydrogen, equation (1) can be limited to three terms :

$$z = \alpha_0 + \alpha_1 \vartheta + \beta \Psi. \tag{2}$$

Two isotherms, ϑ_1 and ϑ_2 (398.15 and 198.15°K) from work [3], were taken as reference isotherms. Since on 198.15°K isotherm experimental data are available only upto $\omega = 1.8$ (Fig. 2), we extrapolated experimental isochores for $\omega = 1.8$-2.4 [3] upto this temperature. It was assumed that $\Psi = 0$ on isotherms ϑ_1 and ϑ_2. Volume functions α_0 and α_1 for the range of reduced densities of 0-2.4 were obtained from the system of equations :

$$z_1 = \alpha_0 + \alpha_1 \, \vartheta_1,$$
$$z_2 = \alpha_0 + \alpha_1 \, \vartheta_2.$$

The elementary functions were determined from isochores in tabular form, as they were eventually to be corrected on the basis of all available experimental data.   Values of $\Delta z_i = z_i - \alpha_0 - \alpha_1 \, \vartheta_i$ on any isotherm can be taken as the volume function β but for obtaining a mean value, the function $\beta = \Sigma \Delta z_i$ was taken and summation was undertaken at equal densities on all isotherms [3] above 110°K.   Values of temperature function Ψ in the range of 110-673.15°K were determined by dividing by β values of Δz_i calculated from experimental data of works [3-7].   From isolated values of α_0, α_1, β, and Ψ, the values of the second virial coefficient were determined

$$B = \left(\frac{\partial z}{\partial \omega} \right)_{\omega=0, \, \theta=\text{const}} = \left(\frac{d \alpha_0}{d \omega} \right)_{\omega=0} +$$

$$\vartheta \left(\frac{d\alpha_1}{d\omega} \right)_{\omega=0} + \Psi \left(\frac{d \beta}{d \omega} \right)_{\omega=0},$$

that is,

$$B = a + b\vartheta + C\Psi, \tag{3}$$

where a, b, and c were determined by graphical differentiation of the elementary functions.

For describing the experimental data at temperatures $T < T_\text{B}$, equation (1) was rearranged as follows :

$$z = \alpha_0 + \alpha_1 \, \vartheta + \beta \left(\frac{B - a - b\vartheta}{c} \right) + \gamma\varphi = \left[\alpha_0 - \frac{a \, \beta}{c} \right] +$$

$$\left[\alpha_1 - \frac{b \, \beta}{c} \right] \vartheta + \frac{\beta}{c} B + \gamma\varphi,$$

that is,

$$z = \bar{\alpha}_0 + \bar{\alpha}_1 \, \vartheta + \bar{\beta} B + \gamma\varphi \dots \tag{4}$$

As mentioned earlier, at temperatures above the Boyle temperature, function φ disappears and equation (4) becomes :

$$z = \bar{\alpha}_0 + \bar{\alpha}_1 \, \vartheta + \bar{\beta} B. \tag{5}$$

Values of the second virial coefficient calculated from equation (3) agree with the values of works [5, 10-13], which were determined from experimental p-v-T measurements (Fig. 3).

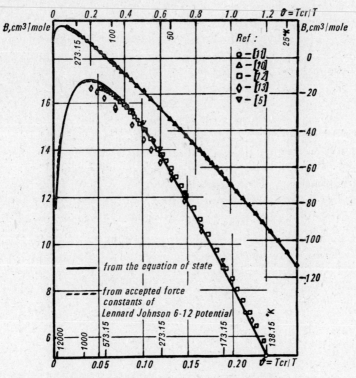

Fig. 3. Values of the second virial coefficient.

The Boyle temperature was observed to be equal to $T_B = 110.1°K$. Force constants b_0 and $\dfrac{\varepsilon}{k}$ of the Lennard-Jones 6-12 potential were isolated from calculated values of the second virial coefficient. From the equation

$$B(T) = b_0 B^*(T^*) \qquad (6)$$

it follows that at the Boyle temperature $T_B = 110 \cdot 1°K$, i.e. at $B = 0$, B^* should also be zero. From the table given in reference [14], values of $T_B^* = 3.418$ and $\dfrac{\varepsilon}{k} = T_B/T_B^* = 32 \cdot 21°K$ were determined. The value of b_0 was determined by averaging the proportionality coefficient between calculated values of $B^*(T^*)$ and the corresponding values of $B(T)$ in the temperature range for which experimental data are available and to which the Lennard-Jones potential ($b_0 = 32.12$ cm³/mole) is applicable.

Using the obtained values of force constants $\dfrac{\varepsilon}{k}$ and b_0, the second virial coefficient was extrapolated into the high-temperature region to 5000°K, which is equivalent to extrapolation of the equation of state to this temperature.

At $T < T_B$, values of B were determined from the experimental data of reference [1] and were compared with the data of reference [10]. Further, the values of

$$\delta z_i = z_i - \bar{\alpha}_0 - \bar{\alpha}_1 \vartheta_i - \bar{\beta} B_i$$

were calculated on all experimental isotherms of reference [1].

It was found that the δz_i values can be represented by the relation $\delta z_i = \gamma \varphi_i$, that is, it was sufficient to introduce here only one term in the curvilinear part of the equation of state so as to describe the experimental data for the lowest temperatures. Assuming function φ to be unity as the critical isotherm, $\delta z_{\theta=1} = \gamma$ was obtained. The values of φ_i on which various isotherms were determined best conform to the experimental data.

Isotherms below the critical temperature [1] and below 273.15 and 298.15°K are up to $\omega = 2.8$. For extending the elementary volume functions to this density, equation of state (4) was rearranged by replacing functions B and φ with new temperature functions $\check{\Psi}$ and $\tilde{\varphi}$ in accordance with :

$$\check{\Psi} = B + a_1 + b_1 \vartheta, \quad \tilde{\varphi} = \varphi + a_2 + b_2 \vartheta. \tag{7}$$

Constants a_1, b_1, a_2, and b_2 were determined from the condition that $\check{\Psi}$ and $\tilde{\varphi}$ are zero on 27 and 298.15°K isotherms, which cover maximum ranges of density. Combining equation (7) with equation of state (4), we obtain :

$$z = \bar{\alpha}_0 + \bar{\alpha}_1 \vartheta + \bar{\beta}(\check{\Psi} - a_1 - b_1 \vartheta) + \gamma(\tilde{\varphi} - a_2 - b_2 \vartheta) =$$
$$(\bar{\alpha}_0 - a_1 \bar{\beta} - a_2 \gamma) + (\bar{\alpha}_1 - b_1 \bar{\beta} - b_2 \gamma)\vartheta + \bar{\beta}\check{\Psi} + \gamma\tilde{\varphi} =$$
$$\tilde{\alpha}_0 + \tilde{\alpha}_1 \vartheta + \bar{\beta}\check{\Psi} + \gamma\tilde{\varphi}. \tag{8}$$

With such a rearrangement of the equation of state, functions $\bar{\beta}$ and γ remain unchanged, and $\tilde{\alpha}_0$ and $\tilde{\alpha}_1$ become linear combinations of the original volume functions. In the interval $\omega = 2.4 - 2.8$, $\tilde{\alpha}_0$ and $\tilde{\alpha}_1$ were determined from the system of equations :

$$z_{T27} = \tilde{\alpha}_0 + \tilde{\alpha}_1 \vartheta_{(27)},$$
$$z =_{T298 \cdot 15} = \tilde{\alpha}_0 + \tilde{\alpha}_1 \vartheta_{(298 \cdot 15)}.$$

Functions $\bar{\beta}$ and γ in the same density interval were determined by linearization of isochores [1] and [3] according to the equation :

$$\frac{z-\tilde{\alpha}_0-\tilde{\alpha}_1\,\vartheta}{\tilde{\Psi}} = F\left(\frac{\tilde{\varphi}}{\tilde{\Psi}}\right).$$

The elementary volume functions obtained for this density interval were smooth extensions of similar functions obtained earlier upto $\omega = 2.4$.

Using ratios (7) and equality (8), the equation of state was further rearranged to the form of equation (4). Elementary functions obtained in tabular form were averaged and rendered more precise to conform to the experimental data in the entire range of change of parameters by repeated linearization of isotherms and isochores.

Using orthogonal polynomials, the elementary volume functions were approximated to agree with the critical point and critical conditions on a URAL–2 computer into the following form :

$$\bar{\alpha}_0 = 1 + \sum_{i=2}^{i=10} a_i\,\omega^i; \quad \bar{\alpha}_1 = \sum_{i=2}^{i=10} b_i\,\omega^i; \quad \bar{\beta} = \sum_{i=1}^{i=10} c_1\,\omega^i;$$

$$\gamma = \sum_{i=2}^{i=10} d_i\,\omega^i.$$

Values of coefficients a_i, b_i, c_i, and d_i are given in Table 1.

Table 1. Coefficients of functions of reduced density in equation [1]

i	a_i	b_i	c_i	d_i
1	—	—	0.01559	—
2	—0.0099	0.49206	0.002326	0.041
3	0.12306	—0.36063	—0.004701	—0.165335
4	—2.57385	8.701637	0.121873	1.851077
5	6.51620	—22.530818	—0.309650	—3.418055
6	—7.98900	28.166434	0.3797683	3.1836804
7	5.464088	—19.519020	—0.2597688	—1.8130507
8	—2.1230419	7.6539207	0.1009351	0.64123564
9	0.43856595	—1.591728	—0.0208506	—0.12824830
10	—0.037444	0.1365997	0.0017802	0.01097327

The analytical expression of function φ, which should become zero at $T > T_B$, has the following form :

$$\varphi = \left(\exp - \frac{0 \cdot 23786}{\vartheta^2} \right) (-0.1536\ \vartheta + 6.9752\ \vartheta^2 - 24.1028\ \vartheta^3 +$$
$$39.479216\ \vartheta^4 - 30.986244\ \vartheta^5 + 12.673656\ \vartheta^6 - 2.591508\ \vartheta^7 + 0.206261\vartheta^8). \quad (9)$$

Considering the difficulties in approximation of the virial coefficient by a single equation (for the sharp maximum, see Fig. 3), the entire range of the virial coefficient is divided into two parts for analytical expression. For $T < T_B$, the coefficient is approximated by a polynomial in ϑ.

$$B_1 = 20.472 - 36.88717\ \vartheta - 176.05256\ \vartheta^2 + 334.22725\ \vartheta^3 - 394.11916\ \vartheta^4 +$$
$$264.42563\ \vartheta^5 - 99.317744\ \vartheta^6 + 19.344366\ \vartheta^7 - 1.502101\ \vartheta^8\ \text{cm}^3/\text{mole} \quad (10)$$

The method of expressing the equation of state through elementary functions enables use of experimental calorific values for correcting temperature functions obtained from thermal data. The most convenient data for this purpose are those on isochoric specific heat, which is expressed as follows :

$$c_V = c_V \sim (T) + R\ \vartheta^2\ [B'' \int_0^\omega \frac{\bar\beta}{\omega}\ d\ \omega + \varphi'' \int_0^\omega \frac{\dot\gamma}{\omega}\ d\ \omega]. \quad (11)$$

From equation (11) functions B'' and φ'' were corrected according to data of Younglove and Diller [15], and were used for deriving expressions (9) and (10) for functions B and φ.

At $T > T_B$ values of B are computed from the expanded equation for the second virial coefficient for the 6-12 Lennard-Jones potential.

$$B_2 = 56.64\ \vartheta^{\frac{1}{4}} - 73.13\ \vartheta^{\frac{3}{4}} - 48.828\ \vartheta^{\frac{5}{4}}\ \text{cm}^3/\text{mole}. \quad (12)$$

At $T = 110°K$, equations (10) and (12) give identical values of B, B', and B''.

Mean deviation of pressure values calculated from equation of state (4) from the data of reference [1] is 0.1%. The maximum deviation above the critical temperature is 0.2%. Below the critical temperature for the liquid, at some points near the saturation curve where the absolute pressures are quite small, the maximum error attains 4%. This is entirely acceptable, since the error corresponding to the large value of the $\left(\dfrac{\partial \rho}{\partial \rho} \right)_T$ derivative does not exceed 0.1% when related to the value of the density. On 33°K iso-therm, which is near the critical curve, the error at some points on either side of the critical point is as high as 0·6%, with different signs before and after the critical point (below critical point, calculated pressures are less than their experimental values). These errors diminish along the isochores as the temperature increases and do not exceed 0·2% at 50°K. The errors in the critical region could be reduced either by decreasing the critical conditions or by increasing the order of the polynomial approximating the critical isotherms to the 15th degree. However, the deviations are apparently the result of inadequate accuracy of the experimental data in this region; hence, these requirements are not necessary. This is shown by a comparison of the calculated and experimental [2] pressures on three near-critical isotherms.

The maximum deviation of calculated pressures from high-temperature data of references [3, 4] is 0.2% with an average value of below 0·1%, and is 0·4% from the data of references [5, 6, 7]. Pressure values calculated from our equation range between the data of references [6] and [7].

Fig. 4 gives an idea of the agreement of the calculated values of the third

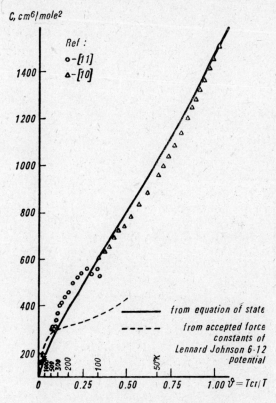

Fig. 4.   Values of the third virial coefficient.

virial coefficient C, determined from equation of state (4) with values of references [10] and [11] determined from experimental p-v-T data as well as with those calculated from the above-mentioned force constants of the Lennard-Jones potential at high temperatures.

Thermal properties at saturation and on the solidification curve

In recent years, studies of the vapor pressure curve for parahydrogen have been frequently reported in the literature, as follows : above the normal boiling point [16, 17], and below [18]. These data agree closely with an earlier work [19]. As no equation accurately representing the data from triple to critical points has been given in the literature for the vapor pressure curve, the present authors obtained the following equation :

$$\lg P = -11 \cdot 01086 + 0 \cdot 005359 \frac{1}{\Theta} + 151 \cdot 1186\ \Theta - 910.2424\ \Theta^2 +$$

$$+ 3071 \cdot 66\ \Theta^3 - 5432 \cdot 9\ \Theta^4 + 3936 \cdot 98\ \Theta^5, \tag{13}$$

where $\Theta = \dfrac{7}{100}$.

The deviation of experimental values from those calculated from equation (13) are given in Fig. 5. Fig. 5 indicates the calculated values to range within the experimental values, showing closer agreement with the recent measurements [17, 18]. Deviations do not exceed experimental error.

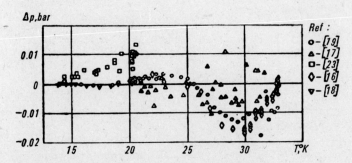

Fig. 5.   Comparison of calculated and experimental data on vapor pressure curve.

The critical temperature of parahydrogen has been determined by Roder *et al* [20], who give a temperature of 32.976±0.015°K. The same value was obtained in an earlier work [2], the reported value being 32.984 ±0.020°K (after a temperature correction of 0.01°K). The present authors accepted a critical temperature of $32 \cdot 98°$K. The critical pressure corresponding to this temperature is, according to equation (13), $p_{cr} = 12 \cdot 933$ bar, coinciding with values reported in references [2, 20].

Table 2 presents the orthobaric densities ρ' and ρ'' determined by joint solution of the equation of state (4) and the equation of vapor pressure curve (13) for the given temperatures along with densities given in work [20].

Table 2. Comparison of calculated and experimental [20] orthobaric densities

T, °K	p, bar	ρ', kmole/m³			ρ'', kmole/m³		
		Experimental values [20]	Calculated values	$\Delta \rho'$, %	Experimental values [20]	Calculated values	$\Delta \rho''$, %
32	11.204	22.7996	22.7790	0.09	8.6917	8.8028	—1.28
31	9.6383	25.0790	25.1193	—0.16	6.7170	6.7659	—0.73
30	8.2404	26.7454	26.7809	—0.13	5.3972	5.4288	—0.59
29	6.9931	28.1314	28.1136	0.06	4.4082	4.4307	—0.51
28	5.8831	29.2443	29.2569	—0.04	3.6197	3.6350	—0.42
27	4.9012	30.2437	30.2572	—0.04	2.9762	2.9851	—0.30
26	4.0394	31.1602	31.1526	0.02	2.4423	2.4449	—0.11
25	3.2901	31.9886	31.9795	0.03	1.9919	1.9932	—0.07
24	2.6447	32.7264	32.7332	—0.02	1.6141	1.6134	0.04
23	2.0955	33.4635	33.4336	0.09	1.2956	1.2942	0.11
22	1.6330	34.1067	34.0832	0.07	1.0273	1.0265	0.08
21	1.2487	34.6992	34.6981	0	0.8030	0.8031	—0.01
20	0.93418	35.2753	35.2734	0.01	0.6176	0.6177	—0.02
19	0.68121	35.7945	35.8166	—0.06	0.4653	0.4654	—0.02
18	0.48196	36.2733	36.3240	—0.14	0.3420	0.3419	+0.03
17	0.32906	36.8288	36.8053	+0.06	0.2440	0.2437	0.04
16	0.21539	37.2552	37.2578	—0.01	0.1678	0.1675	0.18
15	0.13416	37.6984	37.6790	0.05	0.1104	0.1102	0.18
14	0.07880	38.1246	38.0807	0.12	0.0690	0.06883	0.29

The parameters of the triple point, which satisfy vapor pressure curve (13), coincide with values reported in reference [12] : $T_{tr} = 13.803°$K, $P_{tr} = 0 \cdot 0704$ bar. They agree with the latest measurements [18] and have been applied by Goodwin and Roder [21] for obtaining an equation for the solidification curve.

$$(p - p_{tr})/(T - T_{tr}) = 30.7331 \exp\left(\frac{-5.693}{T}\right) + \frac{0.6755}{T}. \qquad (14)$$

Table 3 gives a comparison of densities on the solidification curve as obtained from the equation of state (4) using solidification-curve equation (14) and as reported in reference [21].

**Table 3.   Comparison of calculated and experimental [21] densities
on the solidification curve**

| T, °K | p, bar | ρ, kmole/m³ | | $\Delta\rho$, % |
		Experimental values [21]	Calculated values	
14.171	11.1599	38.50	38.49	0.03
15.247	45.5065	39.39	39.39	0
16.006	71.3301	40.00	39.98	0.05
17.000	107.076	40.76	40.75	0.02
18.000	145.115	41.49	41.48	0.02
19.000	185.138	42.19	42.18	0.02
20.000	227.065	42.86	42.86	0
21.000	270.827	43.52	43.52	0
22.000	316.367	44.14	44.17	—0.07
23.000	363.636	44.77	44.82	—0.11

As can be seen from Table 3, the agreement between calculated densities and the densities graphically derived in references [20, 21] can be considered satisfactory.

REFERENCES

1.   GOODWIN, R. D., D. E. DILLER, H. M. RODER and L. A. WEBER.   *J. Res. NBS*, **67A,** 173, 1963.
2.   HOGE, H. J. and J. W. LASSISTER.   *J. Res. NBS*, **47**, 75, 1951.
3.   MICHELS, A., W. DE GRAAF, T. WASSENAAR, J. M. LEVELT and P. LOUWERSE.   *Physica*, **25**, 25, 1959.
4.   JOHNSTON, H. L. and D. WHITE.   *Trans. ASME*, **72**, 785, 1950.
5.   HOLBORN, L. and J. OTTO.   *Z. für Physik*, **33**, 1, 1925.
6.   BARTLETT, E. P., H. L. CUPPLES and T. H. TREMEARNE.   *J. Am. Chem. Soc.*, **50**, 1275, 1928.
7.   WIEBE, R. and V. L. GADDY.   *J. Am. Chem. Soc.*, **60**, 2300, 1938.
8.   RABINOVICH, V. A.   *IFZh*, **5**, (5), 30, 1962.
9.   VASSERMAN, A. A. YA. Z. KAZAVCHINSKII and V. A. RABINOVICH. *Teplofizicheskie svoistva vozdukha i ego komponentov* (*Thermophysical properties of air and its components*).   Nauka, Moscow, 1966.
10.   GOODWIN, R. D., D. E. DILLER, H. M. RODER and L. A. WEBER. *J. Res. NBS*, **68A**, 121, 1964.
11.   MICHELS, A., W. DE GRAAFF and C. A. TEN-SELDAN.   *Physica*, **26**, 393, 1960

12. WOOLEY, W., R. B. SCOTT and F. G. BRICKWEDDE. *J. Res. NBS*, **41**, 379, 1948.

13. DEMING, E. W. and L. W. SHUPE. *Phys. Rev.*, **40**, 848, 1932.

14. *Termodinamicheskie svoistva individual'nikh veshchestv (Thermodynamic properties of individual substances)*. Acad. V. P. Glushko *et al* (eds.), Izd. AN SSSR, Moscow, 1962.

15. YOUNGLOVE, V. A. and D. E. DILLER. *Cryogenics*, **2** (4), 348, 1962.

16. WEBER, L. A., D. E. DILLER, H. M. RODER and R. D. GOODWIN. *Cryogenics*, **2** (4), 236, 1962.

17. VAN ITTERBEEK, A. *Physica*, **30**, 1238, 1964.

18. BARBER, C. R. and A. HORSFORD. *Brit. J. Appl. Phys.*, **14**, 920, 1963.

19. HOGE, H. J. and R. D. ARNOLD. *J. Res. NBS*, **47**, 63, 1951.

20. RODER, H. M., D. E. DILLER, L. A. WEBER and R. D. GOODWIN. *Cryogenics*, **3**, (1), 16, 1963.

21. GOODWIN, R. D. and H. M. RODER. *Cryogenics*, **3** (1), 12, 1963.

22. STEWART, R. B. and V. J. JOHNSTON. *Adv. Cryogen Eng.*, **5**, 557, 1960.

23. KEESOM, W. H. *Comm. Phys. Lab. Univ. Leiden*, No. 217a, 1931.

UDC 541.27

THERMODYNAMIC PROPERTIES OF PARAHYDROGEN UPTO 1500°K AND 5000 BARS

L. S. Serdyuk

On the basis of the equation of state derived in the preceding article and known thermodynamic relationships, the following expressions for enthalpy, entropy, and isobaric specific heat were obtained :

$$i = u_0(T) + RT_{cr}\left[\int_0^\omega (\alpha_1 + \beta B' + \gamma \varphi') \frac{d\omega}{\omega} + \frac{z}{\vartheta} \right],$$

$$S = S_0(T) - R \int_0^\omega [\alpha_0 + \beta(B - \vartheta B') + \gamma(\varphi - \vartheta \varphi')] \frac{d\omega}{\omega}, \tag{1}$$

$$c_p = c_{v\,\infty} + R \frac{[\alpha_0 + \beta(B - \vartheta B') + \gamma(\varphi - \vartheta\varphi')]^2}{(\alpha_0\omega)' + (\alpha_1\omega)'\vartheta + (\beta\omega)'B + (\gamma\omega)'\varphi}.$$

Values of i_0, s_0, and $c_{v\,\infty}$ were obtained from reference [1], where 0°K served as the initial value point.

A comparison between isochoric specific heats calculated from the equation of state and the measured values [2] showed an average deviation of approximately $1\cdot7\%$, theoretically due to the inconsistency in experimental thermal and caloric determinations and irregularities in the change of second derivatives of temperature functions. The deviations attain 15-20% in the critical region; these values had previously been noted by Kazavchinskii and Serdyuk and attributed to difficulties in attaining equilibrium in the near-critical region.

Van Itterbeek and Van Dael [3, 4], using sonic measurements [5] and data of reference [6] on saturation specific heat c'_s of liquid parahydrogen, determined isochoric and isobaric specific heats on the saturation curve. Table 1 shows c_p and c_v values obtained from the equation of state to agree satisfactorily with calculated values [3, 4].

Table 1. Comparison of calculated values of c_p and c_v at saturation with data of references [3] and [4]

T, °K	C_p, J/(mole . deg)			C_p, J/(mole . deg)		
	Experimental values		Calculated values	Experimental values		Calculated values
	[3]	[4]		[3]	[4]	
14	13.85	12.96	13.25	10.13	9.23	9.74
15	14.52	—	13.98	10.17	—	10.00
16	15.23	14.92	14.60	10.21	10.23	10.02
17	16.11	—	15.34	10.46	—	10.06
18	17.03	17.01	16.35	10.71	10.81	10.30
19	18.03	—	17.61	11.05	—	10.70
20	19.08	19.30	19.04	11.42	11.36	11.17

The heat of evaporation of parahydrogen has been measured by White and colleagues [7], using somewhat obsolete data in orthobaric density calculation. Roder and colleagues [8] corrected these results using orthobaric densities and calculated heats of evaporation according to the Clapeyron-Clausius equation. Fig. 1 shows values calculated from the equation of state to agree closely with the data of reference [8] and the results of reference [9], which are quoted in reference [8]. The average deviation of the calculated values from these data is 0.3%, with a maximum deviation of 1%.

One prerequisite for equilibrium in a two-phase, single-component system is the equality of pressures, temperatures, and chemical potentials of the two phases.

$$p'=p''; \ T'=T''; \ \mu'=\mu''. \tag{2}$$

A single equation of state which reflects all aspects of the behavior of a real gas must also satisfy these conditions. A comparison between

$$\mu'=i'-s' \ T \text{ and } \mu''=i''-s'' \ T, \tag{3}$$

values calculated from the equation of state showed the maximum deviation not to exceed 2 J/mole. The coincidence of calculated values of μ'

and μ'' at equal temperatures indicates the high reliability of the experimental p-v-T data near saturation and satisfactory approximation of these data by the equation of state.

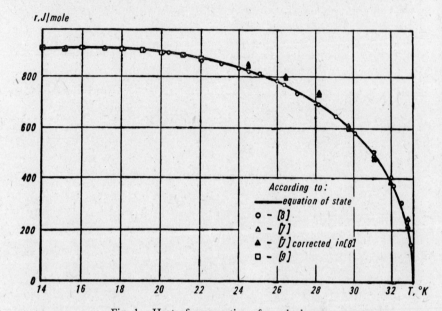

Fig. 1.   Heat of evaporation of parahydrogen.

Equations (3) can be rewritten in the following form :

$$\mu'=u'+p_s v'-Ts'; \quad \mu''=u''+p_s v''-Ts'', \tag{4}$$

where u', u'', v', v'', s', and s'' are the internal energy, specific volume, and entropy of liquid and vapor at saturation, and p_s is the saturation pressure at temperature T.

Since $\mu'=\mu''$, we may derive

$$p_s(v''-v')=u'-Ts'-(u''-Ts'')$$
$$\text{or}$$
$$p_s(v''-v')=f'-f'' \tag{5}$$

where f is the free energy.

However,

$$f'-f''=\int_{v'}^{v''} p\,dv. \tag{6}$$

From equations (5) and (6), we derive

$$p_s (v''-v') = \int_{v'}^{v''} p\,dv. \tag{7}$$

Equation (7) expresses Maxwell's rule, which states that an isobar corresponding to a phase transformation at a given temperature possesses a shape such that areas obtained on intersection with the isotherm are equal. Thus, the equality of chemical potentials calculated from the equation of state indicates that the equation of states and its derivatives, which constitute a continuous function of parameters, satisfy Maxwell's rule.

Table 2. Thermodynamic properties of parahydrogen

p, bar	v, cm³/mole	i, J/mole	s J/(mole . deg)	c_p	v, cm³/mole	i, J/mole	s J/(mole . deg)	c_p
			at 14°K				at 16°K	
0.5	26.25	—622	10.03	13.24	26.83	—594	11.92	14.59
1.0	26.23	—621	10.02	13.23	26.82	—593	11.90	14.57
1.5	26.22	—619	10.01	13.22	26.80	—592	11.89	14.54
2.0	26.20	—618	9.99	13.21	26.78	—591	11.87	14.52
3.0	26.17	—616	9.97	13.19	26.75	—588	11.84	14.48
4.0	26.14	—614	9.96	13.17	26.71	—586	11.81	14.44
5.0	26.11	—612	9.91	13.16	26.68	—584	11.78	14.40
6.0	—	—	—		26.64	—582	11.75	14.36
8.0	—	—	—	—	26.58	—578	11.69	14.28
10.0	—	—	—	—	26.51	—573	11.63	14.20
12.0	—	—	—	—	26.45	—569	11.57	14.13
14.0	—	—	—	—	26.39	—564	11.52	14.06
16.0	—	—	—	—	26.33	—560	11.46	13.99
20.0	—	—	—	—	26.21	—551	11.35	13.86
30.0	—	—	—	—	25.94	—529	11.10	13.57
40.0	—	—	—	—	25.68	—507	10.86	13.31
50.0	—	—	—	—	25.45	—485	10.64	13.08
60.0	—	—	—	—	25.23	—463	10.43	12.87
			at 18°K				at 20°K	
0.5	27.53	—563	13.77	16.35	3,171.3	—397	66.65	22.03
1.0	27.51	—562	13.75	16.32	28.35	—526	15.71	19.03
1.5	27.49	—561	13.73	16.28	28.32	—525	15.69	18.98
2.0	27.47	—560	13.71	16.25	28.29	—524	15.66	18.94
3.0	27.42	—558	13.67	16.19	28.24	—522	15.62	18.84
4.0	27.38	—556	13.64	16.13	28.19	—520	15.57	18.75

Table 2—*Continued*

p, bar	v, cm³/mole	i, J/mole	s J/(mole . deg)	c_p	v, cm³/mole	i, J/mole	s J/(mole . deg)	c_p
			at 18°K				at 20°K	
5.0	27.34	—554	13.60	16.07	28.14	—518	15.53	18.67
6.0	27.30	—552	13.56	16.01	28.09	—516	15.49	18.58
8.0	27.22	—548	13.49	15.90	27.99	—512	15.40	18.42
10.0	27.14	—543	13.42	15.79	27.89	—508	15.32	18.27
12.0	27.07	—539	13.36	15.69	27.80	—504	15.24	18.12
14.0	27.00	—535	13.29	15.59	27.71	—500	15.16	17.98
16.0	26.92	—531	13.23	15.50	27.62	—496	15.08	17.85
20.0	26.79	—522	13.10	15.32	27.46	—488	14.94	17.61
30.0	26.46	—501	12.80	14.92	27.08	—468	14.59	17.08
40.0	26.17	—480	12.53	14.58	26.74	—447	14.28	16.64
50.0	25.91	—458	12.28	14.28	26.43	—426	13.99	16.27
60.0	25.66	—437	12.04	14.01	26.15	—405	13.72	15.95
80.0	25.22	—393	11.61	13.55	25.66	—363	13.24	15.42
100.0	24.84	—350	11.23	13.17	25.23	—321	12.81	14.99
150.0	—	—	—	—	24.35	—215	11.91	14.17
200.0	—	—	—	—	23.66	—110	11.17	13.58
			at 24°K				at 28°K	
0.5	3,874.1	483	70.56	21.61	4,564.6	570	73.92	21.38
1.0	1,875.5	468	64.40	22.59	2,235.0	558	67.88	22.05
1.5	1,206.6	452	60.60	23.80	1,457.4	546	64.23	22.81
2.0	869.8	434	57.73	25.31	1,067.6	532	61.54	23.66
3.0	30.52	—435	19.55	25.55	675.5	504	57.50	25.81
4.0	30.42	—433	19.47	25.29	476.4	472	54.34	28.86
5.0	30.33	—432	19.40	25.05	353.3	435	51.56	33.70
6.0	30.24	—431	19.33	24.82	34.15	—311	23.95	37.32
8.0	30.06	—428	19.20	24.39	33.68	—312	23.67	35.07
10.0	29.90	—425	19.08	24.01	33.27	—312	23.42	33.36
12.0	29.74	—422	18.95	23.66	32.91	—312	23.19	32.00
14.0	29.59	—419	18.84	23.35	32.59	—311	22.98	30.89
16.0	29.45	—415	18.72	23.05	32.29	—310	22.79	29.95
20.0	29.19	—409	18.51	22.53	31.77	—307	22.44	28.47
30.0	28.61	—391	18.03	21.50	30.75	—296	21.72	26.00
40.0	28.12	—373	17.61	20.72	29.96	—282	21.13	24.44
50.0	27.69	—354	17.24	20.11	29.32	—266	20.63	23.33
60.0	27.31	—335	16.90	19.60	28.78	—250	20.19	22.49
80.0	26.66	—295	16.30	18.81	27.90	—214	19.43	21.26
100.0	26.12	—255	15.78	18.21	27.19	—177	18.80	20.39
150.0	25.05	—153	14.71	17.17	25.87	— 79	17.54	18.97
200.0	24.24	— 50	13.85	16.47	24.91	20	16.57	18.06
300.0	—	—	—	—	23.53	220	15.06	16.94

Table 2—*Continued*

p, bar	v, cm³/mole	i, J/mole	s J/(mole . deg)	c_p J/(mole . deg)	v, cm³/mole	i, J/mole	s J/(mole . deg)	c_p J/(mole . deg)
			at 32°K				at 34°K	
0.5	5,247.6	655	76.79	21.23	5,587.2	698	78.06	21.17
1.0	2,586.2	645	70.83	21.71	2,759.8	689	72.13	21.50
1.5	1,698.6	635	67.26	22.23	1,816.9	679	68.58	22.02
2.0	1,254.3	625	64.66	22.79	1,345.2	670	66.02	22.49
3.0	809.0	603	60.85	24.08	872.8	651	62.28	23.54
4.0	585.2	580	57.98	25.64	635.8	630	59.50	24.75
5.0	449.8	555	55.60	27.60	492.9	609	57.22	26.20
6.0	358.4	528	53.50	30.13	397.9	586	55.25	27.94
8.0	240.2	464	49.66	38.60	275.0	535	51.79	32.85
10.0	160.9	373	45.59	63.42	198.6	473	48.60	41.63
12.0	42.07	—125	29.40	92.89	142.7	390	45.18	62.40
14.0	39.69	—147	28.45	62.67	91.25	245	40.22	171.37
16.0	38.30	—159	27.83	51.79	50.25	7	32.83	160.93
20.0	36.52	—172	26.98	41.96	41.66	— 70	30.04	63.49
30.0	34.05	—180	25.62	32.99	36.58	—108	27.78	38.91
40.0	32.57	—176	24.71	29.25	34.35	—114	26.57	32.57
50.0	31.51	—166	24.00	27.07	32.91	—110	25.70	29.40
60.0	30.68	—154	23.41	25.61	31.85	—101	25.01	27.43
80.0	29.42	—125	22.45	23.69	31.01	— 89	24.42	26.05
100.0	28.48	— 92	21.68	22.44	29.21	— 45	23.06	23.54
150.0	26.81	— 1	20.20	20.55	27.33	— 41	21.46	21.39
200.0	25.66	— 94	19.09	19.42	26.07	134	20.28	20.15
300.0	24.08	289	17.42	18.07	24.37	326	18.52	18.69
400.0	22.97	483	16.14	17.30	23.21	518	17.19	17.86
			at 36°K				at 40°K	
0.5	5,925.9	740	79.27	21.12	6,601.1	825	81.50	21.07
1.0	2,932.4	732	73.36	24.48	3,275.2	818	75.63	21.34
1.5	1,934.2	724	69.84	21.85	2,166.4	810	72.14	21.62
2.0	1,435.0	715	67.30	22.25	1,611.8	803	69.63	21.91
3.0	935.2	698	63.62	23.11	1,057.2	789	66.03	22.53
4.0	684.8	680	60.89	24.09	779.6	774	63.39	23.21
5.0	534.2	661	58.69	25.22	612.9	759	61.28	23.95
6.0	433.3	640	56.80	26.51	501.5	743	59.50	24.76
8.0	306.0	598	53.58	29.84	361.9	710	56.55	26.65
10.0	228.0	549	50.76	34.73	277.6	674	54.08	29.00
12.0	174.0	492	48.06	42.65	220.8	636	51.87	31.98
14.0	133.1	421	45.26	57.23	179.8	595	49.86	35.84
16.0	99.25	328	42.03	87.80	148.5	550	47.92	40.87
20.0	56.14	110	35.14	115.08	104.0	446	44.09	55.19
30.0	40.30	— 21	30.24	47.97	55.08	211	36.36	54.08
40.0	36.62	— 44	28.55	36.79	43.64	123	32.98	46.97
50.0	34.60	— 48	27.46	32.13	39.21	93	31.17	38.52
60.0	33.22	— 44	26.63	29.47	36.90	83	29.98	34.07

Table 2—*Continued*

p, bar	v, cm³/mole	i, J/mole	s J/(mole . deg)	c_p	v, cm³/mole	i, J/mole	s J/(mole . deg)	c_p
			at 36°K				at 40°K	
80.0	31.33	— 24	25.40	26.44	33.72	87	28.34	29.46
100.0	30.02	3	24.44	24.68	31.88	106	27.17	27.03
150.0	27.89	85	22.71	22.25	29.12	178	25.16	23.90
200.0	26.50	176	21.45	20.90	27.44	262	23.74	22.42
300.0	24.67	364	19.61	19.34	25.32	444	21.72	20.66
400.0	23.45	555	18.23	18.47	23.96	631	20.25	19.72
500.0	—	—	—	—	22.95	818	19.08	19.20
			at 50°K				at 60°K	
0.5	8,281.1	1,035	86.20	21.10	9,954.6	1,248	90.07	21.50
1.0	4,123.9	1,030	80.37	21.25	4,966.1	1,244	84.27	21.59
1.5	2,738.1	1,025	76.93	21.40	3,303.2	1,240	80.80	21.69
2.0	2,045.2	1,020	74.47	21.56	2,471.8	1,236	78.42	21.79
3.0	1,352.4	1,010	70.97	21.89	1,640.5	1,229	74.96	21.99
4.0	1,005.9	1,000	68.44	22.22	1,224.8	1,221	72.48	22.20
5.0	798.1	990	66.34	22.58	975.5	1,214	70.53	22.41
6.0	659.5	979	64.79	22.94	809.3	1,206	68.93	22.62
8.0	486.3	958	62.12	23.72	601.6	1,191	66.35	23.06
10.0	382.3	937	59.96	24.57	477.1	1,176	64.32	23.51
12.0	313.1	915	58.14	25.48	394.1	1,160	62.62	23.99
14.0	263.6	893	56.55	26.48	335.0	1,145	61.16	24.47
16.0	226.5	870	55.12	27.55	290.7	1,130	59.86	24.98
20.0	174.7	824	52.60	29.95	228.8	1,099	57.64	26.04
30.0	106.8	704	47.49	36.74	147.1	1,024	53.33	28.85
40.0	75.60	596	43.54	41.25	107.3	952	50.05	31.53
50.0	59.91	516	40.60	41.39	84.66	888	47.40	33.48
60.0	51.32	464	38.46	39.48	70.63	835	45.24	34.40
80.0	42.63	415	35.62	35.14	55.09	766	42.02	34.14
100.0	38.26	403	33.78	31.94	47.07	731	39.75	32.88
150.0	32.92	436	30.92	27.63	37.82	725	36.18	29.75
200.0	30.20	503	29.10	25.56	33.58	770	33.97	27.66
300.0	27.15	666	26.66	23.53	29.27	912	31.13	25.42
400.0	25.35	843	24.96	22.43	26.91	1,077	29.22	24.25
500.0	24.09	1024	23.63	21.70	25.34	1,250	27.76	23.50
600.0	23.15	1205	22.55	21.36	24.19	1,427	26.59	22.96
700.0	—	—	—	—	23.30	1,605	25.60	22.61
			at 80°K				at 100°K	
1	5641.7	1694	90.73	23.72	8311.2	2201	96.37	27.07
2	3316.0	1689	84.92	23.83	4154.7	2198	90.58	27.13
5	1320.8	1675	77.16	24.13	1660.6	2189	82.88	27.32
10	656.2	1652	71.17	24.65	829.6	2174	76.97	27.63
20	324.6	1608	64.96	25.70	414.6	2145	70.94	28.23

Table 2—*Continued*

p, bar	v, cm³/mole	i, J/mole	s J/(mole . deg)	c_p J/(mole . deg)	v, cm³/mole	i, J/mole	s J/(mole . deg)	c_p J/(mole . deg)
			at 80°K				at 100°K	
30	21.49	1566	61.15	26.74	276.8	2119	67.31	28.81
40	160.5	1527	58.35	27.75	208.2	2095	64.68	29.36
50	128.4	1491	56.11	28.68	167.4	2072	62.59	29.88
60	107.3	1456	54.24	29.48	140.4	2052	60.86	30.35
80	81.85	1405	51.24	30.59	107.1	2018	58.07	31.16
100	67.40	1367	48.92	31.06	87.53	1992	55.89	31.73
150	49.76	1333	44.91	30.78	62.59	1962	51.92	32.30
200	41.79	1349	42.27	29.98	50.92	1970	49.19	32.20
250	37.22	1391	40.35	29.15	44.23	2002	47.15	31.92
300	34.23	1450	38.85	28.41	39.87	2050	45.53	31.58
400	30.47	1591	36.60	27.26	34.49	2172	43.06	30.88
500	28.13	1749	34.92	26.48	31.24	2316	41.22	30.23
600	26.47	1915	33.58	25.91	29.02	2470	39.76	29.72
700	25.24	2084	32.45	25.44	27.39	2630	38.55	29.31
800	24.26	2255	31.51	25.03	26.12	2793	37.51	28.96
900	23.48	2427	30.69	24.66	25.10	2959	36.60	28.62
1000	—	—	—	--	24.26	3126	35.81	28.27
1200	—	—	—	—	22.99	3465	34.48	27.58
			at 120°K				at 140°K	
1	9979.4	2775	101.5	30.19	11645	3402	106.37	32.11
2	4990.8	2773	95.81	30.23	5825.5	3400	100.59	32.15
5	1997.8	2767	88.14	30.36	2333.6	3396	92.94	32.24
10	1000.3	2757	82.28	30.57	1169.7	3390	87.11	32.39
20	502.0	2738	76.34	30.97	588.1	3378	81.22	32.67
30	336.3	2721	72.79	31.35	394.5	3367	77.72	32.94
40	253.6	2706	70.24	31.71	297.9	3358	75.22	33.20
50	204.3	2692	68.23	32.05	240.0	3350	73.25	33.44
60	171.5	2689	66.57	32.36	201.6	3343	71.63	33.66
80	130.9	2658	63.91	32.93	153.8	3332	69.05	34.07
100	106.8	2643	61.82	33.40	125.3	3324	67.02	34.43
150	75.36	2626	57.97	34.15	87.86	3322	63.29	35.11
200	60.27	2636	55.26	34.41	69.55	3338	60.62	35.48
250	51.50	2665	53.19	34.42	58.83	3369	58.57	35.64
300	45.80	2709	51.54	34.35	51.81	3413	56.97	35.70
400	38.78	2822	48.99	34.11	43.19	3524	54.34	35.69
500	34.57	2956	47.05	33.79	38.04	3654	52.38	35.60
600	31.74	3101	45.51	33.46	34.53	3795	50.80	35.46
700	29.68	3254	44.23	33.16	32.08	3943	49.48	35.29
800	28.11	3111	43.13	32.91	30.18	4096	48.36	35.13
900	26.85	3571	42.18	32.69	28.67	4252	47.37	34.98
1000	25.81	3732	41.33	32.48	27.45	4410	46.50	34.86
1200	24.22	4057	39.89	31.98	25.55	4729	45.00	34.60
1400	23.07	4392	38.73	31.36	24.15	5051	43.76	34.21
1600	—	—	—	—	23.11	5381	42.74	33.65

Table 2—*Continued*

p, bar	v, cm³/mole	i, J/mole	s J/(mole . deg)	c_p J/(mole . deg)	v, cm³/mole	i, J/mole	s J/(mole . deg)	c_p J/(mole . deg)
		at 160°K				at 180°K		
1	13,311	4045	110.74	32.89	14975	4712	114.64	32.82
2	6,659.2	4044	104.97	32.91	7492.4	4711	108.87	32.84
5	2,668.4	4042	97.32	32.98	3002.7	4710	101.22	32.89
10	1,338.3	4038	91.56	33.09	1506.2	4708	95.42	32.98
20	673.4	4031	85.65	33.30	758.1	4705	89.59	33.14
30	452.0	4025	82.19	33.51	508.9	4702	86.15	33.30
40	341.4	4020	79.72	33.70	384.4	4701	83.69	33.45
50	275.1	4016	77.78	33.88	309.8	4700	81.77	33.59
60	231.1	4013	76.18	34.05	260.1	4700	80.20	33.72
80	176.2	4009	73.65	34.36	198.2	4701	77.69	33.96
100	143.4	4008	71.66	34.63	161.1	4705	75.74	34.18
150	100.1	4018	68.01	35.19	112.0	4725	72.14	34.63
200	78.72	4042	65.40	35.57	87.74	4756	69.57	34.97
250	66.11	4077	63.37	35.79	73.31	4796	67.58	35.20
300	57.82	4122	61.73	35.90	63.79	4844	65.95	35.34
400	47.61	4234	59.16	36.00	52.01	4958	63.40	35.49
500	41.53	4364	57.20	36.04	45.03	5089	61.44	35.57
600	37.46	4503	55.61	36.03	40.35	5229	59.86	35.62
700	34.52	4649	54.28	35.98	36.99	5375	58.52	35.64
800	32.30	4800	53.14	35.90	34.44	5525	57.37	35.63
900	30.54	4954	52.14	35.81	32.43	5677	56.36	35.59
1000	29.12	5110	51.25	35.73	30.80	5832	55.47	35.55
1200	26.92	5425	49.72	35.59	28.32	6145	53.93	35.47
1400	25.30	5742	48.45	35.42	26.49	6460	52.64	35.39
1600	24.07	6062	47.36	35.08	25.08	6776	51.53	35.25
1800	23.12	6389	46.46	34.57	23.97	7094	50.58	34.95
2000	—	—	—	—	23.10	7419	49.77	34.77
		at 200°K				at 250°K		
1	16,640	5367	120.49	32.41	20799	6947	125.16	30.89
2	8,325.2	5367	112.33	32.43	10406	6948	119.39	30.90
5	3,336.6	5366	104.70	32.47	4170.3	6949	111.76	30.93
10	1,673.8	5366	98.90	32.54	2091.7	6952	105.98	30.97
20	842.5	5366	93.08	32.67	1052.5	6957	100.19	31.05
30	565.5	5366	89.66	32.79	706.2	6962	96.78	31.13
40	427.1	5367	87.22	32.91	533.0	6968	94.36	31.20
50	344.2	5369	85.31	33.02	429.2	6974	92.48	31.27
60	288.9	5371	83.75	33.13	360.0	6980	90.93	31.34
80	219.9	5377	81.27	33.33	273.5	6994	88.49	31.46
100	178.6	5385	79.33	33.50	221.7	7009	86.58	31.57
150	123.8	5413	75.78	33.87	152.8	7052	83.10	31.82
200	96.64	5450	73.24	34.16	118.4	7101	80.62	32.01
250	80.43	5495	71.27	34.38	97.95	7155	78.68	32.17

Table 2—*Continued*

p, bar	v, cm³/mole	i, J/mole	s J/(mole . deg)	c_p J/(mole . deg)	v, cm³/mole	i, J/mole	s J/(mole . deg)	c_p J/(mole . deg)
			at 200°K				at 250°K	
300	69.70	5546	69.65	34.52	84.30	7213	77.10	32.30
400	56.42	5663	67.12	34.69	67.30	7339	74.61	32.47
500	48.51	5795	65.18	34.78	57.15	7476	72.68	32.57
600	43.24	5937	63.60	34.85	50.40	7621	71.12	32.63
700	39.45	6083	62.27	34.90	45.57	7770	69.80	32.69
800	36.58	6233	61.11	34.94	41.92	7922	68.66	32.75
900	34.33	6386	60.11	34.94	39.07	8077	67.66	32.80
1000	32.50	6540	59.21	34.93	36.78	8232	66.77	32.84
1200	29.72	6852	57.66	34.89	33.24	8544	65.22	32.89
1400	27.69	7165	56.37	34.85	30.69	8857	63.92	32.90
1600	26.12	7479	55.25	34.80	28.73	9170	62.80	32.90
1800	24.87	7794	54.28	34.67	27.18	9482	61.92	32.91
2000	23.87	8111	53.43	34.38	25.91	9793	60.94	32.90
			at 300°K				at 350°K	
1	24958	8466	130.70	29.93	29116	9950	135.28	29.50
2	12466	8467	124.93	29.94	14565	9951	129.51	29.50
5	5003.1	8469	117.31	29.96	5835.4	9954	121.89	29.52
10	2506.8	8473	111.54	29.98	2925.3	9959	116.12	29.54
20	1261.7	8482	105.75	30.04	1470.3	9970	110.34	29.57
30	846.0	8490	102.36	30.09	985.4	9981	106.96	29.61
40	638.2	8499	99.95	30.15	742.9	9991	104.56	29.65
50	513.5	8508	98.37	30.19	597.4	10002	102.69	29.68
60	430.4	8517	96.54	30.23	500.0	10014	101.16	29.71
80	326.5	8536	94.21	30.32	379.2	10036	98.74	29.78
100	264.3	8556	92.23	30.40	306.5	10059	96.87	29.84
150	181.4	8609	88.78	30.59	209.6	10120	93.45	29.96
200	140.0	8686	86.33	30.71	161.2	10183	91.01	30.07
250	115.2	8727	84.42	30.83	132.2	10259	89.12	30.16
300	98.67	8791	82.86	30.93	112.9	10317	87.57	30.23
400	78.06	8925	80.39	31.08	88.72	10458	85.13	30.36
500	65.72	9097	78.49	30.97	74.23	10605	83.23	30.44
600	57.51	9215	76.93	31.23	64.57	10756	81.69	30.50
700	51.63	9367	75.63	31.28	57.66	10940	80.44	30.55
800	47.22	9522	74.50	31.32	52.47	11067	79.27	30.57
900	43.76	9678	73.51	31.36	48.42	11225	78.28	30.61
1000	40.98	9836	72.62	31.41	45.17	11384	77.40	30.63
1200	36.76	10151	71.09	31.49	40.24	11703	75.88	30.70
1400	33.69	10466	69.80	31.54	36.67	12022	74.60	30.77
1600	31.35	10780	68.68	31.57	33.95	12338	73.49	30.82
1800	29.30	11093	67.70	31.60	31.80	12653	72.51	30.86
2000	27.99	11405	66.82	31.62	30.06	12965	71.64	30.89
3000	23.34	12952	63.52	30.90	24.65	14502	68.31	30.89

Table 2—*Continued*

p, bar	v, cm³/mole	i, J/mole	s J/(mole . deg)	c_p	v, cm³/mole	i, J/mole	s J/(mole . deg)	c_p
			at 400°K				at 450°K	
1	33273	11420	139.20	29.34	37431	12884	142.58	29.29
2	16645	11421	133.44	29.34	18724	12885	136.82	29.29
5	6667.4	11425	125.82	29.35	7499.2	12889	129.20	29.30
10	3341.6	11431	120.05	29.36	3757.7	12896	123.43	29.31
20	1678.8	11443	114.28	29.39	1887.0	12909	117.66	29.33
30	1124.5	11455	110.90	29.42	1263.4	12923	114.28	29.35
40	847.3	11468	108.50	29.44	951.6	12936	111.89	29.37
50	681.0	11480	106.63	29.47	764.6	12950	110.02	29.39
60	570.2	11493	105.11	29.49	640.0	12963	108.50	29.41
80	431.7	11518	102.70	29.54	484.0	12991	106.10	29.45
100	348.5	11544	100.83	29.59	390.4	13018	104.23	29.48
150	237.7	11610	97.42	29.68	265.7	13089	100.84	29.56
200	182.3	11678	95.00	29.76	203.4	13160	98.42	29.62
250	149.1	11748	93.12	29.83	166.0	13233	96.55	29.68
300	127.0	11819	91.58	29.89	141.0	13308	95.02	29.73
400	99.30	11966	89.15	29.99	109.8	13459	92.60	29.81
500	82.68	12116	87.27	30.07	91.10	13613	90.72	29.87
600	71.60	12270	85.73	30.12	78.59	13769	89.19	29.92
700	63.67	12426	84.44	30.16	69.65	13927	87.90	29.95
800	57.71	12584	83.32	30.19	62.93	14086	86.79	29.98
900	53.06	12744	82.34	30.21	57.69	14247	85.81	30.00
1000	49.33	12904	81.46	30.23	53.48	14408	84.93	30.01
1200	43.70	13226	79.95	30.27	47.14	14732	83.42	30.04
1400	39.63	13547	78.67	30.32	42.57	15055	82.15	30.07
1600	36.52	13867	77.57	30.38	39.11	15377	81.05	30.11
1800	34.10	14183	76.60	30.43	36.39	15696	80.09	30.16
2000	32.13	14498	75.73	30.46	34.18	16012	79.23	30.20
3000	26.00	16038	72.41	30.59	27.35	17560	75.92	30.34
4000	—	—	—	—	23.78	19664	73.62	30.19
			at 500°K				at 600°K	
400	120.3	14947	95.80	29.70	141.2	17911	101.22	29.61
500	99.48	15104	93.93	29.75	116.2	18092	99.35	29.65
600	85.57	15263	92.41	29.79	99.47	18234	97.84	29.68
700	75.62	15422	91.12	29.82	87.51	18397	96.55	29.70
800	68.13	15583	90.01	29.85	78.52	18559	95.64	29.72
900	62.30	15744	89.03	29.86	71.52	18722	94.47	29.73
1000	57.63	15906	88.15	29.87	65.90	18885	93.60	29.74
1200	50.58	16231	86.65	29.89	57.44	19211	92.09	29.75
1400	46.00	16556	85.38	29.91	51.36	19537	90.83	29.75
1600	41.67	16879	84.29	29.93	46.77	19861	89.73	29.76
1800	38.66	17200	83.32	29.97	43.18	20184	88.78	29.77
2000	36.22	17518	82.47	30.00	40.28	20505	87.92	29.78
3000	28.70	19064	79.18	30.14	31.38	22072	84.66	29.88
4000	24.76	20575	76.87	30.19	26.74	23583	82.37	29.97
5000	—	—	—	—	23.86	25054	80.62	29.94

Table 2—*Continued*

p, bar	v, cm³/mole	i, J/mole	s J/(mole . deg)	c_p	v, cm³/mole	i, J/mole	s J/(mole . deg)	c_p
			at 800°K				at 1000°K	
1	66532	23169	159.55	29.63	83161	29149	166.22	30.21
2	33275	23171	153.79	29.63	41589	29151	160.45	30.21
5	13320	23176	146.17	29.63	16646	29156	152.83	30.21
10	6668.5	23185	140.41	29.64	8331.3	29165	147.17	30.21
20	3342.8	23202	134.64	29.64	4174.1	29183	141.31	30.21
30	2234.2	23219	131.27	29.65	2788.4	29200	137.94	30.22
40	1679.9	23236	128.98	29.65	2095.5	29218	135.55	30.22
50	1347.3	23252	127.02	29.65	1679.8	29235	133.69	30.22
60	1125.5	23269	125.51	29.66	1402.6	29253	132.18	30.22
80	848.4	23303	123.12	29.67	1056.1	29288	129.79	30.23
100	682.1	23337	121.26	29.68	848.3	29323	127.93	30.23
150	460.3	23422	117.89	29.70	571.1	29410	124.57	30.24
200	349.4	23506	115.50	29.71	432.4	29497	122.18	30.25
250	282.8	23590	113.64	29.73	349.2	29584	120.32	30.26
300	238.4	23674	112.13	29.74	293.7	29670	118.81	30.27
400	182.8	23841	109.74	29.77	224.3	29841	116.43	30.28
500	149.5	24017	107.88	29.79	182.6	30010	114.58	30.29
600	127.2	24173	106.37	29.80	154.7	30179	113.07	30.30
700	111.2	24339	105.09	29.82	134.9	30346	111.79	30.31
800	99.23	24504	103.99	29.82	119.9	30512	110.69	30.31
900	89.90	24669	103.01	29.83	108.2	30618	109.71	30.31
1000	82.41	24833	102.14	29.83	98.90	30843	108.84	30.31
1200	71.15	25161	100.64	29.84	84.85	31171	107.34	30.31
1400	63.07	25487	99.38	29.84	74.77	31496	106.08	30.31
1600	56.97	25811	98.29	29.83	67.18	31819	104.98	30.30
1800	52.20	26133	97.33	29.83	61.25	32139	104.02	30.30
2000	48.37	26453	96.47	29.81	56.48	32457	103.16	30.28
3000	36.69	28028	93.22	29.78	41.99	34018	99.90	30.19
4000	30.68	29553	90.95	29.83	34.58	35543	97.63	30.14
5000	26.96	31032	89.21	29.87	32.05	37028	95.89	30.16
			at 1200°K				at 1500°K	
1	99789	35265	171.79	30.99	124730	44759	178.85	32.30
2	49903	35267	166.03	30.99	62374	44761	173.09	32.30
5	19971	35272	158.41	30.99	24960	44767	165.47	32.30
10	9994.0	35281	152.65	30.99	12488	44776	159.71	32.30
20	5005.4	35299	146.89	30.99	6252.2	44794	153.95	32.30
30	3342.5	35317	143.62	31.00	4173.6	44812	150.58	32.31
40	2511.0	35335	141.13	31.00	3134.3	44830	148.19	32.31
50	2012.2	35353	139.27	31.00	2510.7	44848	146.33	32.31
60	1679.6	35371	137.76	31.00	2095.0	44866	144.82	32.31
80	1263.8	35406	135.37	31.00	1575.3	44902	142.43	32.31
100	1014.4	35442	133.51	31.00	1263.5	44937	140.58	32.31

Table 2—*Continued*

p, bar	v, cm³/mole	i, J/mole	s J/(mole . deg)	cp J/(mole . deg)	v, cm³/mole	i, J/mole	s J/(mole . deg)	cp J/(mole . deg)
		at 1200 °K				at 1500 °K		
150	681.8	35530	130.15	31.01	847.8	45027	137.21	32.31
200	515.4	35619	127.76	31.01	639.9	45116	134.82	32.31
250	415.6	35706	125.91	31.01	515.1	45204	132.97	32.31
300	349.0	35794	124.40	31.02	431.9	45282	131.46	32.31
400	265.8	35967	122.01	31.03	327.9	45467	129.08	32.31
500	215.8	36138	120.16	31.03	265.4	45639	127.23	32.31
600	182.4	36308	118.65	31.04	223.7	45810	125.72	32.32
700	158.5	36476	117.38	31.04	193.9	45979	124.45	32.32
800	140.6	36643	116.28	31.05	171.5	46147	123.34	32.32
900	126.6	36809	115.30	31.05	154.1	46313	122.37	32.32
1000	115.4	36974	114.43	31.05	140.1	46477	121.50	32.32
1200	98.56	37301	112.93	31.04	119.1	46803	120.00	32.31
1400	86.49	37625	111.67	31.03	104.1	47125	118.73	32.30
1600	77.41	37947	110.57	31.02	92.78	47443	117.63	32.29
1800	70.32	38265	109.61	31.02	83.95	47759	116.67	32.28
2000	64.62	38581	108.75	31.01	76.87	48072	115.81	32.27
3000	47.32	40124	105.46	30.92	55.39	49594	112.51	32.21
4000	38.50	41632	103.18	30.80	44.43	51064	110.19	32.10
5000	33.12	43113	101.44	30.75	37.76	52513	108.44	31.94

The evaluated accuracy of the tabulated values shows a true average of two to three units of the last figure for s and c_p and one to two units for i and v.

References

1. WOOLEY, W., R. B. SCOTT and F. G. BRICKWEDDE. *J. Res. NBS*, **41**, 1948.
2. YOUNGLOVE, V. A. and D. E. DILLER. *Cryogenics*, **2**, 1962.
3. VAN ITTERBEEK, A. and W. VAN DAEL. *Physica*, **27**, 1961.
4. VAN ITTERBEEK, A. and W. VAN DAEL. *Adv. Cryogen. Eng.*, **9**, 1964.
5. VAN ITTERBEEK, A., W. VAN DAEL and A. COPS. *Physica*, **26**, 1960.
6. YOUNGLOVE, V. A. and D. E. DILLER. *Cryogenics*, **2**, 1962.
7. WHITE, D., J. H. HU and H. L. JOHNSTON. *J. Phys. Chem.*, **63**, 1959.
8. RODER, H. M., D. E. DILLER, L. A. WEBER and R. D. GOODWIN. *Cryogenics*, **3**, 1963.
9. MULLINS, J. O., W. D. ZIEGLER and B. S. KIRK. *Technical Report*, No. 1, Eng. Expt. Station, Georgia Institute of Technology, Nov. 1, 1961.

UDC 541.11

VISCOSITY OF NORMAL HYDROGEN UNDER RAREFACTION

Yu. V. Mamonov and *S. A. Ulybin*

Review of experimental investigations

One of the most complete compilations of the properties of hydrogen was reported by Wooley, Scott, and Brickwedde [1] in 1948, and since then, numerous further experimental data have been obtained on the viscosity of rarefied hydrogen. In the present paper, a fresh analysis of all available experimental data has been attempted regarding compilation of the properties of molecular transport of hydrogen. This analysis evaluates the method and techniques of experiments, errors in individual measurements, and method of calculating viscosity from experimental measurements.

The work of Onnes and colleagues [2], one of the earliest studies covering a wide temperature range, has included the only experiment using the capillary method at 90°K. Experiments were carried out at temperatures of 20-294°K, and the authors estimated the error in experimental values to be ±0.2%. Further analysis, however, shows the scatter of experimental points within these limits at only 80°K, increasing at lower temperatures and reaching ±0.75% at 70.9°K.

Research reported in reference [2] further demonstrated the viscosity to be pressure-dependent at about 20.04°K in the range of 19-39 mm Hg. According to later studies [3], no such dependence was observed in the given pressure range.

Hence, the data of Onnes and colleagues for 20.04°K were considered unreliable and were not used during processing.

Vogel [4] investigated within the same temperature range using the relative, oscillating-disk method. Maxwell's formula [5] was used to calculate the viscosity from the results of measurements. The apparatus was calibrated at the viscosity of air. The maximum error in viscosity of hydrogen, according to the authors, was $\pm 5\%$ at 21°K.

Analyses of these works show Vogel's techniques and method to be somewhat inferior to those used in later studies, for instance in works [6, 7], and reveal Maxwell's approximate formula and calibration of the apparatus applied only at room temperature to yield potentially erroneous results at low temperatures [8, 9]. Furthermore, on comparison with the apparatus reported in reference [6], we estimated the sensitivity of the Vogel apparatus to be potentially inadequate at low temperatures.

The particular comments on Vogel's work also considerably apply to Günther's work [10], which employed a slightly improved version of the same apparatus.

In later investigations by Van Itterbeek and others [3, 6, 7, 11-13], Suzerland and Mass [14], Johnston and McCloskey [15], Kestin *et al.* [9], and Menabde [16], the theory of torsional oscillations and experimental techniques were analyzed. For instance, Van Itterbeek [17], Macwood and then Kestin [9] obtained new expressions for calculation proven more [18], accurate than Maxwell's formula [5].

The viscosity of hydrogen was studied by Van Itterbeek and colleagues [3, 6, 7, 11-13, 19]. The results of their earliest work [19] differ considerably from those of later studies, and thus do not appear to be reliable.

In reference [11], apparatus calibration was closely studied, and the results obtained in this work agree closely with the values obtained by Onnes and colleagues [2] and are about 20% higher than the data of Vogel and Günther for 21°K.

Three more series of experiments [3, 12] were conducted on a similar apparatus and the results coincided with those of earlier experiments.

Van Itterbeek and colleagues constructed two additional improved apparatuses [6, 7, 13], one [6] of which was designed for low-temperature experimentation.

All the data of Van Itterbeek and colleagues, with the exception of data from reference [19], show close agreement. According to the authors, the error in these data is $\pm(2-3)\%$ at 14–80°K and $\pm(1-2)\%$ at higher temperatures.

Measurements by Suzerland and Mass [14] were conducted at 74.76–293.86°K. Johnston and McCloskey [15] subsequently improved their apparatus and experimental procedure, and calculated the experimental error of the improved apparatus to be 0.3-0.15% at 300°K. The results of reference [15] show closer agreement with those of works [3, 6, 7, 11, 12] than do the results of Suzerland and Mass [14].

Menabde's apparatus [16] was calibrated with helium, for which viscosity values with an error of $\pm 2\%$ were proven available [7]. The relative measurements of Menabde were conducted quite accurately, thus rendering the total probable error in the viscosity of hydrogen values to approximately $\pm 2.0\%$.

The oscillating-disk method for gas viscosity measurement was most precisely applied by Kestin [9], and Kestin and Nagashima's [20] values of hydrogen viscosity possess 0.1-0.2% accuracy at room temperature.

Becker and Misenta [21] used the vibrating-cylinder method, with estimated error in measurement of logarithmic decrement in the vibration frequency at $\pm 0.5\%$ and estimated error in calculations of viscosity, according to results obtained on helium [22], at $\pm 5\%$. The values obtained in work [21] thus agree with those of works [6, 7].

Measurement of the viscosity of hydrogen has most frequently been according to the relative, capillary method [23-36], occasionally with temperature below room level [25, 32]. Values reported in reference [32] deviate considerably from previously reported data at $T < 270°K$, yet agree with the results in work [25].

At $T > 270°K$, the relative error of experimental values was estimated at $\pm 0.2\%$ by Trautz and colleagues. Since the present accepted values of viscosities of air [37-39], employed as standard by Trautz to determine the viscosity of other gases, are more accurate, the present authors have corrected the data of works [23-31] by 0.55%.

Subsequent work of Trautz was undertaken on a slightly improved apparatus and the data of his latest publications [25-31] show closer common agreement than with the data of his earlier works [23, 24]. The present authors have thus accepted the data of references [25-31] as more reliable. The experimental data of Golubev [34, 40], Kompaneits [36], and Wobser and Muller [41] agree with the corrected data of Trautz and colleagues [25-31] within limits of experimental error. It is difficult to ascertain the error in Adzumi's data [33] on the basis of his report, as his data insufficiently agree with most of the available data.

Analysis of the results of investigations

When measured results are plotted as $\eta = f(T)$, the scatter is observed as maximum at low temperatures, decreasing inversely with temperature upto room temperature level, and then increasing slightly with further increase in temperature. At $T = 20°K$, the scatter is approximately $\pm 20\%$.

Hence, further analysis has been required, involving comparison of the results of different studies for selection of the most reliable data.

Plots of $\eta = f(T)$ show Vogel's data for 21°K and Gunter's data for 15-21°K to deviate from the generally established relationship, indicating the inadequate reliability of these data.

The averaged results reported by Van Itterbeek and colleagues [6, 7], appearing to be the most reliable data for 14-80°K, have been applied to investigations by the present authors. Other available data in this temperature range agree with these averaged values within limits of experimental error.

The selection of reference points for the temperature range of 80-270°K can be performed simply and statistically, and the same principle as that for the 14-80°K range can be accurately employed. For the 90-260°K range, the present authors concentrated on the data of Johnston and McCloskey [15], Onnes and colleagues [2], and Trautz and Stauf [25]. Other experimental data agree with these within limits of experimental error.

At room temperature level, values obtained by the oscillating-disk method approximate those obtained by the capillary method [25-31], although Trautz's values are higher by a fraction of a percent. Thus, in selection of reference values at 273-500°K, the present authors have estimated the averaged comparable values reported in references [25-31] as increased by $+0.2\%$, within the limits of experimental error. At $T>500°K$, this correction was not included. Our final accepted values for $T>273°K$ agree within limits of experimental error with the majority of other reported experimental values, deviating by 0.2% from the data of Kestin and Nagashima [20].

Table 1 presents experimentally determined viscosities of rarefied hydrogen employed in our investigations.

Table 1.   Experimentally determined viscosities of rarefied hydrogen employed in present investigation

$T, °K$	$\eta \cdot 10^8$ $n \cdot sec/m^2$	Author, year of publication, and reference	$T, °K$	$\eta \cdot 10^8$ $n \cdot sec/m^2$	Author, year of publication, and reference
293.15	{930}	Graham, 1849 [14]	288.15	{970}	Rosander, 1900 [14]
288.71	{968.3}	Maxwell, 1866 [5]	288.15	(889)	
			372.35	1059	
287.45	(894)	Obermayer, 1875 [14]	455.55	1215	Breitenbach, 1901 [14]
326.55	(976)		575.15	1392	
288.15	{923}	Kundt and Warburg, 1875 [14]	287.65	877	Markovski, 1904 [52]
			457.35	1212	
293.15	(890)	Warburg, 1876 [14]			
372.45	{1086}		284.55	(869)	Klyaint, 1905 [14]
289	{928.5}	Puluy, 1876 [14]	287.8	(876.8)	Korsh, 1909 [14]

Table 1—*Continued*

T, °K	$\eta \cdot 10^8$ $n \cdot \sec/m^2$	Author, year of publication, and reference
292.11	(892.46)	Fel'ker 1910 [14]
285.15	{915}	Thomsen, 1911 [53]
285.4	864	Roberts, 1912 [54]
296.15	882.163	Jen, 1919 [56]
296.15	880	Ishida, 1923 [57]
273.15	(849)	Klemens and Remi, 1923 [58]
287.35	{899}	Suhrman, 1923 [59]
15.2	54	Günther, 1924 [10]
15.3	60	
15.4	56	
15.6	59	
20.4	85	
20.5	87	
20.7	88	
20.8	83	
80.4	362	
80.8	365	
81.0	367	
273.1	848	
273.1	850	
273.1	851	
286.21	880	Trautz and Weizel, 1925 [23]
289.23	887	
342.17	994	
364.19	1036	
373.15	1050	
473.15	1239	
290.15	886	Trautz and Narath, 1926 [24]
294.15	895	
318.15	945	
327.15	963	
343.15	994	
365.15	1037	
372.15	1055	
472.15	1237	
523.15	1322	

T, °K	$\eta \cdot 10^8$ $n \cdot \sec/m^2$	Author, year of publication, and reference
293.15	875	Trautz and Binkele, 1930 [28]
323.15	937	
373.15	1029	
423.15	1125	
473.15	1211	
523.15	1296	
473.15	1215	Trautz and Zink, 1930 [29]
572.15	1381	
685.15	1554	
763.15	1672	
864.15	1829	
986.15	1982	
1098.15	2137	
292.65	875	Trautz and Sorg, 1931 [30]
323.45	938	
373.55	1033	
423.15	1126	
472.95	1212	
523.15	1297	
301.25	892	Trautz and Kurz, 1931 [31]
352.25	992.8	
402.55	1086	
447.65	1167	
502.25	1260	
551.15	1344	
14.1	74.5	Van Itterbeek and Claes, 1938 [11]
15.1	80.8	
16.7	90.3	
18.5	102.4	
20.3	108.8	
77.3	345.8	
89.4	387.1	
293.0	882.7	
12.72	69	Van Itterbeek and Paemel, 1940 [3]
14.92	80.7	
17.12	93.6	
20.41	110.7	
68.87	(325.7)	
90.05	394.1	
291.8	(889)	
291.85	(889)	

Table 1—*Continued*

T, °K	η.10⁸ n . sec/m²	Author, year of publication, and reference	T, °K	η.10⁸ n . sec/m²	Author, year of publication, and reference
288.15	866 ⎫		40.03	(212)	
293.15	886 ⎪		44.97	224	
323.15	934.5 ⎭		47.86	236	Coremans, Van
373.15	1032	Golubev, 1940 [34]	55.45	269	Itterbeek, Beenakker,
423.15	1123		59.68	285	Knapp, and
473.15	1212		70.77	327	Zondbergen, 1958[6]
523.15	1296		77.77	353	
273.23	841.1		293.15	(886.4)	Kestin and Leiden-
	842.2				frost, 1959 [62]
286.78	869.2	Johnston and	14.4	79	
	868.5	McCloskey, 1940 [15]		79	
299.95	895.6		20.4	111	
300.05	896.7			108	
	895.3		71.5	326	
293.15	879.3			324	Rietveld, Van
313.15	919.4	Wobser and Muller,	90.1	392	Itterbeek, and
333.15	958.2	1941 [41]		386	Velds, 1959 [7]
353.15	996.3		196.0	670	
371.15	1029			675	
82.2	362		229.0	745	
90.2	392			(757)	
290.4	878		293.1	883	
291.1	877	Van Itterbeek, Paemel,		(886)	
291.7	881	and Lierde, 1947 [12]	20.03	110.9 ⎫	
292.1	882		20.04	110.9 ⎪	
293.3	884		20.04	106.0 ⎪	
293.6	885		20.04	103.5 ⎬	
293.15	(886.6)	Buddenberg and Wilke,	20.04	105.9 ⎪	
		1951 [35]	20.04	107.5 ⎪	
298.15	890		20.06	111.5 ⎭	
323.15	941	Kuss, 1952 [60]	70.9	(316.7)	Onnes, Dorsman,
348.15	993		70.9	319.8	and Weber, 1913 [2]
20.46	(103)		70.9	321.3	
20.46	105	Coremans, Van	89.6	392.1	
20.47	108	Itterbeek, Beenakker,	89.65	392.1	
27.42	146	Knapp, and	89.65	392.5	
28.87	151	Zondbergen, 1958 [6]	170.2	609.2	
29.20	155		170.2	609.4	
33.13	175		293.89	887.2	

Table 1—*Continued*

T, °K	$\eta \cdot 10^8$ $n \cdot \sec/m^2$	Author, year of publication, and reference
293.94	887.2	Onnes and Weber, 1913 [14]
21	{93}	
81.6	{372}	Vogel, 1914[4]
194.6	670	
273.1	(850)	Vogel, 1914 [4]
273.1	(849)	
287.94	(877.2)	Gille, 1915 [55]
192.35	666	
230.45	(734)	
272.15	830	Trautz and Stauf, 1929 [25]
292.55	875	
293.15	876	
294.85	880	
326.55	940	
327.45	942	
328.15	944	Trautz and Stauf, 1929 [25]
368.85	1020	
373.15	1030	
373.25	1030	
288.65	866	
293.55	874	
323.15	937	
326.15	947	
373.15	1029	
373.45	1031	Trautz and Ludewigs, 1929 [26]
423.15	1124	
429.15	1142	
472.85	1209	
473.15	1212	
523.15	1297	
523.55	1296	
293.15	876	
375.15	1031	Trautz and Melster, 1930 [27]
473.46	1210	
523.45	1296	
74.75	336	
77.95	(345)	Suzerland and Maas, 1935 [4]
89.75	388	

T, °K	$\eta \cdot 10^8$ $n \cdot \sec/m^2$	Author, year of publication, and reference
149.45	548	
160.55	577	
159.65	572	
175.65	615	Suzerland and Maas, 1935 [4]
210.55	701	
241.55	767	
273.15	(835)	
93.285	(876)	
288.61	{978}	Van Itterbeek and Keesom, 1935 [19]
90.05	{370.6}	Trautz and Zimmermann, 1935 [32]
194.65	(659)	
273.15		
293.15	924	
303.15	942	
313.15	965	
323.15	989	
333.15	1008	Adzumi, 1937 [33]
343.15	1032	
353.15	1048	
363.15	1072	
373.15	1090	
90.28	390.6	
	391.2	
	390.6	
117.48	474.2	
	474.0	
131.63	513.0	
132.69	515.4	
145.3	548.2	
	549.0	
155.94	576.2	Johnston and McCloskey, 1940 [15]
	575.3	
169.07	(603.9)	
	608.3	
184.01	643.4	
	(639.4)	
200.67	683.1	
	682.1	
216.06	717.2	
	718.2	
231.07	750.7	
	751.5	

Table 1—*Continued*

T, °K	$\eta \cdot 10^8$ $n \cdot \sec/m^2$	Author, year of publication, and references	T, °K	$\eta \cdot 10^8$ $n \cdot \sec/m^2$	Author, year of publication, and references
244.99	780.6		373.15	1035	
	781.7	Johnston and	573.15	1380	Golubev, Shepeleva,
259.87	812.4	McCloskey, 1940 [15]	773.15	1685	1966 [40]
	813.5		928.15	1900	
			1064.15	2080	
284.15	(872.7)				
373.15	1038		77.55	352	Lusternik, Teterina
473.15	1222		291.95	878	and Timrot, 1964
573.15	(1412)	Kompaneits, 1953			
673.15	1547	[36]	295	(907)	Cronin, 1965 [63]
773.15	(1715)				
873.15	1836		300	$2.098 \cdot 10^{-7} +$	Saran and Barua,
				$2.4141 \cdot 10^{-9} T$	1965 [64]
294.15	884.4	Kestin and Pilar-chuk, 1954 [61]	420	$-4.465 \cdot 10^{-13} T^2$	
			77.35	352	
14.52	75.1		90.15	391	
16.05	86.0		111.05	453	
16.97	88.1		133.55	518	
18.77	100	Becker and Misenta,	154.65	574	
20.34	108	1955 [21]	176.25	627	Menabde, 1965 [16]
64.0	(314		200.05	684	
77.2	367		237.55	770	
90.0	411)		293.15	888	
			297.45	897	
14.4	78.9		299.65	902	
20.4	113.2				
71.5	328.7	Rietweld and Van	293.15	882.8	Kestin and
90.1	394.9	Itterbeek, 1957 [13]	303.15	904.2	Nagashima, 1964
196.0	669.7				[20]
229	742.0				
293.15	(866.9)				

Those experimental data considered unreliable by the present authors appear within brackets, and those which deviate from averaged values beyond acceptable limits appear in parentheses.

Compilation of experimental data

Experimental values of the gas viscosities can be interpolated either by the equations of the kinetic theory [42] or by various empirical formulae. At present, the use of model interaction potentials does not allow accurate interpolation of experimental data over a wide temperature range [43, 44, etc.].

It has been shown [45] that some of the empirical potentials in reduced temperature T^* range of ~ 10 to ~ 100 suggest the relation :

$$\eta = AT^n, \tag{1}$$

where A and n are characteristic constants for each gas.

The approximation of experimental data over a wide temperature range would, however, require temperature-related changes in either A or n.

Variable values of n with constant A were applied by Golubev [46], Andryusov [47], and Stiel and Thodos [48]. These authors observed an advantage in having two functional relationships of n over two temperature ranges, rendering simpler approximation without impairment of accuracy, but rendering the derivative $d\eta/dT$ discontinuous at the intersection of the temperature intervals.

The present authors have applied a relationship similar to equation (1) in an analogous manner. On dividing the temperatures into two ranges of 14-95°K and 95-1100°K, we obtained simple expressions for A at $n=\text{constant}=0.6747$,

$$A=19.08 \text{ at } T=95\text{-}1100°\text{K};$$

$$A=19.08 \left(0.9092 + \frac{8.501}{T} \right)^{-1} \text{ at } T=14\text{-}95°\text{K}. \tag{2}$$

It was shown in work [45] that the relation

$$\eta=19.08 \ T^{0.6747} \tag{3}$$

allows some reliable extrapolation to moderately high temperatures. This observation has been considered in the present study during viscosity calculations of $T=1273.15°\text{K}$.

The results of our calculations from equations (1-3) were compared with the results of viscosity equations of numerous other authors. The following diagram shows the deviation of our results on density from the results reported by Golubev [46], Golubev and Shepeleva [40], Andryusov [47], Wooley, Scott, and Brickwedde [1], Rogers, Zeigler, and McWilliams [49], and Thodos *et al* [48] (results of reference [1] were used for the equation of the U. S. National Bureau of Standards [50]).

The diagram shows our results to agree most approximately with the values calculated from the equation of Wooley, Scott, and Brickwedde

$$\eta=855.58 \ \frac{T^{3/2}}{T+19.55} \ \frac{T+650.39}{T+1175.9} \tag{4}$$

over the entire temperature range. A deviation of 1-1.5% is observed only in regions of $T=20°\text{K}$ and $T=95°\text{K}$, and is much smaller than the scatter reported by the present authors at $T\approx20°\text{K}$; hence, we considered this deviation to be accidental. Furthermore, we considered the deviation at $T=95°\text{K}$ to be due to the inapplicability of equation (2) at the boundary

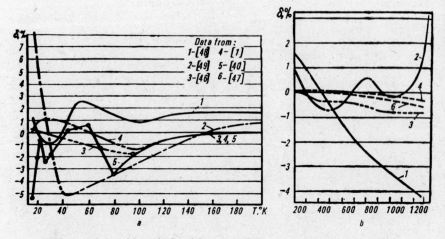

Deviation of viscosities calculated from reported equations from those obtained
in the present study from equations (1–3) *a*—20-180°K; *b*—200-1200°K.

of the temperature intervals. The diagram shows this deviation to be
unsystematic.

Considering these deviations and the fact that formula (4) does not
render the derivative $d\eta/dT$ discontinuous over the entire temperature
range, we have applied equation (4) in tabulation of Table 2, which gives
the recommended values of viscosity coefficients. The steps in Table 2
were selected according to the recommendations in reference [51]. The
viscosity coefficients in Table 2 have been rounded off to whole numbers,
facilitating averaged interpolation.

Table 2.   Recommended viscosity coefficients for normal rarefied hydrogen

T, °K	$\eta \cdot 10^8$ $n \cdot \sec/m^2$	T, °K	$\eta \cdot 10^8$ $n \cdot \sec/m^2$	T, °K	$\eta \cdot 10^8$ $n \cdot \sec/m^2$
10	51±2	350	994±5	850	1806±18
20	109±4	400	1087±5	900	1876±19
30	161±3	450	1177±6	950	1945±19
50	249±5	500	1264±6	1000	2013±20
75	341±5	550	1352±13	1050	2079±21
100	421±6	600	1429±14	1100	2144±21
125	493±7	650	1509±15	1150	2209±22
150	560±7	700	1585±16	1200	2272±23
200	681±7	750	1660±17	1250	2338±23
250	792±8	800	1734±17	1273.15	2361±24
300	896±4				

Selection of tolerances for tabulated viscosities

In determining the tolerances for the tabulated viscosities of hydrogen, we accounted for errors in individual investigations and for the scatter of data, in most cases the scatter constituting the determining factor, exceeding the estimated error in measurement.

We have estimated the following tolerances :

Temperature interval, °K	Tolerances, %
10-20	$\pm 4\cdot 0$
20-50	$\pm 2\cdot 0$
50-100	$\pm 1\cdot 5$
100-150	$-1\cdot 5$
150-250	$\pm 1\cdot 0$
250-500	± 0.5
500-1273.15	± 1.0

We do not consider these allowances to possess 100% accuracy; rather, they represent a first approximation, assuming that greater accuracy can result only following more detailed analysis and further investigation.

Conclusions

1. Analysis of the available data on the viscosity of rarefied, normal hydrogen indicates the experimental data to quite uniformly cover nearly the entire temperature range accepted for the international tables on hydrogen $(T < 1273°K)$.
2. The available data show considerable discrepancy, apparently the result of systematic errors in experimental study.
3. Tabulated viscosities show large allowances.
4. Further narrowing of the allowances would appear to be possible only with further, more accurate investigation.
5. In further investigation, measurement in the temperature range of 14-100°K should be primarily considered.

REFERENCES

1. WOOLEY, H. W., R. B. SCOTT and F. G. BRICKWEDDE. *J. Res. NBS,* **41,** 1948.
2. KAMERLINGH-ONNES, H., C. DORSMAN and S. WEBER. *Commun. Phys. Lab. Univ. Leiden,* **8,** 134a, 1913.
3. VAN ITTERBEEK, A. and O. PAEMEL. *Physica,* **7** (4), 1940.
4. VOGEL, H. *Annalen der Physik,* **43** (8), 1914.

5. MAXWELL, J. C.   *Phil. Trans.*, **156** (1), 1866.
6. COREMANS, J. M. J., A. VAN ITTERBEEK, J. J. M. BEENAKKER, H. F. P. KNAPP and P. ZONDBERGEN.   *Physica*, **24** (12), 1958.
7. RIETVELD, A. O., A. VAN ITTERBEEK and C. A. VELDS.   *Physica*, **25** (3), 1959.
8. KESTIN, J. and H. E. WANG.   *J. Appl. Mech.*, **24** (2), 1957.
9. KESTIN, J.   *Proc. Second Biennial Gas Dynamics Symposium*, Evanston, pp. 27-50, 1958.
10. GÜNTHER, P.   *Z. für Phys. Chem.*, **110**, 1924.
11. VAN ITTERBEEK, A. and A. CLAES.   *Physica*, **5** (10), 1938.
12. VAN ITTERBEEK, A., O. PAEMEL and M. J. LIERDE.   *Physica*, **13** (1), 1947.
13. RIETWELD, A. O. and A. VAN ITTERBEEK.   *Physica*, **23** (9), 1957.
14. LANDOLT-BÖRNSTEIN *Physikalisch-Chemische Tabellen*, I, 176, 1923; I, *Erg. bd.*, **1**, 143, 1927; *Erg. bd.*, **3**, 187, 1935, Berlin.
15. JOHNSTON, H. L. and K. E. McCLOSKEY.   *J. Phys. Chem.*, **44** (9), 1940.
16. MENABDE, N.   *Atomnaya Energiya*, **19** (5), 1965.
17. VAN ITTERBEEK, A.   *Wis. Natur. T.*, **6**, 257, 1934.
18. MAGWOOD, G. E.   *Physica.* **5** (5), 374, 1938; **5** (8), 763, 1938.
19. VAN ITTERBEEK, A. and W. H. KEESOM.   *Physica*, **2** (2), 1935.
20. KESTIN, J. and A. NAGASHIMA.   *Physics of Fluids*, **7** (5), 1964.
21. BECKER, E. W. and R. MISENTA.   *Z. für Physik*, **140** (5), 1955.
22. BECKER, E. W., R. MISENTA and F. SCHMEISSNER.   *Z. für Physik*, **137** (1), 126, 1954.
23. TRAUTZ, M. and W. WEIZEL.   *Annalen der Physik*, **78** (20), 1925.
24. TRAUTZ, M. and A. NARATH.   *Annalen der Physik*, **79** (7), 1926.
25. TRAUTZ, M. and F. W. STAUF.   *Annalen der Physik*, **2** (5), 1929.
26. TRAUTZ, M. and W. LUDEWIGS.   *Annalen der Physik*, **3** (3), 1929.
27. TRAUTZ, M. and A. MELSTER.   *Annalen der Physik.* **7** (4), 1930.
28. TRAUTZ, M. and H. E. BINKELE.   *Annalen der Physik*, **5** (5), 1930.
29. TRAUTZ, M. and R. ZINK.   *Annalen der Physik*, **7** (4), 1930.
30. TRAUTZ, M. and K. G. SORG.   *Annalen der Physik*, **10** (1), 1931.
31. TRAUTZ, M. and F. KURZ.   *Annalen der Physik*, **9** (8), 1931.
32. TRAUTZ, M. and H. ZIMMERMANN.   *Annalen der Physik*, **22** (2), 1935.
33. ADZUMI, H.   *Bull Chem. Soc. Japan*, **12** (5), 1937.
34. GOLUBEV, I. F.   Author's abstract of doctoral dissertation, Moscow Institute of Energy (MEI), 1940.
35. BUDDENBERG, J. W. and C. R. WILKE.   *J. Physical and Colloid Chem.*, **55** (9), 1951.
36. KOMPANEITS, V. YA.   In : *Sb. Nauchnykh trudov Leningradskogo Instituta Mekhanizatsii Sel'skogo Khozyaistva (Collection of works, Leningrad Institute of Technology and Agriculture)*, No. 9, 1953.

37. BEARDEN, J. A. *Phys. Rev.,* **56** (15), 1939.
38. WESTENBERG, A. A. *Advances in Heat Transfer,* No. 3, 1966.
39. KESTIN, J. and W. LEIDENFROST. Thermodynamic and transport properties of gases, liquids, and solids. *Symp. Thermal Properties,* Feb. 23-26, *ASME,* 1959.
40. GOLUBEV, I. F. and R. I. SHEPELEVA. *Gazovaya Promyshlennost',* No. 4, 1966.
41. WOBSER, R. and F. MULLER. *Kolloid-Beihefte,* **52** (6, 7), 1941.
42. GIRSHFELDER, D., C. KERTISS and P. BERD. *Molekulyarnaya teoriya gazev i zhidkostei (Molecular theory of gases and liquids).* IIL, Moscow, 1961.
43. BUCKINGHAM, R. A. *Planetary and space science,* No. 3, 1961.
44. MUNN, R. J. and F. J. SMITH. *J. Chem. Phys.,* **43** (11), 1965.
45. MAMONOV, Yu. V. and S. A. ULYBIN. In : *Teplofizicheskie kharakteristiki veshchestv (Thermophysical characteristics of substances).* Seriya : Fizicheskie Konstanty i Svoistva Veshchestv, No. 1, Izd. Standartov, 1968.
46. GOLUBEV, I. F. *Vyazkost' gazov i gazovykh smesei (Viscosity of gases and gaseous mixtures).* Fizmatgiz, Moscow, 1959.
47. ANDRUSSOV, L. Progress in international research on thermodynamics and transport properties. *Second Symposium on Thermophysical Properties,* Jan. 24-26, *ASME,* 1962.
48. STIEL, L. and G. THODOS. *AIChE Journal,* **7** (4), 1961.
49. ROGERS, J. D., K. ZEIGLER and P. McWILLIAMS. *J. Chem. and Eng. Data,* **7** (2), 1962.
50. HILSENRATH, J. and J. S. TOULOUKIAN. *Trans. ASME,* Aug., 1954.
51. *Instructions, "Thermodynamic Tables",* P. C. D11, London, 1965.
52. MARKOWSKI, H. *Annalen der Physik,* **14** (1), 742, 1904.
53. THOMSEN, E. *Annalen der Physik,* **36** (14), 1911.
54. ROBERTS, J. H. *Philosophical Magazine,* **23** (6), 250, 1912.
55. GILLE, A. *Annalen der Physik,* **48** (22), 1915.
56. JEN, K. *Phil. Mag.,* **38** (227), 1919.
57. ISHIDA, J. *Phys. Rev.,* **21** (5), 1923.
58. KLEMENC, A. and W. REMI. *Monatshefte für Chemie,* **44** (7, 8), 1924.
59. SUHRMAN, R. *Z. für Physik,* **14**, 1923.
60. KUSS, E. *Z. für angewandte Physik,* **4** (6), 1952.
61. KESTIN, J. and K. PILARCHUK. *Trans. ASME,* **76** (6), 1954.
62. KESTIN, J. and W. LEIDENFROST. *Physica,* **25** (11), 1959.
63. CRONIN, D. J. *Am. J. Physics,* **33** (10), 1965.
64. SARAN, A. and A. K. BARUA. *Canad. J. Physics,* **43** (12), 1965.

UDC 541.11

CORRECTION OF EXPERIMENTAL VISCOSITIES OF PARAHYDROGEN

V. E. Lyusternik and *Yu. V. Mamonov*

Until recently, no experimental measurement of the viscosity of parahydrogen over a wide range of temperatures and pressures has been reported, explaining the interest aroused in the work of Diller [1], giving viscosities of liquid and gaseous parahydrogen at 14-100°K and pressures upto 345 atm. Rosenbaum and Thodes's viscosity diagram for hydrogen [2] was almost entirely based on Diller's work.

Diller used a piezoelectric viscometer [3, 4] for measurement, and this method was subsequently applied by other authors [5, 9]. Advantages of the method are the effective design and simplicity of the apparatus and the accuracy in measurement of the initial electrical readings. With such an apparatus, Diller could limit the total error in measurements to $\pm 0.5\%$, and assumed this method to be infallible and not to require any calibration of the viscometer.

There is, however, some basis for doubt regarding the reliability of the viscosity values obtained in reference [1]. Some of the experimental data were eliminated due to their excessively high values. These values give sharp, false peaks on perfectly smooth viscosity curves. The reason for these distortions has not been properly ascertained, but there is a convincing argument that they are caused by a parasitic acoustic effect in the apparatus.

For an evaluation of Diller's method, it is important that similarly high (upto 300%) viscosity values were obtained by Welber and colleagues [5, 7] for helium on a similar apparatus.

Furthermore, viscosities of normal hydrogen measured by Diller on the saturation curve are systematically higher, by six to seven percent, than the data of Rudenko and Konareva [10, 15], Van Itterbeek and colleagues [11], and Keesom and Macwood [12], all of which show close common agreement.

On analyzing these data as well as those of Verschaffelt [13] and Johns [14], the present authors observed the values given in references [10-12] for the range of 14-20°K to form a reliable system of data with an accuracy of 1.5-2% on the viscosity of "liquid normal hydrogen" on the saturation line. This suggests that Diller's method of viscosity measurement gives systematically high values not only in the regions of the peaks.

Hence it is necessary to critically examine the piezoelectric method and introduce the necessary corrections.

While suggesting this method, Mason [3] and Mason [4] indicated the possibility of creating torsional deformations in the piezocrystal by applying an electrical field in the direction perpendicular to the X axis of the crystal (Fig. 1, a). The main component of the viscometer is a polished cylinder cut from monocrystal of quartz or another material in such a way that the axis of cylinder coincides with electrical axis X of the crystal. Using a high-frequency electrical field, elastic torsional oscillations are induced in the crystal, further inducing shear deformations in the viscous liquid surrounding the cylinder. Viscous forces acting on the cylinder cause damping of its oscillations.

The electrical circuit containing the piezocrystal is equivalent to the contour resonance [3, 16]. Measurement of quality Q or decrement Δ of

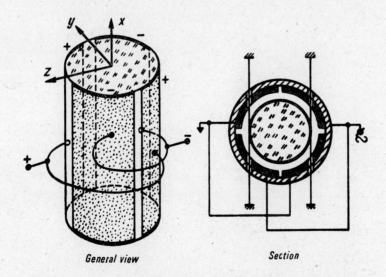

General view   Section

Fig. 1.   Method of application of electrical field to the piezocrystal.

such a contour enables determination of energy W^d expended by the cylinder during oscillation with a constant amplitude in the viscous medium. Viscosity of hydrogen is such that the quality of the contour is at least 10^4. In this case, the following expression applies with the required accuracy for the decrement

$$\Delta = \frac{\pi}{Q} = \frac{W^d}{2 W_k}, \tag{1}$$

where W_k is the energy of elastic oscillations of the crystal.

Experimental determination of the decrement is performed from resonance frequency f and width of resonance curve Δf at one-half maximum power.

$$\Delta = \pi \frac{\Delta f}{f}. \tag{2}$$

The cylindrical crystal is usually suspended in the liquid on two supports passing at the median line of height. Any slight friction in the supports or internal friction in the crystal induces supplementary decrement of oscillations Δ_0, determined by special experiments in vacuum. Assuming, as has Diller, that the main damping of oscillations is due to viscous forces in the liquid and that the supplementary damping is entirely taken into account by Δ_0, the relationship may be expressed as

$$W^d = W_\eta + W_0; \tag{3}$$

$$\Delta = \Delta_\eta + \Delta_0,$$

where W_η is the energy spent in one oscillation cycle in viscous medium,

$$\Delta_\eta = \frac{W_\eta}{2 W_k}. \tag{4}$$

In expression (4)

$$W_k = \frac{1}{2} \pi^2 M f^2 A_\tau^2, \tag{5}$$

$$W_\eta = \frac{S \eta f}{4 \lambda} A_\tau^2, \tag{6}$$

where M and S are the mass and total surface of cylinder; A is the maximum amplitude of torsional oscillations of the cylinder surface (at the edges of extremities); η is shear viscosity of the medium under investigation; $\lambda = \sqrt{\eta \pi f \rho}$ is the effective thickness of the boundary layer of viscous medium of density ρ at the surface of oscillating cylinder.

Considering expressions (1-6), the formula for the determination of viscosity applied by Diller has the following form :

$$\eta_{exp} = \frac{\pi f}{\rho} \left(\frac{M}{S} \right)^2 \cdot \left[\frac{\Delta f}{f} - \left(\frac{\Delta f}{f} \right)_0 \right]^2. \qquad (7)$$

Equation (7) assumes that energy is expended in the medium only to overcome viscous forces, and the development of a method to support this assumption is attributed importance in references [3, 4]. Mason has shown this to apply only to purely torsional oscillations of the cylinder; when these oscillations are accompanied by spurious longitudinal oscillations, the crystal generates ultrasound, which is dissipated in the surrounding liquid. It has been observed [5-9] that the appearance of the longitudinal oscillations is caused by such factors as surface purity of the crystal, anisotropy of its properties, configuration of electric field (Fig. 1), and degree of disorientation of the geometric and electrical axes of the cylinder.

Quartz tends to generate spurious longitudinal oscillations, due to the considerable anisotropy of the elastic properties of the crystal in the YZ plane, and due to the sensitivity of the crystal to deviation of the geometric axis from X (electrical axis). Another source is the ellipticity of the cylinder, which, besides the usual defects of preparations, is caused by anisotropy of the coefficient of thermal expansion, differing by approximately two times along axes Y and Z [3, 16].

Despite these observations, Diller employed in his viscosity measurements a solid cylinder with external electrodes (Fig. 1). Such an arrangement enables considerable expansion of the temperature range of measurements and simplification of the construction, valid even at the cost of accuracy of the method.

While studying a crystal of 5 mm diameter and 50 mm length, Diller observed viscosity peaks on isotherms above 27°K in the pressure range in which the velocity of sound in hydrogen is 750 m/sec. According to references [5, 7], at a torsional oscillation frequency $f = 39.1$ kHz, the wave length of the spuriously generated ultrasound is comparable to crystal perimeter, which induces a static wave in hydrogen. The wave dissipates additional energy and sharply increases the decrement.

Diller avoided peaks in subsequent measurements by changing the crystal diameter from 5 to 3 mm, assuming, as did authors of works [5, 7], that the effect of ultrasound on the measured decrement is caused only on acoustic resonance when a static wave is formed. Since the cylinder apparently emanates acoustic waves, it is correct to assume that the energy dissipation by these waves always effects the measured decrement, but that the effect is not so clearly evident in the absence of acoustic resonance.

Energy W_{ac} emanated by the crystal surface in the absence of static waves is equal to

$$W_{ac} = 2\,\pi^2 f\,a\,\rho\,S\,A_{ac}^2 \tag{8}$$

where a is velocity of sound in the medium; A_{ac} is effective amplitude of longitudinal oscillations of cylinder surface.

Quantity A_{ac} accounts for amplitudes of the longitudinal oscillations of different regions of the cylinder and also for the ratio of the surface undergoing oscillation to total surface S of the cylinder.

In the process of verifying the initial assumptions of the method, we also considered the possible effect of turbulence in the fluid under study, dissipation of electrical energy as a consequence of dielectric losses in the hydrogen filling the gap between the cylinder and electrodes (Fig. 1), and the contribution of interconnected masses of the substance and longitudinal oscillations in the cylinder to the energy W_k of the basic mechanical oscillations of the cylinder.

Calculations showed that these factors can be neglected (error below 0.1%).

The original equation (2) can be rewritten in relation to the aforementioned correction.

$$W^d = W_\eta + W_{ac} + W_0,$$

$$\Delta = \Delta_\eta + \Delta_{ac} + \Delta_0, \tag{9}$$

where

$$\Delta_{ac} = \frac{W_{ac}}{2W_k}, \tag{10}$$

or, using equations (5) and (8)

$$\Delta_{ac} = \frac{2\,a\,\rho\,S}{Mf}\left(\frac{A_{ac}}{A_\tau}\right)^2. \tag{11}$$

We should note that the difference $\Delta - \Delta_0$ is measured in the experiment as $\dfrac{\Delta f}{f} - \left(\dfrac{\Delta f}{f}\right)_0$ and is the starting value in equation (7) for calculating viscosities η experimental.

$$\Delta - \Delta_0 = \frac{S\sqrt{\pi\,\eta_{exp}\,\rho}}{M\sqrt{f}}. \tag{12}$$

Then, applying equations (5), (6), (11), and (12), equation (9) becomes

$$\sqrt{\overline{\eta\rho}} = \sqrt{\eta_{exp}\,\rho} - \frac{2\,a\,\rho}{\sqrt{\pi f}}\left(\frac{A_{ac}}{A_\tau}\right)^2. \tag{13}$$

Thus, equation (13) shows the actual viscosity η to be less than the value calculated, without considering the effect of ultrasound. For any given case, when the difference does not exceed 10%, equation (13) can be written as

$$\eta = \eta_{exp} - \frac{4\,a\sqrt{\eta_{exp}\,\rho}}{\sqrt{\pi f}}\left(\frac{A_{ac}}{A_\tau}\right)^2 \tag{14}$$

or

$$\triangle\eta = \eta_{exp} - \eta = \frac{4\,a\sqrt{\eta_{exp}\,\rho}}{\sqrt{\pi f}}\left(\frac{A_{ac}}{A_\tau}\right)^2 \tag{14a}$$

The correction required in Diller's measured viscosities on the basis of this analysis depends on two groups of factors. First, the physical properties of the fluid under study, sound velocity, viscosity, and density, all depend on the parameters of state, and second, these parameters are the characteristics of the oscillating cylinder and the frequency and ratio of amplitudes.

The frequency of the actual torsional oscillations of the cylinder is expressed by

$$f = \frac{1}{2\,l}\sqrt{\frac{G}{\rho_{cyl}}} \tag{15}$$

where l is length of cylinder; G is shear modulus of cylinder; ρ_{cyl} is density of cylinder.

In Diller's measurements, frequency f was maintained constant with a high degree of accuracy throughout the investigation and was consistent for both cylinders, which differed only in diameter.

Direct determination of A_{ac}/A_τ is impossible due to the complex nature of A_{ac}. It is possible, however, to assume that, since in the present investigation the amplitude of torsional oscillations and the shape of the electrical field were maintained constant, the A_{ac}/A_τ ratio also remained constant.

Thus, on introducing the viscometer constant

$$Z=\frac{4}{\sqrt{\pi f}}\left(\frac{A_{\mathrm{ac}}}{A_\tau}\right)^2, \tag{16}$$

we may derive the formula for correcting the viscosities measured by Diller [1]

$$\Delta\eta=Za\sqrt{\eta_{\mathrm{exp}}\,\rho}. \tag{17}$$

It is interesting to note that Lowry and colleagues [8] also observed a systematic discrepancy due to the sonic oscillations in measurement of the viscosity of liquid argon and standard liquids. Lowry assumed the correction required due to ultrasound in the measured decrement to be proportional to the density of the fluid under study and independent of the sonic velocity. In correcting Diller's viscosities, such a correction, which includes reference to the change in sonic velocity in the fluid, would not potentially render satisfactory results, since the velocity of sound changes manifold in the investigated range of state parameters.

The value of Z in equation (17) required for correcting Diller's data was determined by the present authors on the basis of a comparison with experimental viscosities for liquid hydrogen on the saturation line.

The viscosity of $1555 \cdot 10^{-7} \mathrm{g/cm} \cdot \sec$, measured at 18°K, served as the reference value. Diller's viscosity value for the same point is $1658 \cdot 10^{-7}$ g/cm · sec, yielding $Z=2.495 \cdot 10^{-6}$.

The empirical formula

$$\eta=\eta_{\mathrm{exp}}-2.5 \cdot 10^{-6}a\sqrt{\eta_{\mathrm{exp}}\,\rho} \tag{18}$$

was used for revising the entire data of Diller. The quantities in equation (18) have the following units : $\eta=10^{-7}$ g/cm · sec; $a=$m/sec; and $\rho=$g/cm³.

Values of the viscosity of sound were derived from references [17, 18] and density values were the same as those derived by Diller.

It follows from equation (18) and Tables 1-3 that the value of the correction decreases with decreasing density and barely changes the experimental values obtained at low densities, explaining the close agreement of Diller's data with reliable viscosity data for rarefied hydrogen [19] on extrapolation to low densities. The estimated error in the corrected viscosities is approximately 2%.

Table 1.　Corrected viscosities for parahydrogen (along Isotherms)

p, atm	$\eta \cdot 10^7$, g/cm . sec		$\Delta \eta$, %	p, atm	$\eta \cdot 10^7$, g/cm . sec		$\Delta \eta$, %
	exp	cal			exp	cal	
	$T=15°$K				$T=20°$K		
30.008	2722	2570	6	212.089	3613	3380	6
25.331	2646	2500	6	200.661	3465	3240	6
18.834	2516	2370	6	180.902	3336	3120	6
11.806	2403	2270	6	171.656	3115	2910	6
6.488	2313	2180	6	162.346	3026	2830	6
	$T=16°$K			145.832	2839	2650	7
				134.369	2715	2530	7
				124.941	2615	2440	7
63.878	2947	2770	6	109.649	2466	2280	7
56.219	2823	2660	6	109.057	2448	2280	7
49.834	2725	2560	6	93.542	2280	2130	7
40.488	2589	2440	6	83.429	2196	2050	7
31.179	2433	2290	6	79.567	2150	2010	6
17.352	2227	2090	6	65.755	2011	1880	6
	$T=17°$K			60.865	1975	1840	7
				53.128	1878	1750	7
99.341	3119	2930	6	41.357	1755	1640	6
78.697	2809	2640	6	39.376	1762	1650	6
54.247	2495	2340	6	31.619	1665	1550	7
28.375	2138	2010	6	20.587	1574	1470	7
8.854	1887	1770	6	18.393	1544	1440	7
	$T=18°$K				$T=21°$K		
117.904	3069	2880	6	254.537	3781	3530	7
104.074	2862	2680	6	224.032	3435	3200	7
88.624	2670	2500	6	185.608	3008	2800	7
75.695	2521	2360	6	155.650	2712	2530	7
61.398	2356	2210	6	125.629	2426	2260	7
48.953	2203	2060	6	103.305	2210	2060	7
31.628	1981	1850	6	78.704	1982	1850	7
17.136	1806	1690	6	67.112	1883	1750	7
	$T=19°$K			53.233	1751	1630	7
				41.502	1634	1520	7
126.794	2901	2710	7	34.505	1571	1470	6
111.910	2710	2530	7	21.096	1453	1360	6
95.508	2524	2360	7				
82.219	2367	2210	7		$T=22°$K		
65.581	2196	2050	7				
52.359	2056	1920	7	255.348	3471	3230	7
38.906	1894	1770	7	204.423	2971	2760	7
18.413	1680	1570	7	168.383	2645	2460	7
				164.715	2598	2410	7

Table 1—*Continued*

p, atm	$\eta \cdot 10^7$, g/cm . sec		$\Delta\eta$, %	p, atm	$\eta \cdot 10^7$ g/cm . sec		$\Delta\eta$, %
	exp	cal			exp	cal	
				69.859	1467	1360	7
$T=22°$K				61.449	1413	1310	7
				60.755	1397	1300	7
140.870	2381	2210	7	47.877	1298	1210	7
131.017	2281	2120	7	39.419	1250	1160	7
118.877	2178	2020	7	34.613	1211	1130	7
101.613	2026	1880	7	22.502	1114	1040	7
85.451	1906	1770	7	18.331	1084	1010	7
62.777	1709	1590	7				
59.573	1680	1560	7	$T=27°$K			
44.846	1546	1440	7				
25.889	1409	1310	7	286.861	2672	2460	8
15.133	1293	1210	7	259.479	2489	2290	8
				233.338	2319	2130	8
$T=23°$K				204.540	2141	1970	8
				177.863	1972	1820	8
252.319	3190	2960	7	147.120	1784	1640	8
222.343	2916	2710	7	125.815	1651	1520	8
185.707	2599	2410	7	105.928	1533	1410	8
148.964	2298	2130	7	89.288	1433	1320	8
118.330	2043	1890	7	72.658	1329	1230	7
96.954	1871	1740	7	58.591	1232	1140	7
73.856	1703	1580	7	48.193	1163	1080	7
57.297	1556	1450	7	39.638	1106	1030	7
44.852	1450	1350	7	29.017	1025	950	7
31.705	1352	1260	7	19.285	949	890	7
19.720	1254	1170	7	19.673	953	890	7
				11.723	882	830	6
$T=25°$K							
				$T=30°$K			
278.781	2982	2760	7				
261.872	2839	2620	8	313.044	2456	2250	8
231.121	2602	2400	8	271.159	2240	2050	8
219.289	2535	2340	8	224.901	1953	1790	8
198.736	2365	2190	7	166.780	1650	1510	8
181.841	2261	2090	8	147.971	1553	1430	8
171.015	2178	2010	8	123.871	1421	1310	8
158.121	2094	1930	8	120.652	1407	1300	8
143.873	1985	1830	8	89.974	1241	1150	8
132.581	1890	1750	7	89.267	1239	1140	8
122.101	1848	1710	7	72.961	1146	1060	8
114.114	1775	1640	8	61.137	1070	990	7
102.667	1694	1570	7	46.063	977	910	7
94.863	1651	1530	7	32.183	880	820	7
82.550	1561	1450	7	14.336	723	680	6
81.280	1554	1440	7				

Table 1—*Continued*

p, atm	$\eta \cdot 10^7$, g/cm . sec		$\Delta \eta$, %	p, atm	$\eta \cdot 10^7$, g/cm . sec		$\Delta \eta$, %
	exp	cal			exp	cal	
				19.997	423	410	4
				19.107	384	370	4
$T=33°$K				18.378	352	340	4
331.461	2232	2040	9	17.640	329	320	3
286.630	2021	1840	9	16.846	305	300	3
243.229	1819	1660	9	16.042	282	270	3
215.182	1687	1540	9	15.120	263	260	3
194.062	1592	1460	8	13.874	246	240	3
171.164	1495	1370	8	9.896	212	210	2
151.485	1400	1280	8	$T=40°$K			
124.365	1269	1170	8				
103.720	1168	1080	8	297.459	1655	1500	9
83.711	1065	980	8	269.818	1543	1400	9
65.556	961	890	7	245.657	1464	1330	9
45.165	832	780	7	222.208	1377	1250	9
30.477	723	680	6	197.214	1283	1170	9
21.211	630	600	5	175.091	1196	1090	9
14.421	530	510	4	150.187	1102	1010	8
12.920	429	420	3	126.062	1003	920	8
12.802	356	350	3	107.377	923	850	8
12.788	329	320	3	94.929	870	800	8
12.776	314	310	3	88.825	840	780	7
12.723	290	280	3	84.426	817	760	7
12.703	286	280	3	71.932	755	700	7
12.593	270	260	3	70.355	746	690	7
12.375	256	250	3	61.821	696	650	7
12.344	255	250	3	58.023	673	630	6
11.446	229	220	3	50.475	623	590	6
9.355	204	200	2	46.083	594	560	6
8.093	199	200	2	42.229	563	530	6
4.193	182	180	2	36.155	513	490	5
				35.07	498	470	5
$T=36°$K				31.203	446	430	4
				26.779	403	390	4
258.429	1700	1550	9	26.082	385	370	4
209.760	1496	1370	9	24.197	346	330	4
108.837	1329	1210	9	21.024	297	290	3
132.794	1172	1080	8	17.336	262	250	3
105.715	1049	970	7	10.649	227	220	2
75.687	903	840	7	5.154	215	210	2
57.204	797	740	7	$T=50°$K			
42.166	695	650	6				
31.087	601	570	5	345.722	1429	1290	10
24.517	517	490	5	319.804	1357	1230	10
22.133	485	470	4	278.013	1239	1120	10
21.005	472	450	4				

Table 1—*Continued*

p, atm	$\eta \cdot 10^7$, g/cm . sec		$\Delta \eta$, %	p, atm	$\eta \cdot 10^7$, g/cm . sec		$\Delta \eta$, %
	exp	cal			exp	cal	
	$T=50°$K				$T=70°$K		
249.095	1158	1050	9	326.525	1026	930	9
208.884	1039	950	9	296.857	960	870	9
187.380	975	890	9	245.829	854	780	9
162.565	820	820	9	195.527	745	690	8
144.598	838	770	8	159.854	664	610	8
125.191	770	710	8	124.009	582	540	7
109.916	714	660	8	103.150	529	500	6
96.057	661	610	8	88.298	491	460	6
89.580	632	590	7	68.119	441	420	5
76.010	574	540	6	40.223	380	370	3
68.786	538	500	6	19.679	345	340	1
61.438	501	470	6		$T=80°$K		
48.787	434	410	5				
41.244	384	370	4	234.883	943	850	10
28.444	324	310	4	274.350	856	780	9
18.223	287	280	3	226.731	750	690	8
9.422	261	260	0	186.062	672	620	8
	$T=60°$K			150.152	606	570	7
346.354	1203	1080	10	122.676	552	520	6
308.726	1118	1010	10	101.394	508	480	6
277.634	1046	950	9	82.548	473	450	5
248.652	976	890	9	63.680	438	420	4
214.894	891	810	9	42.852	404	390	4
186.810	819	750	8	17.746	371	360	3
156.286	736	680	8		$T=100°$K		
135.502	679	630	7				
113.439	619	580	7	339.566	845	770	9
94.661	552	520	6	308.982	803	730	9
82.397	509	480	6	275.364	757	700	8
67.717	458	430	6	234.671	701	650	7
56.727	420	400	5	188.834	639	600	7
45.890	390	370	5	150.838	588	550	6
32.552	344	330	4	123.086	549	520	5
21.792	318	310	3	95.370	512	490	4
13.097	301	290	3	66.817	480	460	4
7.331	293	290	1	36.159	446	430	3
				14.845	432	420	2

Table 2. Corrected viscosities for liquid hydrogen on saturation line

T, °K	$\eta \cdot 10^7$, g/cm . sec exp	cal	$\Delta \eta$, %	T, °K	$\eta \cdot 10^7$, g/cm . sec exp	cal	$\Delta \eta$, %
14	2543	2400	6	21	1284	1200	7
15	2302	2170	6	22	1187	1110	7
16	2039	1920	6	23	1105	1030	7
17	1829	1720	6	24	1026	960	6
18	1656	1550	6	25	957	900	6
19	1515	1420	6	26	890	840	6
20	1392	1300	7				

Table 3. Corrected viscosities for liquid parahydrogen on saturation line

T, °K	$\eta \cdot 10^7$ g/cm . sec exp	cal	$\Delta \eta$, %	T, °K	$\eta \cdot 10^7$ g/cm . sec exp	cal	$\Delta \eta$, %
14	2507	2370	5	24	1008	940	7
14.5	2341	2210	6	25	935	880	6
15	2213	2090	6	26	872	820	6
15.5	2073	1950	6	26.5	841	790	6
16	1975	1860	6	27	810	760	6
16.5	1856	1740	6	27.5	781	730	7
17	1777	1670	6	28	752	710	6
17.5	1685	1580	6	28.5	724	680	6
18	1605	1510	6	29	696	660	5
18.5	1538	1440	6	29.5	670	630	6
19	1470	1380	6	30	649	620	4
19.5	1413	1320	7	30.5	612	580	5
20	1354	1270	6	31	581	550	5
20.5	1306	1220	7	31.5	557	530	5
21	1253	1170	7	32	519	500	4
21.5	1206	1130	6	32.5	475	460	3
22	1161	1090	6	32.7	439	420	4
23	1081	1010	7	32.976	335	350	1

Figs. 2 and 3 display the viscosities of liquid normal hydrogen and parahydrogen on the saturation line. The corrected Diller data in either case agree closely with reliable data within limits of experimental error.

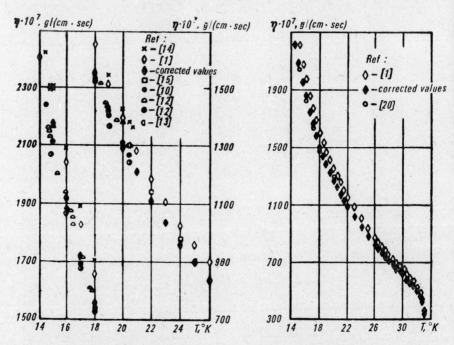

Fig. 2. Saturation curve for liquid normal hydrogen.

Fig. 3. Saturation curve for liquid parahydrogen.

The value of Z derived above allows calculation (from equation 16) of the ratio A_{ac}/A_τ to be $3 \cdot 10^{-5}$. Thus, in order to induce an error of 10% due to longitudinal oscillations in the piezoelectric viscometer, the effective amplitude of sonic oscillation can be as small as 0.003% of the amplitude of torsional oscillations. This indicates the necessity for thorough calibration of piezoelectric viscometers, especially for measurements on liquids or dense gases.

REFERENCES

1. DILLER, D. E. (NBS) *J. Chem. Phys.*, **42**, No. 6, 1965.
2. ROSENBAUM, B. and G. THODES. *J. Spacecraft and Rockets*, **4** (1), 1967.

3. MASON, U. *P'ezoelektricheskie kristally i ikh primenenie v ul'tra-akustike* (*Piezoelectric crystals and their use in ultrasonics*). IIL, Moscow, 1952.

4. MASON, W. P. and H. MURRAY. *Trans. ASME*, **69** (4), 1947.

5. WELBER, B. *Phys. Rev.* **119** (6), 1960.

6. BARLOW, A. J., G. HARRISON, J. RICHTER, H. SEGUIN and J. LAMB. *Lab. Practice*, **10** (10), 1961.

7. BETTS, D. E., D. W. OSBORNE, B. WELBER and J. WILKS. *Phys. Rev.*, **8** (90), 1963.

8. LOWRY, B. A., S. A. RICE and P. GRAY. *J. Chem. Phys.*, **40** (12), 1964.

9. DE BOCK, A., W. GREVENDONK, and H. AWOUTERS. *Physica*, **34** (1), 1967.

10. RUDENKO, N. S. and V. G. KONAREVA. *Zh. Fiz. Khim.*, **37** (12), 2761, 1963.

11. VAN ITTERBEEK, A., H. ZINK and O. VAN PAEMEL. *Cryogenics*, **4** (3), 1962.

12. KEESOM, W. H. and G. E. MACWOOD. *Physica*, **5** (8), 1938.

13. VERSCHAFFELT, J. E. *Commun. Phys. Lab. Univ. Leiden*, No. 153b, 1917.

14. JOHNS, H. E. *Canad. J. Research*, **17a** (12), 1939.

15. KONAREVA, V. G. and N. S. RUDENKO. *Zh. Fiz. Khim.* **41** (9), 1967.

16. BERGMAN, L. *Ul'trazvuk i ego primenenie v nauke i tekhnike* (*Ultrasound and its use in science and engineering*). IIL, Moscow, 1957.

17. RODER, H. M., L. A. WEBER and R. D. GOODWEEN. *NBS Monograph*, 94, 1965.

18. VAN DAEL, W., A. VAN ITTERBEEK and J. THOEN. *Cryogenics*, **5** (4), 1965.

19. COREMANS, J. M. J., A. VAN ITTERBEEK, J. J. M. BEENAKKER, H. I. P. KNAPP and P. ZANDBERGEN. *Physica*, **24** (12), 1958.

20. RUDENKO, N. S. and V. G. KONAREVA. *Zh. Eksp. Teoret. Fiz.*, **48** (2), 1965.

UDC 541.27

AN EQUATION OF STATE FOR HELIUM AT TEMPERATURE OF 20-1500°K AND PRESSURE UPTO 1000 BAR

V. I. Kudashev and *V. N. Taran*

Study of the thermodynamic properties of helium over a wide temperature range is of interest from both engineering and scientific viewpoints, as it allows analysis of the behavior of a real gas at high reduced temperatures (upto 100-200 T_{cr}) and derivation of equations of state for substances within this temperature range.

The experimental data of Holborn and Otto [1], Wiebe, Gaddy, and Heins [2], Canfield, Leland, and Kobayashi [3], Dobrovol'skii and Golubev [4], and Hill and Lounasmaa [5] were studied and analyzed to obtain an equation of state for helium. On the basis of these data and by adjustment along two sections, a skeleton diagram of the most reliable values was obtained.* In the process of development of the reference skeleton, discrepancies upto 0.5% were observed in the p-v-T data of various authors. Analysis of the reference values shows all the investigated isochores to possess a curvature with the same sign, suggesting the equation of state to have the form

$$z = \alpha_0 + \alpha_1 \vartheta + \beta \psi, \tag{1}$$

where α_0, α_1, and β are density (volume) dependent functions; $\vartheta = \dfrac{T_{cr}}{T}$ is inverse reduced temperature ($T_{cr} = 5.1994°K$) ; and ψ is function of temperature.

---

*Michel's data [14] were considered while mapping the reference skeleton, but were omitted from comparison tables for reasons discussed in reference [15].

When isochoric cross-sections were compared according to the method of Kazavchinskii [6], their curvilinear portions were observed to be affine, further suggesting feasibility of an equation of state of the same form as equation (1).

For investigating thermodynamic similarity and common nature of the elementary functions at high reduced temperatures, it is convenient to use the reduced second virial coefficient B/v_{cr} as function ψ. Determination of B/v_{cr} was performed under coordinates z-$1/\omega$ and $\omega = v_{cr}/v$ using the data of references [1-5, 7]. The data of Schneider and colleagues [8, 9] were applied at high temperatures.

The data of Mage [10] on differential Joule-Thomson effect (at $p \to 0$) were used to check the agreement of thermal virial coefficient with caloric values according to the relationship

$$\frac{B}{T} - \int_{T_0}^{T} \frac{\mu_0\, C^\circ_p}{T^2}\, d\,T = \frac{B_0}{T_0}, \tag{2}$$

This relationship shows that when B and μ_0 are matched, the left side of equation (2) becomes independent of temperature and is equal to B_0/T_0. Fig. 1 indicates experimental values of the virial coefficient to be somewhat inconsistent over the entire temperature range.

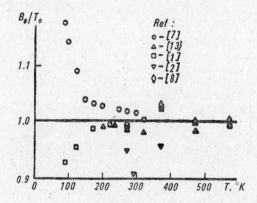

Fig. 1.   Agreement of the second virial coefficient with
data on Joule-Thomson effect.

Values of the second virial coefficient accepted by the present authors can be approximated by the relation

$$\frac{B}{v_{cr}} \quad 0.3035636 - 1.335531 \; \vartheta - 0.0101968 \; \vartheta^2 - 0.00006945 \; \vartheta^3 -$$

$$-0.2823762 \; x + 0.0810073 \; x^2 - 4.1242084 \; x^6, \qquad (3)$$

where $\qquad\qquad v_{cr} = 57.614 \text{ cm}^3/\text{mole};$

$$x = \frac{T}{519.94 + 1.8 \; T}.$$

Calculated values of B/v_{cr} satisfy two conditions : (1) they are consistent with experimental values within possible tolerances (see Table 1), and (2) they show satisfactory agreement with values of the Joule-Thomson effect. By using equation (3), volume elementary functions of equation (1) can be isolated and expressed from experimental p-v-T data as :

$$\left.\begin{array}{l} \alpha_0 = 1 - 0.0952426 \; \omega^2 - 0.00412116 \; \omega^3 + 0.000965381 \; \omega^4 - \\ - 0.001478587 \; \omega^5 + 0.000385145 \; \omega^6 - 0.0000404213 \; \omega^7 \\ \alpha_1 = 0.8853308 \; \omega^2 + 0.06419341 \; \omega^3 + 0.05472136 \; \omega^4 + \\ \quad + 0.07660029 \; \omega^5 - 0.02068234 \; \omega^6 + 0.002123534 \; \omega^7 \\ \beta = \omega + 0.5736679 \; \omega^2 + 0.01857956 \; \omega^3 - 0.00503396 \; \omega^4 + \\ \quad + 0.00543497 \; \omega^5 - 0.000609572 \; \omega^6 \end{array}\right\}, \qquad (4)$$

where $\qquad\qquad\qquad \omega = \dfrac{v_{cr}}{v}$

**Table 1.   Comparison of calculated and experimental values
of the second virial coefficient**

T, °K	B/v_{cr} cal	exp	Reference	T, °K	B/v_{cr} cal	exp	Reference
20.35	−0.0485	−0.0486	[1]	373.15	0.2006	0.1975	[1]
20.58	−0.0448 ⎫	−0.0455				0.1962	[2]
60.03	0.1616 ⎬	0.1654	[7]			0.1982	[8]
100.02	0.1820 ⎭	0.2059					
123.15	0.2024	0.1980	[1]	473.15	0.1942	0.1919	[1]
150.04	0.2064 ⎫	0.2110	[7]			0.1859	[2]
200.11	0.2083 ⎭	0.2124				0.1923	[8]
203.15	0.2083 ⎫	0.2070	[2]				
238.15	0.2076 ⎭	0.2060		673.15	0.1815	0.1759	[1]
						0.1814	[8]
				873.15	0.1700	0.1704	[8]
						0.1701	[9]
273.15	0.2062	0.2028	[2]				
		0.2054	[1]	1073.15	0.1600	0.1592	
		0.2097	[7]	1273.15	0.1513	0.1503	[9]
		0.2043	[8]	1473.15	0.1438	0.1422	

Equation (1), in which elementary functions have been substituted from equations (3) and (4), describes the thermodynamic properties of helium for temperature 20-1500°K, density upto 0.28 g/cm³, and pressure upto 1000 bar within limits of experimental error. The deviation from experimental values on certain characteristic isotherms is shown in Table 2.

The lower temperature limit (19-20°K) of the equation of state was fixed from both p-v-T and isochoric specific heat data [5].

Table 2. Deviation of calculated values of z from its experimental values on certain characteristic isotherms

ω	z_{exp}	Δz, %	Reference	ω	z_{exp}	Δz, %	Reference

ω	z_{exp}	Δz, %	Reference	ω	z_{exp}	Δz, %	Reference
T=20.35°K				T=123.15°K			
0.0455	0.9981	—0.01	[1]	0.5334	1.1251	—0.04	[1]
0.2854	0.9962	—0.19	[5]	0.9054	1.2254	0.60	
0.4081	0.9973	0.06	[1]	1.2463	1.3331	1.10	[4]
0.4534	1.0013	—0.15	[1]	1.5279	1.4478	0.67	
0.5122	1.0042	0.08	[5]	1.7717	1.5607	0.34	
0.8089	1.0328	0.12	[1]	T=273.15°K			
0.8645	1.0348	0.29	[5]	0.0336	1.0069	0.01	[1]
1.0665	1.0905	—0.88	[5]	0.0621	1.0130	0	[3]
1.2187	1.1176	0.24	[1]	0.1166	1.0250	—0.04	[3]
1.4210	1.1860	0.62	[7]	0.1634	1.0347	0.01	[1]
1.4365	1.1864	0.64	[4]	0.2094	1.0454	—0.04	[3]
1.4690	1.2086	—0.06	[1]	0.2441	1.0531	—0.04	[2]
1.4536	1.1957	0.55	[5]	0.2563	1.0556	—0.04	[1]
1.4953	1.2145	0.39	[1]	0.3140	1.0693	—0.08	[3]
1.5863	1.2606	—0.82	[5]	0.3930	1.0879	—0.08	[3]
1.7122	1.3257	0.13	[1]	0.4655	1.1044	0.02	[2]
1.815	1.3858	0.35	[1]	0.4708	1.1065	—0.05	[3]
2.043	1.5548	0.46	[1]	0.5891	1.1361	—0.05	[3]
2.0646	1.5854	—0.05	[5]	0.7058	1.1661	—0.03	[3]
2.1102	1.5990	1.23	[4]	0.8543	1.2035	0.18	[2]
2.1944	1.6551	2.69	[1]	0.8882	1.2143	—0.03	[3]
2.1943	1.7042	—0.33	[5]	1.0579	1.2643	—0.05	[3]
2.3617	1.7520	—0.20	[5]	1.1852	1.3013	0.05	[2]
2.7578	2.4346	1.03	[4]	1.4758	1.3935	0.13	[2]
3.1304	3.2118	1.12	[4]	1.7311	1.4849	0.01	[2]
0.0739	1.0148	0.05		0.0579	1.0112	0.01	[1]
0.1456	1.0301	0.06	[1]	0.1146	1.0225	0.01	[1]
0.2153	1.0455	0.09		0.1443	1.0286	0	[2]
0.2648	1.0635	—0.54	[4]	0.1517	1.0300	0	[1]
0.2828	1.0610	0.10		0.2810	1.0563	0.04	
0.3484	1.0767	0.09	[1]	0.5357	1.1081	0.30	
0.4119	1.0927	0.06		0.7648	1.1643	—0.05	[2]
0.4736	1.1089	0.02		0.9793	1.2123	0.14	
0.5006	1.1139	0.20	[4]	1.1735	1.2646	—0.05	

Thus, the equation of state given here applies for the temperature ranges of McCarty's [11] and Tsederberg's [12] equations which are valid for pressures upto 100 and 200 kg/cm², respectively.

REFERENCES

1. HOLBORN, L. and J. OTTO. $\mathcal{Z}$. *für Physik*, **38**, 359, 1926.
2. WIEBE, R., V. L. GADDY and C. HEINS.   *J. Am. Chem. Soc.*, **53**, 1721, 1931.
3. CANFIELD, F. B., T. W. LELAND and R. KABAYASHI.   *J. Chem. Eng. Data*, **10** (2), 1965.
4. DOBROVOL'SKII, O. A. and I. F. GOLUBEV.   *Gazovaya Promyshlennost'*, No. 7, 1965.
5. HILL, R. W. and O. A. LOUNASMAA.   *Phys. Trans. Roy. Soc., London*, **A252** (1013), 1960.
6. KAZAVCHINSKII, Y. ZA.   *IFZh,* **7** (6), 1964.
7. WHITE, D., T. RUBIN, P. CAMKY and H. L. JOHNSTON.   *J. Phys. Chem.*, **64**, 1607, 1960.
8. SCHNEIDER, W. G. and J. A. H. DUFFIE.   *J. Chem. Phys.*, **17**, 751, 1949.
9. YNTEMA, J. U. and W. G. SCHNEIDER.   *J. Chem. Phys.*, **18**, 641, 1950.
10. MAGE, D. T.   *J. Chem. Phys.*, **42** (8), 1965.
11. McCARTY, R. D. and R. B. STEWART.   In : *Progress in international research on thermodynamic and transport properties.*   1962.
12. TSEDERBERG, N. V., V. N. POPOV and N. A. MOROZOVA.   *Teplofizicheskie svoistva geliga* (*Thermophysical properties of helium*).   Gosenergoizdat, Moscow, 1961.
13. KEESOM, W. H. and J. VAN SANTEN.   *J. Proc. Roy. Acad. Amsterdam*, **36**, 813, 1933.
14. MICHELS, A. and H. WOUTERS.   *Physica*, **8** (8), 1941.
15. MICHELS, A. *et al.   Physica*, **25** (1), 1959.

UDC 541.27

AN EQUATION OF STATE FOR LIQUID AND GASEOUS HELIUM

V. N. Taran

A single equation of state should cover the entire temperature range of interest to modern technology and should be applicable to both liquid and gaseous phases, enabling calculation of the thermodynamic properties of the substance over the entire homogeneous region including points on the saturation curve. The equation is supposed to have the following form

$$z = \alpha_0 + \alpha_1\,\vartheta + \beta\,B + \gamma\,\varphi + \delta\,\varepsilon$$

with expanded elementary functions. The number of functions can change in the general case. The problem of selecting a single equation for helium is simplified because of the availability of equation of state (I)* which describes the thermodynamic properties of this gas at temperatures above the Boyle temperature T_B. This equation has been accepted by the present authors, but contains only the first three terms.

Analysis of experimental p-v-T properties showed that for attaining the required accuracy in describing the thermal properties through a single equation, terms $\gamma\varphi$ and $\delta\varepsilon$ are necessary, together with all the elementary functions in equation (I)*. Applicability of equation (I) is enhanced by reducing temperature functions φ and ε to zero at temperature functions and to zero at temperatures above T_B. Actually, since the experimental

*The equation of state derived in the preceding article will be indicated by [I].

data have limited accuracy, functions φ and ε can have values differing from zero if they do not significantly contribute to thermal and calorific properties in this temperature range.

The elementary functions in the very low temperature region were determined following the general procedure for similar equations [1] using the method of consecutive approximations.

In addition to equation (I), the critical isotherm and isochore were used as reference curves, primarily to satisfy critical conditions.

Values of elementary functions obtained and tabulated at discrete values of arguments were approximated by polynomials and have the form as follows :

$$\gamma = 0.9\,\omega^2 - 2.692995\,\omega^3 + 8.9865164\,\omega^4 - 4.4483362\omega^5 - 7.2433935\,\omega^6 +$$
$$9.3056234\,\omega^7 - 4.3097793\,\omega^8 + 0.92399394\,\omega^9 - 0.07710676\omega^{10};$$
$$\delta = 0.4\,\omega^2 - 0.76022894\,\omega^3 - 0.508792211\,\omega^4 + 2.4815536\,\omega^5 - 2.4785120\omega^6 +$$
$$+1.1151107\omega^7 - 0.23806487\omega^8 + 0.019624982\,\omega^9;$$
$$\varphi = 0.00903666 - 0.0582075\,\vartheta + 0.105\,\vartheta^2 + 0.046117333\,\vartheta^3 - 0.01591775\,\vartheta^4$$
$$+0.0004603\,\vartheta^6 - 0.05053309\,x + 0.07581814\,x^2;$$
$$\varepsilon = 0.0004529 - 0.0415299\,\vartheta + 0.92899\,\vartheta^3 - 1.3638926\,\vartheta^4 +$$
$$0.55265989\,\vartheta^5 - 0.076680383\,\vartheta^6.$$

It was accepted that $T_{cr} = 5.1994°K$ and that $\rho_{cr} = 0.06948$ g/cm^3.

The sole criterion for checking the accuracy of the equation is comparison with experimental data. Comparison of calculated thermal properties with experimentally derived values shows that the equation describes, within limits of experimental error, the main data for temperatures from 2.25 to 1500-2000°K and densities of 0-0.2 g/cm^3.

Due to the numerous investigations and experimental points of p-v-T properties of helium, the average deviation of calculated values will be discussed in the present work.

The data of Holborn and Otto [2] are described by the equation with an error not exceeding 0.1% on isotherms above 60°K. On 20°K and 15°K isotherms, the error is 0.6%, exceeding the 0.1% deviation from the data of Canfield and colleagues [3] only at certain points. The data of Wiebe and colleagues [4] are systematically 0.1-0.2% below the calculated values with an internal inconsistency of upto 0.35%.

Dobrovol'skii and Golubev's data [5] show large scatter and deviations from these data, averaging 0.5-0.6%.

The most detailed investigation of the thermodynamic properties of helium at low temperatures has been that of Hill and Lounasmaa [6], who estimated the error in their pressure measurements to be 0.7%. Exactly identical deviation is observed between calculated and experimental [6] values at temperatures of 2.6-20°K.

Comparison of the calculated densities of the liquid with values of Edeskuty and Sherman [7] demonstrates the average deviation to be 0.2% and 0.5% at individual points. A similar error is observed at saturation.

It should be noted that the peculiar behavior of helium near the λ-curve does not permit an equation sufficiently approximating the λ-transition and valid for the region of helium II. There is also a region near the critical point with a sharp change in isochoric specific heat C_V [8]. These features cannot be described by any of the known equations of state and require the introduction of special functions [9].

Hill and Lounasmaa [6] experimentally determined the derivatives $\left(\dfrac{\partial p}{\partial T}\right)_\rho$. Derivative values calculated from the equation of state agree with most of the experimental values within 1%, within the possible error limits in determination of the derivatives [6]. Some increase in the deviation is observed at densities above 2.6 ρ_{cr}. An overall analysis of the deviation at temperatures from 2°K to 500°K, pressures upto 1000 bar, and densities below 0.2 g/cm³ indicates the possible error in pressures calculated from the equation of state for the change of parameters to be as follows :

Temperature interval, °K	Possible error in calculated pressures, %
2.25-5	0.2*
5-20	0.5-0.7
20-100	0.3
100-500	0.15
above 500	upto 0.05

The experiments above 500°K were performed upto pressures of only 100 bar. However, the coincidence of virial coefficients (experimental and theoretical) with the temperature coefficients of the equation at corresponding densities and the relatively small contribution of the higher virial coefficients suggest that the equation can be extrapolated to 1000 bar upto temperatures in the region of 1500-2000°K with error below 0.5%, and that the error will not exceed 1% on extrapolation to pressures of 2000 bar for densities below 0.2 g/cm³ ($\omega=2.9$).

The suggested equation of state agrees closely with the large number of calorific data and quantitatively reflects the course of characteristic curves. A comparison of inversion pressures is given in tabulated form :

---

* For the liquid state, this value applies for the possible error in the calculated value of the density.

Inversion pressures, bars

Author and reference	p at T, °K								
	6	8	10	12	14	16	18	20	25
Zel'manov [11]	—	15.2	20.1	24.5	28.8	32.8	35.3	35.9	—
Keesom [17]	—	—	—	26.9	30.1	33.2	35.2	—	—
Baer [18]	—	16	21.5	25.9	30.4	35.5	38.9	37.3	—
Hill and Lounasmaa [6]	—	14.2	20.3	25.5	29.6	32.5	34.4	35.3	—
Averaged values	7.4	14.6	20.8	26.1	30.6	33.9	36.1	37.1	37.0

The present author has compared the calculated and experimental values of enthalpy, isobaric and isochoric specific heats, and latent heat of evaporation. In regions where experimental calorific data were unavailable, values calculated from the reported equations were compared. Calorific calculations were based on a value of isochoric specific heat for the ideal gas equal to $3/2 R$ [6, 13, 19]. A volume tending to infinity was taken as the zero point, insuring negligible contribution of any quantum-effect correction to $c_{v \infty}$ even at the lowest calculation temperature.

Enthalpies of helium were tabulated in works [6, 10, 12, 13]. At low temperatures, deviation from values of Hill and Lounasmaa was negligible (below ± 3 J/mole), and deviation from the values of Zel'manov [10], 9 J/mole. Zel'manov's data, however, disagree with the enthalpy data in the ideal-gas state, apparently due to incorrect thermometer calibration in experimental determination of enthalpy at one atmosphere. The deviation can be reduced to 6-7 J/mole with proper correction.

McCarty's equation [13] applies for the temperature interval of 20-300°K at pressures upto 100 kg/cm². In this region, enthalpies calculated from the equations of McCarty and the present author differ by an average of 6 J/mole, whereas the equations of Tsederberg [12] and the present author yield close values of corrections for nonideal behavior in the common region. These corrections do not exceed the limits estimated in reference [12].

The entropy values can only be compared with the calculated values of various authors. Values derived by the present author deviate by an average of 0.2 J/mole · deg from the values given in references [6, 10, 13].

The single equation of state may be applied for calculation of the thermal and calorific properties at saturation point, including saturated vapor pressures. The calculation of vapor pressures with low error, however, requires a high-precision equation of state. As the objective of the present work is formulation of an equation for technical calculations, all calculations at saturation point have been performed with vapor pressure on T_{58} scale.

Calculated values of heats of evaporation range between the averaged values of Van Dijk [14] and Borman [15], with 0.7% common deviation. The deviation between calculated and experimental values is shown in Fig. 1. The possible error in heats of evaporation calculated from our equation is estimated to be 0.3-0.4%.

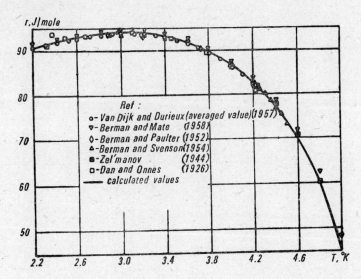

Fig. 1. Comparison of calculated and experimental heats of evaporation.

The calculation of specific heats c_p and c_v require determination of the derivatives of thermal properties. Hence, agreement of calculated specific heats, especially at $T > 20°K$, with large nonideality correction, provides a sensitive criterion for the reliability of the equation.

Specific heats c_p were determined by Hill and Lounasmaa [6] with an accuracy of 1.5%. Fig. 2 shows the agreement between these values and the calculated isobaric specific heats. The deviation does not exceed 5%, and averages 2%.

As compared to c_p the calculated values of heat capacity c_v reflect clearly all the errors and defects in the equation of state compiled on the basis of independent variables T and v. The verification of our equation shows that the values of the isochoric heat capacity agree well in the limit of 2-2.5% with the values taken from [6], at temperatures over 2.5°K and upto densities of 0.17-0.18 g/cm³. At higher densities and low temperatures the error may reach ±5%.

Thus, the obtained equation of state contains information on the thermodynamic properties of helium at temperatures from 2.25°K to 1500-2000°K and densities upto 0.2 g/cm³ in the gaseous and liquid states,

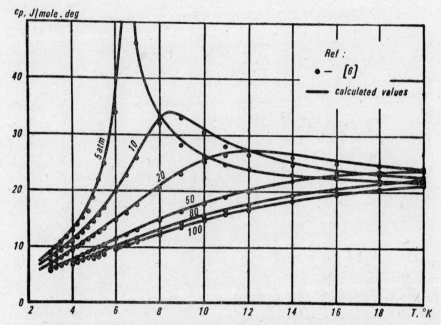

Fig. 2.   Comparison of calculated and experimental [6] isobaric specific heats.

i.e. it may be considered as unique. The recently published data [16] vary significantly (upto 10%) from the carefully conducted studies [6], and at present may not serve as a basis for compiling the equation of state at higher densities.

REFERENCES

1. KAZAVCHINSKII, YA. Z.   *IFZh*, **7** (6), 1964.
2. HOLBORN, L. and J. OTTO.   *Z. für Physik.* **38,** 359, 1926.
3. CANFIELD, F. B., T. W. LELAND and R. KOBAYASHI. *J. Chem. and Eng. Data,* **10** (2), 1965.
4. WIEBE, R., V. L. GADDY and C. HEINS. *J. Am. Chem. Soc.,* **53**, 1721, 1931.
5. DOBROVOL'SKII, O. A. and I. F. GOLUBEV. *Gazovaya Premyshlennost',* No. 7, 1965.
6. HILL, R. W. and O. V. LOUNASMAA. *Phys. Trans. Roy. Soc., London,* **A252** (1013), 1960.
7. EDESKUTY, E. F. and R. H. SHERMAN. *Proc. Fifth Internat. Conf. Low-Temp. Phys. and Chem.,* Madison, 1958.

8. MOLDOVER, M. R. and W. A. LITTLE. *Phys. Rev. Letters,* **15** (2), 1965.

9. AZBEL', M. YA., A. V. VORNEL' and M. SH. GITERMAN. *Zh. Eksper. i Teoret. Fiz.,* **46** (2), 1964.

10. ZEL'MANOV, I. L. *Zh. Eksper. i Teoret. Fiz.,* **14** (12), 1944.

11. ZEL'MANOV, I. L. *Zh. Eksper. i Teoret. Fiz.,* **10** (6), 1940.

12. TSEDERBERG, N. V., V. N. POPOV and N. A. MOROZOVA. *Teplofizicheskie svoistva geliga (Thermophysical properties of helium).* Gosenergoizdat, Moscow, 1961.

13. MCCARTY, R. D. and R. B. STEWART. In : *Progress in low-temperature physics* (Gorter, ed.), Vol. **II**, 1957.

14. VAN DIJK, H. and M. B. DURIEUX. In : *Progress in low-temperature physics* (Gorter, ed.), Vol. **II**, 1957.

15. BORMAN, R. and C. F. MATE. *Phyl. Mag.,* **8** (3), 1958,

16. GLASSFORD, A. P. M. and J. L. SMITH. *Cryogenics,* **6** (4), 1966.

17. KEESOM, V. *Gelii (Helium).* IIL, Moscow, 1949.

18. BAER, H. D. *Electrochem. z.,* **60** (5), 1956.

19. GUREVICH, A. B. *Termodinamicheskie svoistva individual'nykh veshchestv (Thermodynamic properties of individual substances).* Moscow, 1962.

UDC 541.11

THERMODYNAMIC PROPERTIES OF NEON, ARGON, KRYPTON AND XENON AT SATURATION POINT

V. A. Rabinovich and *L. S. Veksler*

Inert gases are attracting the attention of investigators in cryogenics and many other fields of technology and as ideal monatomic gas models for formulation and verification of the main laws evolved from the theories of gaseous, liquid, and more recently, solid states. Subsequently, considerable experimental data have been obtained on the properties of inert gases. No systematic compilation of the data, however, has yet been attempted in connection with critical evaluation and extrapolation to nonexperimental parameter ranges.

The objective of the present study is the selection of reliable experimental data and analysis and formulation of optimal methods for calculating the vapor and liquid properties of saturation points of four inert gases, neon, argon, krypton, and xenon. Analysis of the properties of helium is not included in the present work, as a number of special studies and monographs (e.g., [1]) are available on this subject.

Analysis of saturation vapor pressure data, selection of reference values, and parameters of characteristic points

Because of the numerous available experimental studies of the vapor pressure curve of each of the gases, the reliability of the available data was comparatively studied and evaluated. Experimental data were compared by plotting against coordinates $\log p$ and $1/T$. The relationship between saturation pressure p and temperature T is a line of small curvature. For analysis, all temperatures were converted to the International Temperature Scale of 1948.

The reliability of the experimental data on the saturation vapor pressure curve was evaluated in respect to (1) reliability of method, (2) purity of materials utilized in experiments, (3) reproducibility of results, and (4) consistency with the results of subsequent investigations.

On the basis of selected reliable experimental data, saturation vapor pressure p and temperature T were interpolated by the least-square method.

The relationship was assumed to represent an equation of the following form :

$$\log p = A + B/T + C \log T + DT \tag{1}$$

An equation of this type is obtained by integration of the Clausius-Clapeyron equation in a region remote from the critical point where the specific volume of the liquid is negligible and the gas can be considered ideal. A further assumption is that the dependence of the heat of evaporation on temperature can be expressed in the form of an exponential polynomial.

The coefficients in equation (1), where p is expressed in atmospheres and T in degrees Kelvin, were calculated on a computer and are presented in Table 1.

Table 1. Coefficients in equation (1)

Substance	A	B	C	D
Neon	14.078171	— 141.90732	—7.1660509	0.052727894
Argon	19.944207	— 529.29524	—7.8525130	0.015604304
Krypton	24.280217	— 783.79619	—9.2991376	0.013276991
Xenon	24.004066	—1056.5316	—8.5979329	0.0088676567

Parallel, simultaneous calculations showed that rendering equation (1) more complex by increasing either the number of terms in the first part or the order of the last terms does not increase accuracy of reference data representation.

Analyses of the experimental data on the saturation vapor lines of neon, krypton, argon, and xenon are shown in Table 2, indicating the accuracy of describing these data by equation (1) and selection of optimal data on the parameters of the characteristic points, triple points, normal boiling points, and critical points of the four inert gases.

Neon. Experimental data on temperature dependence of vapor pressure of neon on the saturation curve are given in references [2-7], and the data of these six studies show close common agreement. The most accurate and complete data are those of Grilly [7], and have been applied to obtain an equation for the dependence of saturated neon vapor pressure on temperature. The parameters of characteristic points are also in accordance with Grilly's work.

Table 2. Characteristic points for inert gases

Substance	Characteristic point	T, °K	p, atm	ρ', g/cm³	ρ'', g/cm³
Neon	Triple point	24.55	0.428	1.248	0.00438
	Normal boiling point	27.09	1.00	1.204	0.00950
	Critical point	44.40	26.18	0.483	
Argon	Triple point	83.81	0.682	1.415	0.00407
	Normal boiling point	87.29	1.00	1.393	0.00579
	Critical point	150.65	48.00	0.535	
Krypton	Triple point	115.76	0.720	2.452	0.00652
	Normal boiling point	119.78	1.00	2.420	0.00882
	Critical point	209.39	54.25	0.911	
Xenon	Triple point	161.36	0.805	2.985	0.00820
	Normal boiling point	165.03	1.00	2.956	0.01001
	Critical point	289.74	57.52	1.100	

Fig. 1 shows Grilly's data [7] to be represented by equation (1) with an error of less than 0.25%, and the data of an earlier work [5] are also shown in Fig. 1. These data, similar to those of references [2-4, 6], are best described by equation (1). However, it is impossible to attain greater accuracy in representing these data, due to numerous accidental experimental errors.

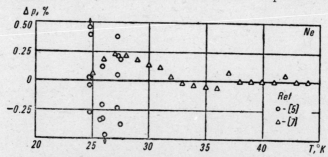

Fig. 1. Deviation of experimental saturated vapor pressures of neon from values calculated from equation (1).

Argon. Numerous reports [8-19] are available on the saturated vapor pressure of argon. The data of works [8-11] do not display a high degree of accuracy, whereas the data of works [12-19] show close common agreement, confirming their reliability. The data of works [14, 17, 19], considered the most accurate on saturated vapor pressure over the temperature range between triple and critical points, provide reference points for equating the saturation line.

Fig. 2 shows considerable scatter of the experimental data on the saturated vapor pressure of argon. Equation (1), however, describes these data optimally.

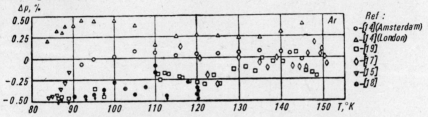

Fig. 2. Deviation of experimental values of saturated vapor pressures of argon from values calculated from equation (1).

The temperature and saturated vapor pressure at the triple point of argon have been measured frequently [11-14, 18, 20, 45, 46, 48]. The variety of techniques employed for approaching the triple point is more significant than the large number of studies. Parameters of the triple point have been determined in respect to the intersection point of the boiling, melting, and sublimation curves selectively plotted from these studies.

The normal boiling temperature has been determined by many authors. All experimentally derived values show close common agreement and agreement with the saturation curve for argon.

All available data on the critical point for argon were analyzed to fix this point :

Year of publication and reference	T_{cr}, °K	p_{cr}, atm
1912 [22]	150·68	48·0
1958 [17]	150·86	48·34
1966 [21]	150·62	48·62
1968 [49]	150·64	—
1967 [47]	150·65	47·92

Radovskii's sonically obtained data [21] deviate from the general temperature-saturation pressure relationship and, therefore, seem unreliable. Michels's values of the critical parameters [17], recommended by the majority of data books, appear too high, in comparison with later data and following detailed analysis of the experimental procedure.

The present authors recommend values of critical constants based on works [22, 47, 49], adjusted with the general course of the saturation vapor pressure line.

Krypton. Experimental data obtained after 1930 on saturation vapor pressure of liquid krypton have been reported in works [15, 23–30]. Peters's data [23] for krypton and xenon considerably differ from those of other authors, and may hence be considered erroneous. Analysis of the experimental results of work [25] exhibits considerable systematic error. The data of work [24] are considered unsuitable for formulating an equation, due to the large scatter and poor reproducibility evidenced by the discrepancy between the results of two separate sets of experiments. The results of work [15], represented by the equation log $p=A+B/T$, are also not sufficiently accurate.

The data obtained by Meihuizen and Crommelin [27] and Michels and colleagues [28] cover nearly the entire temperature range from triple to critical points, and have been employed for reference. Near the triple point, the absolute saturation pressures are very low, resulting in high relative error; thus the results of the precise experiments of Beaumont and colleagues [29] near the triple point have been additionally used.

Fig. 3 shows the equation to represent these data with an error of under 0.3% and reveals the calculated values to deviate from the data of work [29] by less than 0.1%.

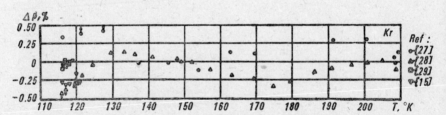

Fig. 3. Deviation of experimental saturated vapor pressure for krypton from values calculated from equation (1).

In our opinion, the most reliable values of the pressure and temperature at the triple point for krypton are those reported in reference [29]. Quite close values for the triple point were obtained by approaching the triple point from the direction of sublimation [31] and melting [20]. Table 2 gives averaged values. The normal boiling point was calculated from data in reference [28]. Critical constants for krypton were determined in only one study [27]. These values can be considered reliable, since the other data from this study are confirmed by subsequent, extremely precise experiments [28], which, unfortunately, were not undertaken upto the critical point.

Xenon. Experimental data on temperature and saturation pressure for liquid xenon were reported in references [15, 23, 24, 32-34]. As was mentioned previously, the second and third reports are not sufficiently reliable. The most reliable among reported data are those of Michels and Wassenaar [34], obtained over almost the entire range of parameter variation. These data are described by equation (1) with an accuracy of 0.2% (Fig. 4).

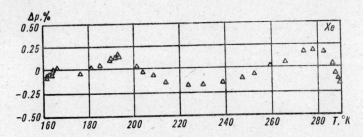

Fig. 4. Deviation of experimental saturated vapor pressures of xenon [34] from values calculated by equation (1).

The triple point for xenon has been reported in numerous studies, the most reliable of which appear to be works [20, 32, 38]. Michels and Wassenaar's value [34] of the normal boiling temperature was accepted. Incidentally, this value was confirmed in the majority of experimental studies. Critical constants for xenon have been accurately established, since certain studies [35-37] have been specifically directed toward investigation of the critical region of xenon, due to its peculiar behavior in the near-critical region.

Analysis, processing and extrapolation of experimental data on orthobaric densities of inert gases

Important studies on experimental densities of liquid and vapor of neon, argon, krypton, and xenon are listed in Table 3.

Data of the saturation curve were processed according to a single scheme. The original data were initially analyzed and their reliability estimated. The most reliable data were then interpolated within the experimental temperature range. Values of the critical density were calculated for all four substances by the rule of linear diameter, as directly measured values of densities were not available in the literature. Precise experimental measurements in the near-critical region for xenon [36-37], however, confirm the value of ρ_{cr} obtained by calculation, suggesting the rule of linear diameter to provide sufficiently reliable values of the critical density for the four substances.

Extrapolation of the experimental segment of the saturation curve to the triple-point temperature was especially complicated. In the low-density region, data for krypton, argon, and xenon on the gas side were calculated from equations of state with two virial coefficients. These equations were obtained from the experimental data for the single-phase region on the basis of the law of corresponding states following the procedure described in reference [51]. The two-phase curve on the liquid side was extrapolated to the triple point following the rule of linear diameter.

Table 3. Investigations of orthobaric densities of neon, argon, krypton and xenon

Substance	Year of publication and reference	Property investigated	Experimental temperature interval, °K
Neon	1923 [40]	ρ', ρ''	25.18- 43.03
	1966 [44]	ρ'	25.20- 43.14
Argon	1912 [22]	ρ', ρ''	89.96-147.95
	1958 [17]	ρ', ρ''	116.82-150.80
	1964 [50]	ρ'	84.10- 86.85
Krypton	1937 [41]	ρ', ρ''	125.96-208.21
Xenon	1912 [39]	ρ', ρ''	206.31-289.16
	1965 [43]	ρ', ρ''	161.9 -273.20

For assaying the reliability of the density values for the vapor and liquid at the triple point and, consequently, the reliability of the course of orthobaric density curves in the low-temperature region, the heats of phase transitions were checked at the triple point for all four gases. The calculations included supplementary data on the melting curves of neon [57], argon, krypton, and xenon [20]. Equations for sublimation curves were obtained from original experimental data reported in the literature. Wherever possible, calculated values of heats of phase transitions were compared with their experimentally determined values. Besides assaying the accuracy of the extrapolation of experimental data to the triple point, these calculations helped in checking the mutual consistency of the values of various properties at the triple point.

The original experimental material and method for processing the data on the two-phase boundary are analyzed separately below for each of the four substances.

Orthobaric densities of neon obtained experimentally at the Leiden Laboratory [40] seem to be sufficiently reliable on the basis of confirmation by data of a later work [44]. Interpolation applied only the data of work [40], since the data of work [44] show considerable scatter. The densities of liquid and gas at the triple point were adjusted by assay of the thermodynamic consistency of heats of evaporation, melting, and sublimation.

Experimental values of the densities of liquid argon on the saturation curve [17, 22] agree in their common temperature interval within 0·2%. In the narrow temperature interval between the triple and normal boiling points, densities of liquid argon on the saturation curve were measured in work [50]. The accuracy of the data of reference [50] was estimated by the results of reliable liquid-density measurements [52, 53]. A comparison showed the saturation curve reported in work [50] to shift by almost 1% toward the liquid region. Therefore, results obtained on extrapolation to saturation pressures of isotherms for the liquid [52, 53] were selected as reference points on the saturation line.

Saturated vapor densities for argon were obtained by direct processing of the results of works [17, 22]. Near the triple point, these values were adjusted using the equation of state with two virial coefficients, allowing consistency between data for this segment of the saturation curve and data for the gaseous phase.

The reliability of the density values of the liquid and gas at the triple point of argon was estimated by calculating the heats of transitions at this point and comparing these heats with the available experimental data [18, 54].

The Leiden Laboratory has provided the sole experimental data on the density of krypton at the saturation curve [41], and data on neon [40] and argon [22] which have also proved quite reliable and have been confirmed by subsequent measurements by other researchers. The present authors have thus employed the data of work [41] as reference data. The correction of the gas branch of the saturation curve for krypton and its extension from the final experimental value of ρ'' at $T=144.04°K$ to the triple point applied the equation of state with two virial coefficients. Density values for liquid krypton in the same temperature interval were calculated using the rule of linear diameter. As in the case of argon, the values of ρ' and ρ'' at the triple point were additionally checked from data on heats of phase transitions.

Experimental data on the two-phase line for xenon have been reported in two works [39, 43]. In 1912, the densities of liquid and gaseous xenon at -66.8 to $16°C$ were measured [39], and the results are presented in all handbooks and articles on xenon. In 1965, data on the density of liquid xenon from the triple point to $0°C$ [43] showed a 4-5% decrease from the 1912 values, and this required investigative selection of the preferred data. For evaluating the accuracy of the data on the saturation curve, the values of ρ' at the triple point were calculated from the available experimental values of the heat of melting [56] and density of crystal [55] at the triple point of xenon using the equation for the melting curves from work [20]. The value of the density of the liquid at the triple point, calculated from the Clausius-Clapeyron equation, agreed within 0.3% with the data of work [43] and was 4% below the data of work [39]. However, extrapolation of the compressibility isochore for single-phase xenon [42] to the saturation pressure provides points on the two-phase curve, confirming the general course of the curve [43] within 0.3%. This indicates the data of work [43] to be sufficiently reliable, whereas the data of work [39] are too high on the liquid side.

The values of ρ'' were checked and corrected using all available information on gaseous xenon, including experimental results for the near-critical region [37] and the data on compressibility of xenon above 0°C [42]. Reference points were determined by extrapolating the compressibility isochores reported in these works on the p-T coordinates upto the intersection point with the vapor pressure curve. The extrapolation is sufficiently accurate because of the small curvature of compressibility isochores near the vapor pressure line. In the region near the triple point, the gas density on the saturation line was calculated for the equation of state with two virial coefficients. Comparison between these values and those of work [39] showed the experimental values of the densities of saturated vapor, similar to the densities of saturated liquid, to be on an average 4% too high.

Table 4.   Thermodynamic properties of neon at saturation

T, °K	p, bar	ρ', g/cm³	ρ'', g/cm³	v', cm³/g	v'', cm³/g	r, kJ/kg
24.55	0.4334	1.2475	0.00438	0.8016	228.3	89.7
25	0.5107	1.2400	0.00510	0.8065	196.1	89.2
26	0.7197	1.2232	0.00695	0.8175	143.9	88.1
27	0.9876	1.2061	0.00927	0.8291	107.9	86.9
28	1.3239	1.1882	0.01213	0.8416	82.44	85.5
29	1.7383	1.1699	0.01556	0.8548	64.27	83.9
30	2.2411	1.1510	0.01972	0.8688	50.71	82.1
31	2.8427	1.1315	0.02477	0.8838	40.37	80.1
32	3.5539	1.1108	0.03076	0.9003	32.51	77.9
33	4.3858	1.0893	0.03790	0.9180	26.39	75.3
34	5.3500	1.0665	0.04624	0.9377	21.63	72.7
35	6.4583	1.0425	0.05605	0.9592	17.84	70.0
36	7.7232	1.0175	0.06730	0.9828	14.86	67.2
37	9.1878	0.9905	0.08056	1.010	12.41	64.1
38	10.776	0.9610	0.09655	1.041	10.36	60.7
39	12.592	0.9292	0.1152	1.076	8.681	56.9
40	14.622	0.8945	0.1376	1.118	7.267	52.6
41	16.881	0.8548	0.1648	1.170	6.068	47.8
42	19.389	0.8080	0.1979	1.238	5.053	42.3
43	22.163	0.7472	0.2407	1.338	4.155	35.3
44.40	26.527	0.4830			2.070	

Table 5. Thermodynamic properties of argon at saturation

T, °K	p, bar	ρ', g/cm³	ρ'', g/cm³	v', cm³/g	v'', cm³/g	r, kJ/kg
83.81	0.6914	1.415	0.004074	0.7067	245.4	164.2
84	0.7068	1.413	0.004156	0.7077	240.6	164.0
85	0.7918	1.407	0.004613	0.7107	216.8	163.3
86	0.8846	1.401	0.005105	0.7138	195.9	162.5
87	0.9856	1.395	0.005637	0.7168	177.4	161.7
88	1.095	1.389	0.006211	0.7199	161.0	160.8
89	1.214	1.382	0.006826	0.7236	146.5	159.9
90	1.342	1.376	0.007485	0.7267	133.6	159.1
91	1.480	1.370	0.008190	0.7299	122.1	158.2
92	1.629	1.363	0.008944	0.7337	111.8	157.4
93	1.788	1.357	0.009747	0.7369	102.6	156.6
94	1.959	1.351	0.01060	0.7402	94.32	155.7
95	2.142	1.344	0.01151	0.7440	86.86	154.7
96	2.338	1.338	0.01248	0.7474	80.11	153.8
97	2.546	1.332	0.01351	0.7508	74.02	153.9
98	2.768	1.325	0.01460	0.7547	68.51	152.0
99	3.004	1.318	0.01575	0.7587	63.50	151.1
100	3.225	1.311	0.01697	0.7628	58.93	150.1
101	3.520	1.304	0.01825	0.7669	54.78	149.1
102	3.802	1.298	0.01962	0.7704	50.98	148.1
103	4.099	1.291	0.02105	0.7746	47.51	147.1
104	4.413	1.284	0.02255	0.7788	44.34	146.1
105	4.745	1.276	0.02415	0.7837	41.41	145.1
106	5.094	1.269	0.02581	0.7880	38.74	144.1
107	5.461	1.262	0.02757	0.7924	36.27	143.0
108	5.848	1.255	0.02943	0.7968	33.98	141.9
109	6.253	1.247	0.03135	0.8021	31.90	140.8
110	6.679	1.240	0.03339	0.8068	29.95	139.7
111	7.125	1.232	0.03551	0.8117	28.16	138.6
112	7.593	1.224	0.03775	0.8167	26.49	137.5
113	8.082	1.217	0.04008	0.8218	24.95	136.4
114	8.593	1.209	0.04254	0.8269	23.51	135.2
115	9.127	1.201	0.04509	0.8323	22.18	134.0
116	9.685	1.193	0.04778	0.8379	20.93	132.7
117	10.27	1.185	0.05058	0.8437	19.77	131.5
118	10.87	1.177	0.05348	0.8496	18.70	130.3
119	11.50	1.169	0.05653	0.8556	17.69	129.0
120	12.16	1.161	0.05977	0.8618	16.73	127.5
121	12.85	1.152	0.06332	0.8684	15.79	125.8
122	13.56	1.143	0.06715	0.8752	14.89	124.0
123	14.30	1.134	0.07109	0.8820	14.07	122.2
124	15.06	1.125	0.07514	0.8892	13.31	120.4
125	15.86	1.116	0.07938	0.8966	12.60	118.6
126	16.68	1.106	0.08369	0.9043	11.95	116.9
127	17.54	1.096	0.08827	0.9124	11.33	115.2
128	18.43	1.086	0.09313	0.9208	10.74	113.4
129	19.34	1.076	0.09822	0.9294	10.18	111.5

Table 5—*Continued*

T, °K	p, bar	ρ', g/cm³	ρ'', g/cm³	v', cm³/g	v'', cm³/g	r, kJ/kg
130	20.29	1.066	0.1036	0.9385	9.653	109.5
131	21.28	1.055	0.1092	0.9481	9.158	107.5
132	22.29	1.044	0.1152	0.9581	8.681	105.4
133	23.35	1.033	0.1216	0.9685	8.224	103.1
134	24.43	1.021	0.1284	0.9794	7.788	100.8
135	25.56	1.009	0.1355	0.9909	7.380	98.4
136	26.71	0.9970	0.1430	1.003	6.993	95.9
137	27.91	0.9842	0.1510	1.016	6.623	93.3
138	29.15	0.9709	0.1596	1.030	6.266	90.6
139	30.42	0.9560	0.1688	1.046	5.924	87.7
140	31.73	0.9416	0.1787	1.062	5.596	84.6
141	33.09	0.9259	0.1896	1.080	5.274	81.3
142	34.48	0.9107	0.2015	1.098	4.963	77.7
143	35.92	0.8929	0.2146	1.120	4.660	73.8
144	37.40	0.8734	0.2291	1.145	4.365	69.6
145	38.92	0.8525	0.2452	1.173	4.078	65.1
146	40.49	0.8299	0.2633	1.205	3.798	60.2
147	42.11	0.8032	0.2843	1.245	3.517	54.7
148	43.77	0.7734	0.3097	1.293	3.230	48.3
149	45.48	0.7364	0.3426	1.358	2.919	40.3
150.65	48.39		0.535		1.869	

Table 6.   Thermodynamic properties of krypton at saturation

T, °K	p, bar	ρ', g/cm³	ρ'', g/cm³	v', cm³/g	v'', cm³/g	r, kJ/kg
115.76	0.7292	2.452	0.00652	0.4068	153.4	109.6
116	0.7442	2.450	0.00664	0.4072	150.6	109.5
118	0.8785	2.434	0.00773	0.4100	129.4	108.7
120	1.031	2.418	0.00895	0.4129	111.7	107.9
122	1.202	2.402	0.01031	0.4156	96.99	107.1
124	1.395	2.386	0.01182	0.4184	84.60	106.2
126	1.610	2.370	0.01349	0.4214	74.13	105.3
128	1.849	2.355	0.01533	0.4244	65.23	104.4
130	2.114	2.339	0.01735	0.4275	57.64	103.5
132	2.406	2.322	0.01956	0.4307	51.12	102.6
134	2.728	2.305	0.02197	0.4338	45.52	101.7
136	3.080	2.288	0.02459	0.4371	40.67	100.7
138	3.465	2.271	0.02743	0.4403	36.46	99.8
140	3.884	2.254	0.03050	0.4437	32.79	98.9
142	4.339	2.237	0.03382	0.4470	29.57	97.9
144	4.832	2.220	0.03740	0.4505	26.74	97.0
146	5.364	2.203	0.04125	0.4539	24.24	96.0
148	5.938	2.185	0.04538	0.4577	24.04	95.1
150	6.556	2.167	0.04981	0.4615	20.08	94.1
152	7.218	2.149	0.05456	0.4653	18.33	93.1

Table 6—*Continued*

T, °K	p, bar	ρ', g/cm³	ρ'', g/cm³	v', cm³/g	v'', cm³/g	r, kJ/kg
154	7.928	2.130	0.05966	0.4695	16.76	92.1
156	8.687	2.111	0.06513	0.4737	15.35	91.0
158	9.497	2.092	0.07100	0.4780	14.08	89.9
160	10.36	2.073	0.07729	0.4824	12.94	88.7
162	11.28	2.053	0.08402	0.4871	11.90	87.5
164	12.25	2.032	0.09121	0.4921	10.96	86.2
166	13.29	2.011	0.09889	0.4973	10.11	84.9
168	14.38	1.990	0.1071	0.5025	9.337	83.6
170	15.54	1.968	0.1158	0.5081	8.636	82.3
172	16.76	1.945	0.1251	0.5141	7.994	80.9
174	18.06	1.922	0.1351	0.5203	7.402	79.4
176	19.42	1.897	0.1459	0.5271	6.854	77.8
178	20.85	1.872	0.1575	0.5342	6.349	76.2
180	22.36	1.846	0.1699	0.5417	5.886	74.5
182	23.95	1.819	0.1833	0.5498	5.456	72.6
184	25.62	1.791	0.1978	0.5583	5.056	70.7
186	27.37	1.762	0.2136	0.5675	4.682	68.6
188	29.20	1.731	0.2310	0.5777	4.329	66.3
190	31.12	1.699	0.2502	0.5886	3.997	63.7
192	33.14	1.666	0.2716	0.6002	3.682	60.9
194	35.25	1.631	0.2953	0.6131	3.386	58.0
196	37.45	1.593	0.3214	0.6277	3.111	54.9
198	39.76	1.553	0.3505	0.6439	2.853	51.5
200	42.17	1.508	0.3839	0.6631	2.605	47.8
202	44.68	1.456	0.4239	0.6868	2.359	43.4
204	47.31	1.395	0.4742	0.7168	2.109	38.1
206	50.05	1.317	0.5401	0.7593	1.852	31.5
208	52.91	1.209	0.6325	0.8271	1.581	22.9
209.39	54.97	0.911			1.098	

Table 7. Thermodynamic properties of xenon at saturation

T, °K	p, bar	ρ', g/cm³	ρ'', g/cm³	v', cm³/g	v'', cm³/g	r, kJ/kg
161.36	0.8159	2.985	0.00820	0.3354	121.95	96.98
162	0.8480	2.980	0.00850	0.3358	117.65	96.76
164	0.9546	2.964	0.00947	0.3373	105.60	96.29
166	1.071	2.948	0.01053	0.3392	94.967	95.80
168	1.199	2.932	0.01167	0.3411	85.690	95.30
170	1.337	2.917	0.01290	0.3428	77.519	94.79
172	1.488	2.902	0.01423	0.3446	70.274	94.27
174	1.651	2.886	0.01566	0.3465	63.857	93.74
176	1.827	2.871	0.01719	0.3483	58.173	93.20
178	2.017	2.857	0.01883	0.3500	53.107	92.65
180	2.222	2.841	0.02059	0.3520	48.567	92.09
182	2.442	2.826	0.02247	0.3539	44.504	91.52

Table 7—*Continued*

T, °K	p, bar	ρ', g/cm³	ρ'', g/cm³	v', cm³/g	v'', cm³/g	r, kJ/kg
184	2.678	2.812	0.02447	0.3556	40.866	90.95
186	2.930	2.797	0.02659	0.3575	37.608	91.38
188	3.200	2.782	0.02884	0.3595	34.674	89.81
190	3.487	2.768	0.03124	0.3613	32.010	89.24
192	3.794	2.753	0.03378	0.3632	29.603	88.66
194	4.119	2.738	0.03647	0.3652	27.420	88.07
196	4.465	2.725	0.03932	0.3670	25.432	87.48
198	4.832	2.710	0.04234	0.3690	23.618	86.88
200	5.220	2.695	0.04551	0.3711	21.973	86.27
202	5.631	2.680	0.04886	0.3731	20.467	85.65
204	6.064	2.664	0.05240	0.3754	19.084	85.01
206	6.522	2.650	0.05613	0.3774	17.819	84.37
208	7.004	2.635	0.06005	0.3795	16.653	83.72
210	7.511	2.620	0.06417	0.3817	15.584	83.07
212	8.045	2.605	0.06850	0.3839	14.599	82.41
214	8.605	2.589	0.07305	0.3862	13.690	81.74
216	9.194	2.573	0.07783	0.3887	12.849	81.05
218	9.810	2.557	0.08285	0.3911	12.070	80.35
220	10.46	2.540	0.08812	0.3937	11.348	79.63
222	11.13	2.522	0.09365	0.3965	10.678	78.90
224	11.84	2.503	0.09945	0.3995	10.055	78.17
226	12.58	2.485	0.1055	0.4024	9.4787	77.42
228	13.35	2.467	0.1119	0.4054	8.9366	76.63
230	14.15	2.449	0.1186	0.4083	8.4317	75.80
232	14.99	2.431	0.1257	0.4114	7.9554	74.92
234	15.87	2.411	0.1333	0.4148	7.5019	73.99
236	16.78	2.391	0.1412	0.4182	7.0822	73.00
238	17.72	2.372	0.1496	0.4216	6.6845	71.96
240	18.71	2.352	0.1585	0.4252	6.3091	70.88
242	19.73	2.330	0.1679	0.4292	5.9559	69.75
244	20.79	2.308	0.1778	0.4333	5.6243	68.59
246	21.90	2.286	0.1883	0.4374	5.3107	67.38
248	23.04	2.263	0.1993	0.4419	5.0176	66.18
250	24.23	2.241	0.2109	0.4462	4.7416	64.92
252	25.46	2.217	0.2231	0.4511	4.4823	63.65
254	26.74	2.197	0.2359	0.4552	4.2391	62.38
256	28.06	2.173	0.2494	0.4602	4.0096	61.07
258	29.43	2.148	0.2638	0.4655	3.7908	59.68
260	30.84	2.120	0.2793	0.4717	3.5804	58.18
262	32.31	2.093	0.2960	0.4778	3.3784	56.57
264	33.82	2.062	0.3140	0.4850	3.1847	54.85
266	35.39	2.035	0.3334	0.4914	2.9994	53.06
268	37.00	2.002	0.3543	0.4995	2.8225	51.16
270	38.67	1.970	0.3768	0.5076	2.6539	49.18
272	40.40	1.934	0.4011	0.5171	2.4931	47.10
274	42.18	1.895	0.4276	0.5277	2.3386	44.88
276	44.01	1.855	0.4569	0.5391	2.1887	42.49

Table 7—*Continued*

T, °K	p, bar	ρ', g/cm³	ρ'', g/cm³	v', cm³/g	v'', cm³/g	r, kJ/kg
278	45.91	1.812	0.4898	0.5519	2.0416	39.87
280	47.87	1.764	0.5274	0.5669	1.8961	36.95
282	49.88	1.711	0.5711	0.5845	1.7510	33.68
284	51.96	1.650	0.6227	0.6061	1.6059	29.96
286	54.10	1.573	0.6860	0.6357	1.4577	25.56
288	56.31	1.475	0.7831	0.6780	1.2770	19.33
289.74	58.28	1.100		0.9091		

Since the values of ρ'' densities of xenon (see Table 7) are not based on direct experimental measurement, due to the unreliability of the experimental values of work [39], the possible relative error of the values recommended by the present authors may be $\pm 0.6\%$. The saturation temperature T, pressure p, and densities ρ' of the liquid and ρ'' of the gas for neon, argon, krypton and xenon are given in Tables 4-7.

These tables also contain specific volume, v' of the liquid and v'' of the gas for neon, argon, krypton, and xenon, as well as heats of evaporation r, calculated from the Clausius-Clapeyron equation :

$$r = T \frac{dp}{dT} (v'' - v'),$$

where the values of derivatives dp/dT were calculated by differentiating equation (1).

References

1. KEESOM, V. *Gelii (Helium)*. IIL, Moscow, 1949.
2. KAMERLINGH-ONNES, H., C. A. CROMMELIN and P. G. CATH. *Commun. Phys. Lab. Univ. Leiden*, No. 151b, 1917.
3. CATH, P. G. and H. KAMERLINGH-ONNES. *Commun. Phys. Lab. Univ. Leiden*, No. 152b, 1927.
4. CROMMELIN, C. A. and R. O. GIBSON. *Commun. Phys. Lab. Univ. Leiden*, No. 185b, 1927.
5. HENNING, F. and J. OTTO. *Z. Physik*, **37**, 633, 1936.
6. BIEGELEISEN, J. and E. ROTH. *J. Chem. Phys.*, **35**, 1, 1961.
7. GRILLY, E. R. *Cryogenics*, **2**, 4, 1962.
8. OLSZEWSKY, K. *Trans. Roy. Soc., London*, **A186**, 253, 1895.
9. RAMSAY, W. and M. TRAVERS. *Trans. Roy. Soc., London*, **A197**, 47, 1901.
10. RAMSAY, W. and M. TRAVERS. *Z. Phys. Chem.*, **38**, 641, 1901.

11. BORN, F.   *Ann. Phys.*, **69**, 473, 1922.
12. CROMMELIN, C.   *Commun. Phys. Lab. Univ. Leiden*, No. 138c, 1913 ; No. 140a, 1914.
13. CLAUSIUS, K. and A. FRANK. $\mathcal{Z}$. *Electrochem.*, **49**, 308, 1943.
14. CLARK, O., F. DIN, J. ROBB, A. MICHELS, T. WASSENAAR and T. ZWEITERING.   *Physika*, **17**, 10, 1951.
15. FREEMAN, M. and C. HALSEY.   *J. Phys. Chem.*, **60**, 8, 1956.
16. NARINSKII, G. B.   *Kislorod*, No. 3, 1957.
17. MICHELS, A., J. LEVELT and W. DE GRAAF.   *Physica*, **24**, 659, 1958.
18. FLUBACHER, P., A. LEADBETTER and J. MORRISON.   *Proc. Roy. Soc., London*, **78**, 1449, 1961.
19. VAN ITTERBEEK, A., I. DE BOELPAEP, O. VERBEKE, F. THEENWES and K. STAES.   *Physica*, **30**, 2119, 1964.
20. MICHELS, A. and C. PRINS.   *Physica*, **28**, 2, 1962.
21. RADOVSKII, I. S.   In :   *Teplo- i massoobmen (Heat and mass transfer)*, Vol. **7**, Energiya, Moscow-Leningrad, 1966.
22. MATHIAS, E., H. KAMERLINGH-ONNES and C. A. CROMMELIN. *Commun. Phys. Lab. Univ. Leiden*, No. 131a, 1912.
23. PETERS, K. and K. WEIL. $\mathcal{Z}$. *Phys. Chem.*, **A148**, 27, 1930.
24. ALLEN, F. J. and R. B. MOORE.   *J. Am. Chem. Soc.*, **53**, 2522 , 1931.
25. JUSTI, E.   *Physik.* $\mathcal{Z}$., **36**, 4, 1935.
26. KEEZOM, W. H., J. MAZUR and J. J. MEIHUIZEN.   *Physica*, **2**, 669, 1935.
27. MEIHUIZEN, J. J. and C. A. CROMMELIN.   *Physica*, **4**, 1, 1937.
28. MICHELS, A., T. WASSENAAR and T. N. ZWEITERING.   *Physica*, **18**, 1, 1952.
29. BEAUMONT, R. H., H. CHIHARA and J. A. MORRISON.   *Proc. Roy. Soc., London*, **78**, part 6 (1), No. 505, 1961.
30. CLAUSIUS, K. and K. WEIGAND. $\mathcal{Z}$. *Phys. Chem.*, **B46**, 1, 1940.
31. THOMAES, G. and R. STEENWINKEL.   *Nature*, **193**, 160, 1962.
32. HEUSE, W. and J. OTTO. $\mathcal{Z}$. *Tech. Physik*, **13**, 277, 1932.
33. CLAUSIUS, K. $\mathcal{Z}$. *Phys. Chem.*, **B50**, 403, 1941.
34. MICHELS, A. and T. WASSENAAR.   *Physica*, **16**, 253, 1950.
35. WEINBERGER, M. A. and W. G. SCHNEIDER.   *Canad. J. Chem.*, **30**, 422, 1952.
36. WHITEWAY, S. G. and S. G. MASON.   *Canad. J. Chem.*, **31**, 569, 1953.
37. HABGOOD, H. W. and W. G. SCHNEIDER.   *Canad. J. Chem.*, **32**, 2, 1954.
38. HEARTY, R. and C. LEFEBRE.   *Proc. Roy. Soc., London*, **76**, 180, 1960.
39. PATTERSON, H. S., R. S. CRIPPS and R. WHITLAW-GRAY.   *Proc. Roy. Soc., London*, **A86**, 591, 1912.
40. MATHIAS, E., C. A. CROMMELIN and H. KAMERLINGH-ONNES.   *Commun. Phys. Lab. Univ. Leiden*, No. 162b, 1923.

41. MATHIAS, E., C. A. CROMMELIN and J. J. MEIHUIZEN. *Physica*, **4**, 11, 1937.

42. MICHELS, A., T. WASSENAAR and P. LOUWERSE. *Physica*, **20**, 99, 1954.

43. LEADBETTER, A. J. and H.E. THOMAS. *Trans. Far. Soc.*, **61**, part 1, 10, 1965.

44. GLADUN, C. *Cryogenics*, **6**, 1, 27, 1966.

45. POOL, R. A. H., B. D. C. SHIELDS and L. A. K. STAVELY. *Nature*, **181**, 831, 1958.

46. POOL, R. A. H., G. SAVILLE, T. M. HERRINGTON, B. D. C. SHIELDS and L. A. R. STAVELEY. *Trans. Far. Soc.*, **58**, 1692, 1962.

47. McCAIN, W. D. and W. T. ZEIGLER. *J. Chem. Eng. Data*, **12**, 199, 1967.

48. THOMAES, G., R. STEENWIENKEL and W. STONE. *Mol. Phys.*, **5**, 301, 1962.

49. CHASHKIN, YU. R. Author's abstract of Kandidat's dissertation, Moscow State University, 1968.

50. SAIJ, Y. and S. KOBAJASHY. *Cryogenics*, **4**, 136, 1964.

51. RABINOVICH, V. A., L. S. VEKSLER and P. T. SLOBODYANIK. *Trudy III Vsesoyiznoi Teplofizicheskoi Konferentsii po Svoistvam Veshchestv pri Vysekikh Temperaturakh* (*Transactions of the Third All-Union Thermophysical Conference on High-Temperature Properties of Substances*). Nauka, Moscow, 1969.

52. VAN ITTERBEEK, A. and O. VERBEKE. *Physica*, **26**, 931, 1960.

53. VAN ITTERBEEK, A., O. VERBEKE and K. STAES. *Physica*, **29**, 742, 1963.

54. CLAUSIUS, K. *Z. Phys., Chem.*, **B31**, 459, 1936.

55. PACKARD, I. and C. SWENSON. *J. Phys. Chem. Solids*, **24**, 1405, 1963.

56. CLAUSIUS, K and J. RICCOBONI. *Z. Phys. Chem.*, **B38**, 81, 1938.

57. MILLS, R. and E. GRILLY. *Phys. Rev.*, **99**, 480, 1955.

UDC 541.11

EXPERIMENTAL p-v-T DATA FOR NEON IN THE TEMPERATURE RANGE OF 65-273°K AND PRESSURES UPTO 250 BARS

E. V. Osnovskii and *A. I. Moroz*

Neon has recently attained increasing importance in cryogenic technology as a prospective refrigerant for obtaining temperatures lower than those obtained with the use of liquid oxygen or nitrogen [1-5].

By evacuating the space above solid neon, 20.3 and 17.8°K, temperatures corresponding to the normal boiling point for hydrogen and to the upper limit of transition to the superconducting state respectively, can be consecutively reached.

Because of the large volume heat of evaporation, the cooling effect of neon per unit volume of the liquid is 3.3 times greater than that of hydrogen and 40 times greater than that of helium.

The higher cooling capacity of neon compares favorably with the loss of liquid during evaporation. Advantages of neon, in comparison with hydrogen, are its complete inertness and the fact that it is explosion-proof.

Neon has been variously applied as a refrigerant; it has been employed for cooling and thermostatting of radioelectronic apparatuses and infrared detectors, in microcoolers, cryogenic pumps, and other equipment.

For application of neon in cryogenics, reliable data are required on its thermodynamic properties.

A short survey of the available data on the compressibility of neon

Few experimental studies on the p-v-T relationships for neon at low temperatures are available, and these studies have been undertaken at limited temperature and pressure ranges and have yielded inconsistent data.

The first significant studies were performed at the Leiden Laboratory during 1915-1919 [6, 7], in which eight isotherms were obtained at 56-273°K and pressures of 20-90 atm. The experimentation of Holborn and Otto [8-10] covered nearly identical parameter ranges, with six isotherms obtained over the temperature range of 65-273°K.

Further studies on neon were directed toward application of the available experimental data for extrapolation to wider temperature and pressure ranges. Thus, Jendall [11] suggested an equation of state from which he calculated the thermodynamic properties of neon at temperatures from normal boiling point to 320°K and pressures upto 200 atm. The present authors have compared Jendall's calculated thermal properties with the values reported in works [8-10], showing an average discrepancy between the two sets of data of 0.2%, and maximum $\sim 1.9\%$.

The present authors regard the use of the calculated values in the extrapolation region to potentially yield considerable error [11]; a similar conclusion was drawn in reference [12]. A similar attempt [12] was undertaken to obtain an equation of state for neon on the basis of the theory of thermodynamic similarity and the law of corresponding states. Fig. 1 shows the deviation of the calculated data of McCarty and Stewart from the data of other authors in a diagram with $\Delta\varepsilon/\varepsilon \cdot 100\%$ and p as the coordinates ($\varepsilon = pv/p_0v_0 =$ degree of compressibility). Fig. 1 also displays the deviation of the calculated values from experimental values in references [6, 8-10] to average 0.3%, exceeding 1% on 80°K and 65°K isotherms. In the nonexperimental region, the authors of reference [12] estimate their values to possess an error of 1.5-2%.

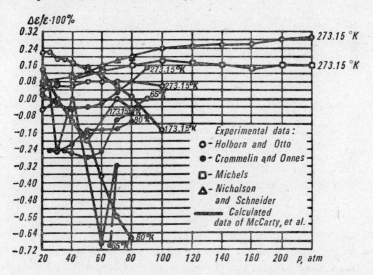

Fig. 1. Comparison of available data on thermal properties of neon.

This comparison evinces the need for experiments to evaluate and extend the available data. Such an experimental investigation was conducted at the Physicotechnical Laboratory of the All-Union Scientific Research Institute of Cryogenic Machines, and the experimental procedure and results obtained thus far are described as follows.

Experimental procedure

During installation of experimental equipment, preference was given to the use of the unrelieved constant-volume piezometer, which is relatively simple, widely used, and does not require precise equipment. Experimental compressibility of neon was determined along isotherms with the measurement of the amount of neon in a low-pressure gasometer.

Analysis of corrections for temperature and pressure reveals a high accuracy of $\pm(0\cdot01\text{-}0.02)\%$. For applying corrections to the change in piezometer volume with temperature and pressure variations, numerical values of the corresponding coefficients and the calculation procedure described in references [13-15] were used.

For estimating the effect of ballast volume, which is the volume of a region of the gas-supply connections to the piezometer, the soldered capillary method was employed on a number of isotherms. Separate calibration experiments were similarly performed with argon, for which extensive and reliable compressibility data are available. A schematic diagram of the apparatus employed in these experiments is given in Fig. 2.

Compressibility of neon in the temperature range of 173-273°K was measured on an apparatus with liquid cryostat and automatic temperature control [16]. Petroleum ether served as the intermediate refrigerant and was cooled by liquid nitrogen supplied at the desired rate from a KPZh-30 gasifier through cooling spiral. The piezometer was a thick-walled welded vessel (1) of Kh18N9T steel and was calibrated with benzene. The required weight measurements were performed in the Mass Measurement Laboratory of the VNIIK (the All-Union Scientific Research Institute of Cryogenics). Uniform temperature in the liquid bath of the cryostat was obtained with the mechanical stirrer (3) and the required temperature was obtained using the electric heater (6) connected to the circuit of an electronic temperature controller. The heater was comprised of a winding mechanism on a textolite cylinder.

Temperature of the liquid bath was measured with a standard platinum resistance thermometer included in the circuit of a P308 potentiometer. A technical platinum resistance thermometer installed in a manner similar to the standard thermometer served as the temperature monitor for the temperature controller. Pressure of the gas introduced into the piezometer was measured with the piston manometer (14) with the weights suspended from the bottom of the piezometer and with forced rotation of the piston. Individual readings of the manometer were checked by comparison with parallel measurements with another MP-60 piston manometer of 0.05 class. For measurement of pressure in the piezometer, the gas and oil

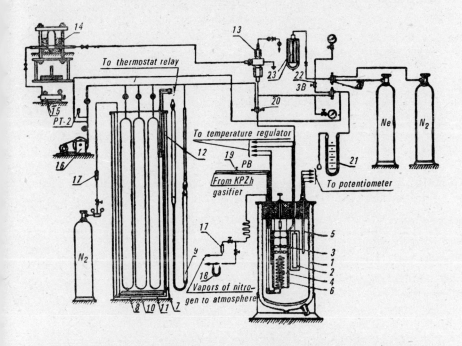

Fig. 2. Schematic diagram of experimental apparatus with liquid cryostat.
1—*vessel* ; 2—*piezometer* ; 3—*stirrer* ; 4—*cooling spiral* ; 5—*standard platinum resistance thermometer*; 6—*textolite cylinder* ; 7—*outer shell of thermostat* ; 8—*thermostat vessels*; 9—*U-shaped manometer*; 10—*stirrer*; 11—*electric heater*; 12—*standard platinum resistance thermometer*; 13—*null-point instrument*; 14—*piston manometer*; 15—*oil-operated press*; 16—*vacuum pump*; 17—*rotameter*, 18—*membrane rheometer* ; 19—*valve for liquid-nitrogen supply* ; 20—*microvalve* ; 21—*U-shaped water manometer* ; 22—*clamping valve* ; 23—*thermal booster*.

lines were separated by a mercury-membrane null-point instrument (13) with a secondary arrow indicator. Sensitivity of the membrane of the null-point instrument was 50-60 mm H_2O. For raising the pressure in the piezometer above the gas pressure in the cylinder, the compact thermobooster (23) was used. Quantity of neon contained in the piezometer was determined from the pressure fluctuation in thermostat vessels (8), wherein gas was introduced on expansion in the piezometer. Gasometer pressure was measured by the U-shaped mercury manometer (9), assisted by a KM-8 catherometer. The left arm of the U-shaped manometer had previously been evacuated to a pressure of 10^{-3} to 10^{-4} mm Hg. The volume of the gasometer vessel was determined by calibration with water.

In the process of alignment all the main apparatus components and measurement instruments were thoroughly checked in accordance with the standard specifications for experimental work of this type.

The accuracies of determination of the main parameters, determining the accuracy of experimental results, are given below :

Cryostat temperature, °K	±0.02
Gasometer temperature, °K	±0.05
Gas pressure in piezometer, % total pressure	±0.02
Gas pressure in gasometer, mm Hg	±0.03
Piezometer volume, % total volume	±0.04
Volume of gasometer vessels, % total volume	±0.03

Experimentation at lower temperatures was undertaken using another type of cryostat, described in the article in the present collection by Moroz, Onosovskii, and Mil'man.

Experimental results

Processing of the obtained results included analysis of all factors potentially affecting the final numerical value of the density of neon corresponding to experimental conditions. The required corrections were accomplished in the calculations on this basis.

Corrections due to temperature, pressure, and ballast volume of the piezometer have already been mentioned. The effect of hydrostatic pressure of the gas in the piezometer and capillary depression of the mercury in the U-shaped manometer were also calculated, with the necessary corrections for change in free-fall acceleration, deformation of piston pair, and so on.

Tables 1-6 display the experimentally obtained values of the thermal properties of neon on six isotherms : 273.15°K, 223.15°K, 173.15°K, 123.15°K, 77.65°K, and 65°K at pressures of 20-250 bars.

The following values of physical constants were used in processing the experimental data : $\rho_0 = 0.90004$ g/cm^3, $R = 8.3143$ J/mole · °K, and $M = 20.183$.

The results obtained by the present authors were compared with the experimental and calculated values of other authors. The comparison was performed at identical isotherms and at those for which interpolation could be accomplished without exceeding the temperature by 2–3 deg.

At high temperatures (273.15, 223.15 and 173.15°K isotherms), our data agree closely with those of Holborn and Otto at pressures of 20-100 atm. In this range, the deviation in ε values is within 0.1-0.15%. The maximum deviation from the data of Crommelin and Onnes on the given isotherms is 0.3-0.5%.

Table 1. Thermal properties of neon at 273.15°K

p, bar	ρ, kg/m³	ε	$z=pv/RT$	p, bar	ρ, kg/m³	ε	$z=pv/RT$
22.338	19.63	1.0107	1.0113	187.25	151.8	1.0958	1.0963
39.453	34.43	1.0192	1.0197	187.78	152.1	1.0968	1.0973
59.04	50.99	1.0286	1.0291	207.71	166.6	1.1074	1.1079
78.56	67.19	1.0386	1.0391	215.40	172.1	1.1115	1.1120
78.62	67.21	1.0391	1.0396	226.48	180.0	1.1175	1.1181
97.53	82.65	1.0482	1.0487	241.52	190.5	1.1262	1.1267
109.07	91.86	1.0547	1.0552	244.16	192.4	1.1274	1.1280
128.68	107.4	1.0649	1.0648	244.35	192.5	1.1275	1.1281
148.11	122.4	1.0747	1.0752	244.35	192.5	1.1277	1.1283
166.24	136.2	1.0846	1.0851	245.10	193.1	1.1276	1.1282
181.39	147.4	1.0931	1.0936				

Table 2. Thermal properties of neon at 223.15°K

p, bar	ρ, kg/m³	ε	$z=pv/RT$	p, bar	ρ, kg/m³	ε	$z=pv/RT$
20.021	21.56	0.8249	1.0103	137.54	139.0	0.8789	1.0764
20.130	21.67	0.8250	1.0104	156.26	156.3	0.8881	1.0876
29.795	31.92	0.8291	1.0153	157.05	157.0	0.8883	1.0879
89.477	42.08	0.8334	1.0207	157.41	157.3	0.8887	1.0884
59.13	62.41	0.8416	1.0307	176.35	174.4	0.8982	1.1000
59.42	62.69	0.8420	1.0312	177.61	175.5	0.8989	1.1008
78.60	82.06	0.8508	1.0419	177.88	175.8	0.8990	1.1010
79.01	82.51	0.8506	1.0417	198.35	193.7	0.9094	1.1137
98.01	101.3	0.8598	1.0530	207.05	201.2	0.9139	1.1192
98.34	101.5	0.8603	1.0536	207.44	201.7	0.9136	1.1188
98.88	102.1	0.8602	1.0535	224.78	216.2	0.9235	1.1310
117.77	120.4	0.8689	1.0641	227.93	219.0	0.9245	1.1322
119.02	121.5	0.8699	1.0653	245.10	233.1	0.9343	1.1438
120.35	122.8	0.8705	1.0661	247.57	235.2	0.9350	1.1450

Table 3. Thermal properties of neon at 173.15°K

p, bar	ρ, kg/m³	ε	$z=pv/RT$	p, bar	ρ, kg/m³	ε	$z=pv/RT$
20.809	28.86	0.6405	1.0109	59.39	80.77	0.6531	1.0307
22.671	31.41	0.6411	1.0118	78.58	105.69	0.6504	1.0423
39.435	54.19	0.6464	1.0202	78.79	106.02	0.6601	1.0418
40.114	55.12	0.6465	1.0204	97.64	129.92	0.6676	1.0537
59.02	80.31	0.6528	1.0303	98.06	130.50	0.6675	1.0535

Table 3—*Continued*

p, bar	ρ, kg/m³	ε	$z=pv/RT$	p, bar	ρ, kg/m³	ε	$z=pv/RT$
117.37	154.4	0.6754	1.0660	177.09	224.3	0.7013	1.1068
117.21	154.2	0.6753	1.0658	177.23	224.4	0.7015	1.1072
137.04	178.1	0.6835	1.0788	197.21	246.6	0.7103	1.1210
137.80	179.0	0.6839	1.0794	197.27	246.5	0.7110	1.1222
156.08	200.4	0.6920	1.0922	234.33	285.6	0.7289	1.1504
156.39	200.7	0.6922	1.0925	235.47	286.7	0.7295	1.1513

Table 4. Thermal properties of neon at 123.15°K

p, bar	ρ, kg/m³	ε	$z=pv/RT$	p, bar	ρ, kg/m³	ε	$z=pv/RT$
20.479	40.29	0.4515	1.0019	156.51	287.6	0.4833	1.0725
20.777	40.88	0.4515	1.0019	173.74	315.0	0.4900	1.0874
39.712	77.73	0.4538	1.0070	174.41	316.3	0.4898	1.0869
40.511	79.30	0.4538	1.0071	187.72	336.4	0.4957	1.1000
58.40	113.6	0.4565	1.0130	193.29	344.8	0.4979	1.1049
58.54	113.9	0.4565	1.0130	195.50	348.1	0.4989	1.1071
76.52	147.8	0.4600	1.0208	197.80	351.5	0.4999	1.1093
77.19	149.0	0.4602	1.0212	198.36	352.5	0.4998	1.1091
93.08	178.3	0.4638	1.0292	198.52	352.6	0.5001	1.1098
104.97	199.8	0.4669	1.0361	215.40	377.0	0.5075	1.1262
106.60	202.6	0.4675	1.0374	216.02	377.9	0.5078	1.1267
115.46	218.2	0.4701	1.0432	220.90	384.7	0.5100	1.1318
132.15	247.1	0.4750	1.0541	226.68	392.6	0.5129	1.1382
137.00	255.2	0.4768	1.0581	245.51	418.1	0.5216	1.1575
155.90	286.9	0.4827	1.0712	246.18	418.8	0.5221	1.1586

Table 5. Thermal properties of neon at 77.65°K

p, bar	ρ, kg/m³	ε	$z=pv/RT$	p, bar	ρ, kg/m³	ε	$z=pv/RT$
20.080	65.33	0.2730	0.9608	102.71	359.8	0.2536	0.8925
20.525	66.82	0.2729	0.9603	117.85	409.5	0.2556	0.8996
39.962	134.41	0.2641	0.9295	137.48	469.0	0.2604	0.9165
39.965	134.36	0.2642	0.9298	156.66	520.5	0.2674	0.9409
40.131	135.98	0.2641	0.9295	177.06	568.8	0.2765	0.9731
40.463	136.09	0.2641	0.9295	178.08	570.9	0.2771	0.9752
59.26	204.3	0.2577	0.9066	196.88	609.8	0.2868	1.0094
60.84	210.0	0.2573	0.9056	213.45	640.7	0.2959	1.0414
78.15	273.2	0.2541	0.8942	217.03	646.9	0.2980	1.0488
78.77	275.5	0.2540	0.8939	235.04	677.0	0.3084	1.0854
97.86	343.2	0.2533	0.8915	235.67	678.1	0.3087	1.0865
98.39	345.3	0.2531	0.8908				

Table 6. Thermal properties of neon at 65°K

p, bar	ρ, kg/m³	ε	$z=pv/RT$	p, bar	ρ, kg/m³	ε	$z=pv/RT$
10.429	40.61	0.2281	0.9590	95.87	470.5	0.1810	0.7610
19.894	80.43	0.2197	0.9237	101.91	498.4	0.1816	0.7636
20.791	84.41	0.2188	0.9199	107.33	521.6	0.1828	0.7684
30.699	129.61	0.2104	0.8846	119.43	567.6	0.1869	0.7858
41.126	181.2	0.2016	0.8477	120.02	569.8	0.1871	0.7866
41.188	181.5	0.2016	0.8476	139.07	631.2	0.1957	0.8228
51.50	235.4	0.1943	0.8169	148.28	656.3	0.2007	0.8438
56.94	265.2	0.1907	0.8018	157.20	679.8	0.2054	0.8636
64.11	304.8	0.1868	0.7854	176.97	722.8	0.2175	0.9145
73.41	356.2	0.1830	0.7696	199.42	763.5	0.2320	0.9754
79.17	387.3	0.1816	0.7635	217.12	791.4	0.2437	1.0246
87.36	429.2	0.1808	0.7601	250.86	838.4	0.2658	1.1175

The deviation of our data from those of Holborn and Otto and Crommelin and Onnes is higher (0.3-0.6%) on 80 and 123°K isotherms. At 65°K in the pressure region upto 70 bars, our data coincide with those of Crommelin and Onnes, with maximum deviation from the data of Holborn and Otto at 0.25%.

The reliability of our results on the density and compressibility of neon was checked by comparison of all available data for the 273.15°K isotherm. In addition to the works already mentioned, the data of Nicholson and Schneider [17] and Michels and colleagues [18] are available for this temperature. Michels and colleagues determined the compressibility of neon at this temperature upto pressures of 2000 atm. Furthermore, the 273.15°K isotherm was the only isotherm on which Holborn and Otto obtained experimental points in the pressure range of 20-185 atm.

Fig. 3 gives a diagram of deviations under coordinates $\triangle\varepsilon/\varepsilon$. 100% and p for comparison of our data with the p-v-T data available in the literature, and shows our compressibility values for neon to generally agree with the experimental data of most authors. The maximum deviation does not exceed 0.1% over the entire pressure range. Hence, it can be assumed that the main parameters of volume, temperature, and pressure were determined with final accuracy in our investigation.

The reliability of our p-v-T data at low temperatures was assayed by special comparative experiments at the boiling point of nitrogen on two cryostats differing in design, piezometer volume, and thermostat method. The results coincided within $\pm(0.05$-$0.1)\%$.

Our results may perhaps enable evaluation of the calculated data of McCarty and Stewart, whose data apparently correspond to the accuracy indicated by these authors. At pressures upto 100 atm, where calculations could be based on the available experimental data, the deviation is $0.2 \pm$ 0.4%. The deviation increases at higher pressures, attaining a value of above 1% on individual isotherms.

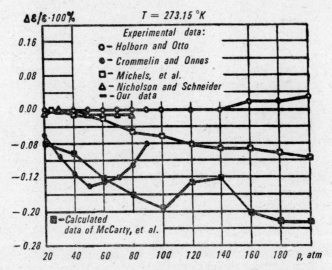

Fig. 3.   Comparison of data on the compressibility of neon for 273.15°K isotherm.

The range of present experiments will be extended to lower temperatures in future investigations.

REFERENCES

1. BEWILOGUA, L.   *Die Technik,* No. 2, 107-111, 1963.
2. BEWILOGUA, L.   *Monatsberichte der Deutschen Akademie der Wissenschaft zu Berlin,* Vol. **4** (3-4), 180, 1962.
3. BEWILOGUA, L.   *Kältetechnik,* **17** (6), 185-187, 1965.
4. GRAHAM, F. G.   *Advances in Cryogenic Engineering,* **7**, 562-566, 1962.
5. FRADKOV, A. B.   *Pribory i Teknika Eksper.,* No. 1, 184-185, 1963.
6. KAMERLINGH-ONNES, H. and C. A. CROMMELIN.   *Commun. Phys. Lab. Univ. Leiden,* No. 147d, 1915.
7. CROMMELIN, C. A., I. P. MARTINEZ and H. KAMERLINGH-ONNES. *Commun. Phys. Lab. Univ. Leiden,* No. 154a, 1919.
8. HOLBORN, L. and J. OTTO.   *Z. für Physik,* **23**, 77, 1924.
9. HOLBORN, L. and J. OTTO.   *Z. für Physik,* **33**, 1, 1925.
10. HOLBORN, L. and J. OTTO.   *Z. für Physik,* **38**, 359, 1926.

11. JENDALL, E. F. *Thermodynamic tables for neon.* Linde Company, Engineering Laboratory , New York, January 15, 1960.
12. McCARTY, R. D., R. B. STEWART and K. D. TIMMERHAUS. *Advances in Cryogenic Engineering*, **8**, 135-145, 1963.
13. TULYAKOV, A. P. *Khimicheskoe Mashinostroenie*, No. 2, 1935.
14. ZHOKHOVSKII, M. K. *Izmeritel'naya Tekhnika*, No. 7, 1959.
15. FEDOSEEV, V. I. *Soprotivlenie materialov (Strength of materials).* Moscow, Mashgiz, 1960.
16. ROGOVAYA, I. A. and M. G. KAGANER. *Zh. Fiz. Khim.*, **34** (9), 1960.
17. NICHOLSON, E. A. and W. G. SCHNEIDER. *Canada J. Chem.*, **33**, 589, 1955.
18. MICHELS, A., T. WASSENAAR and P. LOURENSE. *Physika*, **26**, 539, 1960.

UDC 541.11

MOLAL VOLUMES AND THERMODYNAMIC PROPERTIES OF ARGON AT PRESSURES UPTO 10,000 ATM AND TEMPERATURES UPTO 400°C

E. V. Polyakov and *D. S. Tsiklis*

Molal volumes of argon were measured by the apparatus described in reference [1] by the displacement method at pressures upto 10,000 atm and temperatures between 100-400°C. Argon utilized in these experiments contained approximately 0.05% impurities.

It was shown [1] from the example of nitrogen that the accuracy of data obtained by the displacement method is about 1.5% in the pressure range of 1500-2500 atm and 0.3% at higher pressures.

The results obtained were averaged on isotherms of pv-p relationship and are given in Table 1.

The data on the compressibility of argon are described using the Tait equation of state

$$v = v_0 \left[1 - C \ln \frac{B+p}{B+p_0} \right],$$

where v=gas volume at pressure p and temperature T; v_0=gas volume at pressure p_0 used as the zero reading; C=constant; B=a temperature function.

It is interesting to note that the values of C were identical for both argon and nitrogen [3], i.e., $C=0.1597$.

The selected values of function B were graphically averaged (see Fig. 1).

The Tait equation was used to compute molal volumes of argon in the pressure range of 3000-12,000 atm and temperature range of 100-400°C. These values were compared with experimental values (see Table 2 and Fig. 2). Fig. 2 shows the deviations for argon to be accidental, similar to those for nitrogen.

The thermodynamic properties of argon were calculated from equations similar to those employed for nitrogen. The required values of $(dv_0/dT)_p$ and dB/dT were determined by graphical differentiation.

Under v-T coordinates, the 3000 atm isobar assumes a straight line and $(\delta v_0/\delta T)_{p_0} = 0.2817$ cm³/mole·deg=constant.

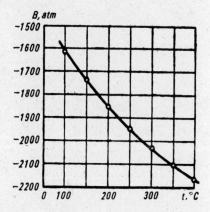

Fig. 1. Dependence of B on temperature.

Table 1. Averaged molal volumes for argon, cm³/mole

p, atm	v, at t, °C			
	100	200	300	400
1500	41.20	46.93	52.80	58.80
2000	36.75	41.00	45.40	49.80
2500	34.24	37.72	41.20	44.52
3000	32.52	35.40	38.33	41.17
3500	30.94	33.43	36.09	38.60
4000	29.65	31.80	34.22	36.52
4500	28.71	30.67	32.75	34.80
5000	27.90	29.72	31.56	33.32
5500	27.09	28.82	30.58	32.16
6000	26.43	28.03	29.67	31.20
6500	25.91	27.37	28.95	30.38
7000	25.43	26.78	28.29	29.64
7500	25.03	26.27	26.68	29.00
8000	24.62	25.82	27.18	28.41
8500	—	25.40	26.67	27.87
9000	—	25.00	26.20	27.33
9500	—	24.66	25.78	26.86
10,000	—	24.36	25.42	26.39

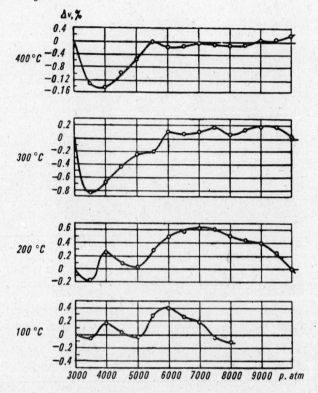

Fig. 2. Deviation of molal volumes of argon calculated from Tait equation from experimentally obtained values.

Table 2. Molal volumes of argon calculated from Tait Equation and deviation from experimental values

p, atm	at $t=100°$C		at $t=200°$C		at $t=300°$C		at $t=400°$C	
	v, cm³/mole	Δv, %	v, cm³/mole	Δv, %	v. cm³/mole	Δv, %	v, cm³/mole	Δv, %
3000	32.52	—	35.40	—	38.33	—	41.17	—
3500	30.92	—0.06	33.37	—0.18	35.79	—0.83	38.08	—1.35
4000	29.70	+0.17	31.88	+0.25	33.99	0.67	35.99	—1.45
4500	28.72	+0.03	30.70	+0.09	32.61	—0.43	34.41	—1.12
5000	27.89	—0.04	29.73	+0.03	31.48	—0.25	33.13	—0.57
5500	27.17	+0.29	28.90	+0.28	30.52	—0.20	32.06	—0.03
6000	26.54	+0.42	28.17	+0.50	29.70	+0.10	31.14	—0.19
7000	25.48	+0.20	26.95	+0.63	28.32	+0.11	29.62	—0.07
8000	24.59	—0.12	25.95	+1.50	27.20	+0.07	28.38	—0.10
9000	23.84	—	25.10	+0.40	26.25	+0.19	27.34	+0.04
10,000	23.18	—	24.36	0	25.43	+0.04	26.44	+0.19
11,000	22.59	—	23.71	—	24.71	—	25.65	—
12,000	22.07	—	23.12	—	24.06	—	24.94	—

*Pressure of 3000 atm taken as the zero reading.

Values of dB/dT were averaged with respect to temperature (see Fig. 3). Averaged values of constant B and dB/dT at various temperatures are given below.

t, °C	B, atm	dB/dT, atm/deg
100	—1610	—2.800
150	—1740	—2.404
200	—1852	—2.068
250	—1948	—1.788
300	—2030	—1.556
350	—2102	—1.364
400	—2165	—1.192

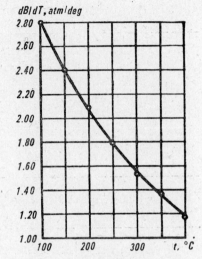

Fig. 3. Dependence of dB/dT on temperature.

Volatility ratio f/f_0, isothermal entropy differences $s_{p,T}-s_{p_0,T}$, and isothermal enthalpy difference $H_{p,T}-H_{p_0,T}$ for argon are displayed in Tables 3-5 for different temperatures and pressures.

The relatively low accuracy of our data in the pressure range of 1500-2500 atm and their deviation from the data of Din [2] somewhat disproves the reliability of our data.

Table 3. Volatility ratio for argon, atm

p, atm	f/f_0 at t, °C			
	100	200	300	400
3000	1	1	1	1
4000	2.7	2.4	2.1	2.0
5000	7.0	5.2	4.3	3.7
6000	17.1	11.0	8.2	6.7
7000	40.1	22.4	15.3	11.6
8000	90.9	44.2	27.6	19.6
9000	200.6	85.2	48.7	32.4
10,000	432.6	161.1	84.4	52.8
11,000	914.3	299.0	144.0	84.7
12,000	1897.3	546.2	242.0	133.9

Table 4.　Isothermal entropy difference for argon, cal/mole . deg

p, atm	$s_{p,T}-s_{p_0, T}$ at t,°C			
	100	200	300	400
3000	0	0	0	0
4000	0.59	0.57	0.56	0.56
5000	1.06	1.03	1.00	0.98
6000	1.47	1.42	1.38	1.34
7000	1.83	1.76	1.71	1.66
8000	2.16	2.07	2.00	1.95
9000	2.47	2.36	2.28	2.22
10,000	2.75	2.63	2.53	2.46
11,000	3.02	2.87	2.77	2.69
12,000	3.27	3.11	2.99	2.90

Table 5.　Isothermal enthalpy difference for argon, cal/mole

p, atm	$H_{p,T} H_{p_0, T}$ at t, °C			
	100	200	300	400
3000	0	0	0	0
4000	531.2	537.8	546.0	552.1
5000	1051.0	1067.0	1085.7	1099.7
6000	1557.2	1582.9	1611.9	1633.3
7000	2050.9	2086.0	2124.8	2153.3
8000	2533.3	2577.6	2625.9	2661.0
9000	3005.6	3058.8	3116.3	3157.7
10,000	3468.8	3530.7	3597.1	3644.6
11,000	3923.6	3994.1	4069.2	4122.5
12,000	4370.9	4449.8	4533.3	4592.4

REFERENCES

1. TSIKLIS, D. S. and E. V. POLYAKOV.　See article in the present collection.
2. DIN, F.　*Thermodynamic functions of gases.*　Vol. **2**, 1956.
3. TSIKLIS, D. S.　*Doklady Akademii Nauk SSSR*, No. 79, 289, 1951.

UDC 541.11

AN EXPERIMENTAL APPARATUS FOR THE DETERMINATION OF ISOCHORIC SPECIFIC HEATS OF LIQUIDS AND GASES OVER A WIDE RANGE OF PARAMETERS

V. A. Rabinovich and *O. M. Oleinik-Dzyadik*

Experimental data on isochoric specific heats of liquids and gases over a wide range of temperatures and pressures have recently received considerable attention, as such data would presumably facilitate obtaining rational equations of state and isolating the curved segments [1]. However, one complication in experimental determination of isochoric specific heats of liquids and gases at high pressures is the tenuity of calorimeter walls. The available experimental data on C_V of various substances in the liquid and gaseous states (excluding water and steam) have therefore been measured at pressures below 100 atm, and the objective of the present work is the development of an experimental apparatus for measuring specific heats at higher pressures.

The requirements for direct measurement of C_V are : (1) the calorimetric system should be highly adiabatic, (2) the calorimeter should have a much lower specific heat than the substance under study, and (3) the parameters of the substance under study should be flexible over a sufficiently wide range.

These requirements are generally satisfied in the known calorimetric apparatuses, in the majority of which [2] the system is rendered highly adiabatic by high vacuum (10^{-5} to 10^{-6} mm Hg) around the calorimetric vessel. Heat loss by radiation is considerably reduced by providing polish to the calorimeter walls and by using shields. In some investigations [18] the calorimeter is submerged in a thermostat bath, the temperature of tained which is main-equal to the temperature of the substance in the calorimeter.

These adiabatic methods have one important disadvantage, however. The calorimeters used in these procedures cannot be applied at high pressure, and the requirement for a thick-walled calorimeter raises the heat capacity, and accuracy of specific heat measurement decreases to such an extent that the experiments are no longer justifiable.

The present authors consider these difficulties to be most successfully overcome in the method recommended by Amirkhanov and Kerimov [4]; hence we have designed our apparatus by utilizing the advantages of this method and by avoiding some of the disadvantages.

The apparatus operates on the principle of direct heating of the substance in a constant-volume calorimeter. A measured amount of heat is introduced into a calorimeter containing a known quantity of the substance and the resultant temperature increase is measured.

Specific heat c_V is calculated from the formula :

$$c_V = \frac{W \delta \tau}{m \delta t} - \frac{A}{m},\qquad (1)$$

where W=heater capacity; $\delta\tau$=time of heating; m=mass of substance under study; δt=temperature increase; A=heat capacity of calorimeter.

The actual calorimeter is thin-walled as it is not under pressure, enabling decrease in heat capacity to 210 J/deg. The calorimeter consists of a 93-mm diameter sphere (see Fig. 1) produced by welding two halves with argon-arc. The wall thickness is 1 mm and the material is Kh18N9T stainless steel. The external surface of the calorimeter is polished after welding.

The high pressure exerted by the substance in the calorimeter is adjusted by concentrically placed thick-walled shielding shell (2). The high pressure is transmitted through Cu$_2$O powder (3) which fills the gap between the calorimeter and the shield. The shield is sphere-shaped and constructed of Kh18N9T steel with an internal diameter of 97 mm and wall thickness of 3.5 mm.

The cuprous oxide powder, while transmitting pressure from calorimeter to shield, also serves as a highly sensitive differential thermocouple registering the temperature difference between calorimeter and shield. The sensitivity of the cuprous oxide thermoelement considerably depends on the uniformity and density of the packed Cu$_2$O in the gap, which is filled by pouring the powder through a hole in the shield with administration of a continuous light knock to the shield. The calorimeter is water-cooled while the shield is heated and the hole in the shield is closed on filling the gap. On cooling, the shield causes further pressing of the powder in the gap, considerably decreasing the resistance of the powder layer and thereby raising the sensitivity of the thermoelement.

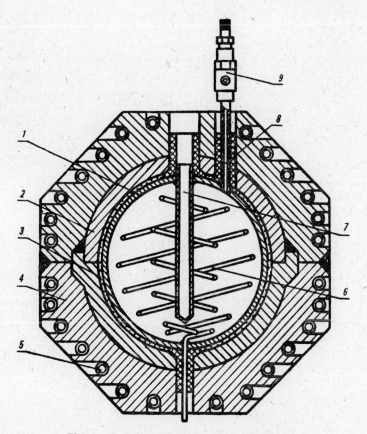

Fig. 1.   Constant-volume adiabatic calorimeter.

The adiabatic property of the calorimeter is achieved by continuously maintaining the shield temperature equal to the calorimeter temperature. For ensuring temperature uniformity throughout the shield, an important condition for creating adiabatic conditions, the shield is enclosed in the copper block (4).   The insulated heater (5) is fitted into grooves machined on the   surface of the copper block.   The heater is a nichrome spiral of 0.2 mm diameter wire and is insulated from the block with porcelain beads.

The substance in the calorimeter is heated by the insulated heater (6), which is constructed of PESHOK constatan wire of 0.2 mm diameter with a total length of 3 m.   The wire, wrapped in silk insulation soaked in BF-2 insulating gum, is folded and passed through a 1 mm diameter copper tube 1.5 m long.   The copper tube, presoldered with silver to the center of the bottom hemisphere, is then closed with solder at the free end and is formed into a spiral inside the calorimeter, providing uniform heat liberation therein.   Use of a magnetic stirrer inside the calorimeter is planned for future work to decrease the time required in attaining thermal equilibrium; this will be especially important for investigations of the critical region.

For work at temperatures above 450° K, a heater insulated with double-bore refractory porcelain beads has been designed.   The heater is placed inside a tube of Kh18N9T steel with an internal diameter of 3.5 mm, and is fitted inside the calorimeter in the manner described above.

A resistance thermometer is placed inside a 5 mm diameter, 0.5 mm thick tube (7) along the vertical axis of the calorimeter.   The open end of the tube is soldered to the top hemisphere of the calorimeter.   The calorimeter is filled with the gas under study through the steel tube (8) joined to the constant-volume valve (9).   The tube is 1.4 mm in diameter and has a wall thickness of 0.3 mm.

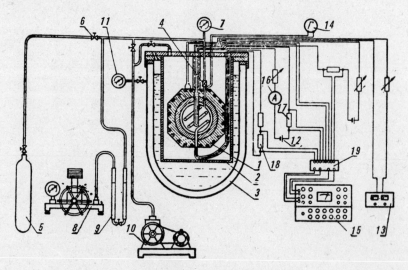

Fɪɢ. 2.   Schematic diagram of installation.

The apparatus for the determination of isochoric specific heat is shown in Fig. 2.   The calorimeter block (1) described above is placed inside the vacuum chamber (2) in the Dewar flask (3).   The vacuum chamber, a cylindrical vessel 140 mm in diameter and 360 mm in height with a hermetically sealing cover, is of Kh18N9T steel.   The calorimetric block is suspended inside the chamber from a prop fixed to the cover.   The stem of the constant-volume valve (4) and the tube connecting the valve with the filling system pass through a gasket in the chamber cover.   Connecting pipes from the vacuum chamber are directed outside through four openings in the cover.   The openings are packed with double-layer teflon washers.

The vacuum chamber is thermostatted in the metallic Dewar flask (3). Cylindrical walls of the flask are of Kh18N9T steel with thicknesses of 1 and 0.2 mm, and the bottom region is of 1 mm thick copper. For thermostatting at low temperatures, the Dewar flask is filled with liquid nitrogen.

The calorimeter is connected with the filling system, pressure measurement system, and vacuum connections through a copper tube and constant-volume valve (4). The calorimeter is filled with the gas to be studied from the cylinder (5) through the valve (6). Coarse measurement of the pressure in the calorimeter is performed by the 0.4 class spring manometer (7). Accurate pressure measurement is achieved with the 0.02 class loaded-piston manometer (8). Oil in the piston manometer is separated from the gas in the calorimeter by the U-shaped manometer (9). A vacuum is created in the calorimeter, vacuum chamber, and Dewar flask with the pump (10) and is measured with the vacuumometer (11).

The storage battery (12) supplies electric power to the calorimeter heater. The heater, encased in the shield, receives power from UIP-1 dc current source (13). Leads from the Cu_2O thermoelement are connected to terminals of a M17/12 galvanometer (14), which can register a temperature difference of less than 10^{-4} deg. between calorimeter and shield.

Temperature of the calorimetric substance is measured with a standard TS-Pn-1 platinum resistance thermometer with resistance $R_0 = 100.6605$ ohm and temperature coefficient $R_{100}/R_0 = 1.3924$. The thermometer can be used in the temperature range of 12-273.15°K; however, additional calibration may allow application upto 450°K. The resistance of the thermometer is measured with a bridge circuit employing a self-checking semiautomatic 0.005 class P-309 potentiometer (15).

The power expended in the heater is determined by measuring the current flowing through it and the voltage across its ends. On switching on the heater, the current is coarsely measured with a 0.5 class ampermeter (16). Current is accurately measured by calculating the voltage drop across the terminals of the standard resistance (17) connected in series with the heater circuit. The voltage across terminals of the heater is remeasured with the potentiometer (15), using the attenuator (18) connected in parallel with the heater. Another potentiometer (15) is alternately switched across the terminals of the heater and standard resistance thermometer with the change over switch (19).

The potentiometric block uses a standard circuit. The F-305 amplifier of the potentiometer is supplied with stabilized ac voltage of 220 V. The working circuits of the potentiometer operate on large-capacity dry cells. All standard resistance coils are reserved for thermostatting in an oil bath of thermometer-measured temperature.

The heating time is measured with a 51SD stopwatch with an error of below 0.025%. The calorimeter volume at room temperature and atmospheric pressure is determined from the difference in weights of the calorimeter filled with deaerated distilled water and empty calorimeter with a small correction due to the weight of air in the empty calorimeter.

As the calorimetric block is a vessel containing three layers, it is difficult to determine the change in its volume due to thermal expansion and isothermal deformation. The dependence of the calorimetric volume on temperature and pressure is therefore determined experimentally.

The amount of gas in the calorimeter is determined by either "relative" or "absolute" methods. In the relative method, the gas can be determined from compressibility data, for which temperature and pressure of the gas are measured after its saturation within the calorimeter. The amount of gas is then determined from the density of the gas under these conditions and the volume of the calorimeter. The absolute method requires gas recondensation in the calorimeter from the cylinder and determination of gas weight from the difference between weights of the cylinder prior to and following recondensation.

The absolute gas pressure in the calorimeter is represented by the algebraic sum of the pressure measured by piston manometer p_{man}, barometric pressure p_{bar}, hydrostatic pressure of oil p_{oil}, and hydrostatic pressure of mercury in the differential manometer p_{Hg}. The barometric pressure is measured with a standard barometer with an error below 0.2 mm Hg. By proper adjustment of the position of the piston and differential manometers, the hydraulic pressure due to oil is reduced to a minimum. Hydrostatic pressure of the mercury in the differential manometer is measured with an error below 0.2 mm Hg. Heat capacity of the calorimeter proper is determined experimentally after filling it with helium at low pressure. Helium is used for the calibration because of its high thermal conductivity and low atomic weight. Heat capacity A of the calorimeter is calculated from the formula :

$$A = \frac{W_T . \delta \tau_T}{\delta t_T} - c_{He} m_{He},\qquad (2)$$

where W_T=rate of heating during calibration ; $\delta\tau_T$=time of heating; δt_T=temperature difference; c_{He}=specific heat of helium; m_{He}=amount of helium in the calorimeter.

Dependence of the heat capacity of the calorimeter on temperature is established from the results of a number of experiments with helium at different temperatures.

Relative error of the specific heat thus determined is calculated from a formula directly derived from equation (1).

$$\frac{\Delta c_v}{c_v} = \frac{1+\varphi}{\varphi} \left[\frac{\Delta W}{W} + \frac{\Delta(\delta\tau)}{\delta\tau} + \frac{\Delta(\delta t)}{\delta t} \right] + \frac{\Delta m}{m} + \frac{1}{\varphi}\frac{\Delta A}{A}, \quad (3)$$

where $\varphi = \dfrac{c_V m}{A}$ is a complex term characterizing the perfection calorimeter.

Specific heats can be determined with great accuracy in calorimeters with a high value of φ. For a given calorimeter, the value of φ will increase with increased specific heat of the investigated substance. In the case of argon, for instance, the value of φ is 0.5 at specific volume $v = 1.5$ cm³/g, and only 0.2 at $v = 3.0$ cm³/g, and the maximum relative error in the determination of specific heat increases from 1.5 to 3%.

The value of specific heat c_V should be related to that state of the substance under which measurements are performed. In the single-phase region, the state is determined by two parameters, such as temperature and specific volume. The errors in measurement of state parameters cause the error in the specific heat. The error is expressed by the formula:

$$\left(\frac{\Delta c_V}{c_V} \right)_{\text{err}} = \left(\frac{\partial c_V}{\partial v} \right)_T \frac{\Delta v}{c_V} + \left(\frac{\partial c_V}{\partial T} \right)_v \frac{\Delta T}{c_V}, \qquad (4)$$

which clearly shows that the error will be high in the region where c_V is a strong function of temperature and volume, particularly near the critical point. The derivatives in formula (4) are computed from experimental values of c_V on isotherms and isochores.

The authors express their deep gratitude to F. G. El'darov for helpful suggestions and assistance during all stages in the development of the experimental apparatus.

REFERENCES

1. RABINOVICH, V. A. *IFZh,* **3** (6), 107, 1960.
2. KIRILLIN, V. A. and A. E. SHEINDLIN. *Issledovaniya termodinamicheskikh svoistv veshchestv (Investigation of thermodynamic properties of substances).* Moscow-Leningrad, Energiya, 1963.
3. MICHELS, A. and J. STRIJLAND. *Physica,* **18** (8), 613, 1952.
4. AMIRKHANOV, KH. I. and A. M. KERIMOV. *Teploenergetika,* No. 9, 1957; No. 6, 1962.

UDC 541.11

CRYOSTAT FOR EXPERIMENTAL DETERMINATION OF GAS COMPRESSIBILITIES AT LOW TEMPERATURES

A. I. Moroz, E. V. Onosovskii and *S. B. Mil'man*

The experimental methods for the determination of low-temperature thermal properties of gases can be divided into two main piezometric methods using loaded and unloaded constant or variable-volume piezometers, and hydrostatic methods [1]. Each method possesses peculiar advantages and disadvantages, and method selection is influenced by both objective and subjective factors, which include : (1) range of parameters in which measurements are to be performed, (2) availability of proper equipment and instruments, and (3) experience and skill of the research team in employing a given method.

The present authors preferred the loaded constant-volume piezometer for determining the p-v-T relationships for neon in the temperature range of 27-273°K and pressures upto 250 bar. Corrections for changes in the effective volume of the piezometer with changes in temperature and pressure in the given ranges can be calculated with an error of below $\pm(0.01\text{-}0.02)\%$ [2-7]. Corrections for ballast volume of the piezometer can be calculated with similar accuracy. The method of analyzing this error will be considered in the present paper, along with the construction of a cryostat with constant-volume piezometer developed particularly for work below the nitrogen temperature. A schematic diagram and general view of the cryostat are presented in Figs. 1 and 2.

Cooling system of piezometer

The piezometer is cooled and thermostatted at a given temperature by the liquid in the inner vessel (3), which boils at a lower temperature.

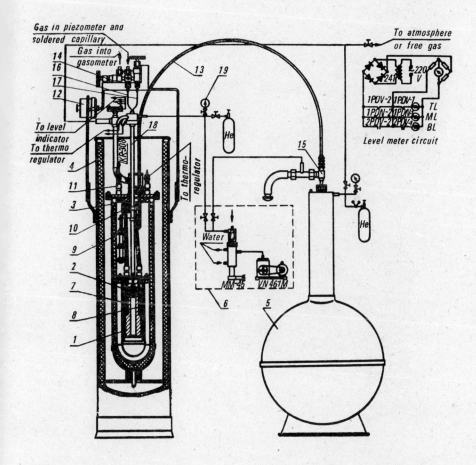

Fig. 1. Schematic diagram of cryostat for compressibility measurements.

1—piezometer ; 2—cup ; 3—inner vessel ; 4—outer vessel ; 5—helium container ; 6—vacuum assembly ; 7—TSPn-1 standard platinum resistance thermometer ; 8—TSP-0.3 secondary platinum resistance thermometer ; 9—level-meter ; 10—spool for winding leads ; 11—glass insulation ; 12— common circuit breaker ; 13—overflow siphon ; 14—composite valve ; 15—vacuum valve ; 16—working capillary ; 17—soldered capillary ; 18—tube ; 19—vacuum manometer : TL, ML, and BL=top, middle, and bottom levels respectively.

This metallic vessel of 3.5 liter capacity possesses multilayer vacuum insulation; at the temperature of the surrounding medium, the loss in case of nitrogen is 50 g/h. The entire inner area of the cryostat is mounted on the flange provided at the top of the vessel (3).

Depending on the temperature interval of the experiments, the vessel (3) can be filled with liquid nitrogen, neon, hydrogen or helium.

For reducing the loss of thermostatting liquid, the inner vessel is immersed in liquid nitrogen contained in the outer vessel (4), which is an open cylindrical Dewar flask of 18 liter capacity with multilayer vacuum insulation.

Fig. 2.   General view of cryostat.

For filling the inner vessel (3) with the thermostatting liquid and restoring the liquid lost during the experiment, the cryostat is fed from the standard 10 liter helium cylinder (5) with the flexible siphon (13). The siphon, 3.5 m long, consists of two thin stainless steel tubes. Thermal contact between the two tubes is prevented by winding glass rope on the inner tube ($4 \times$ 0.2 mm) in a spiral with a pitch of 6-8 mm along the entire length of the tube. The size of the outer tube is 6×0.3 mm. After assembling the tubes, they are carefully bent to the desired form of the siphon.

The space between the two tubes is evacuated through the special vacuum valve (15), fitted into one of the arms of the siphon along with bellows for thermal compensation. A similar construction of the siphon has been described by another author [8]. The construction is simple, quite reliable, and effective.

Variation in the level of liquid in the inner vessel is measured with the level-meter (9), consisting of three copper resistances of 100 ohm each wound on small teflon spools. The spools are fixed on a metallic tube and separated by a distance of 30 mm. The liquid level is determined by connecting the windings across a potentiometric bridge with a needle indicator, applying a power of 2 watts to the winding for 3-5 sec. The principle of level measurement is shown in the right-hand region of Fig. 1.

Rapid cooling of the piezometer (1) is achieved by passing gaseous helium from a cylinder into the metallic cup (2). Gas pressure in the cup is measured with the vacuum manometer (19). On attaining the required temperature, helium is evacuated from the cup with vacuum assembly (6). For easier control of piezometer temperature with the thermoregulator, a vacuum can be created in the cup with either mechanical or diffusion-vacuum pumps, depending on the temperature gradient between the piezometer and cryostat bath. Sealing of flange connection of the cup (2), immersed in liquid during the experiment, is achieved using an indium gasket, inducing a possible vacuum of 10^{-5} mm Hg in the cup.

Construction of piezometer and thermoregulation

The piezometer (1) is obtained from 50 mm diameter, 150 mm high copper block, weighs 2.5 kg, and has a working volume of 20 cm³. Its inner surface is polished and chrome-plated. Heat transferred from the piezometer to cryostat bath is compensated for by an electric heater in the thermoregulation circuit. The heater is constructed of enameled PEVKM-2 constantan wire of 0.15 mm diameter and has a total resistance of 350 ohm.

To minimize thermal inertia in the system, the heater winding is arranged for maximum thermal contact with the piezometer. A right-angle spiral groove of 2.5×1.5 mm is machined along the outer surface of the piezometer. The groove contains a two-way channel for mounting the winding. The piezometer with the wound heater is placed inside a glass vessel with a gap of about 1 mm. The gap is filled with low-melting Cerrlow-117 alloy (Bi 44.7%, Pb 22.6%, Sn 8.3%, Cd 5.3%, In 19.1%) with a eutectic point of 47°C. When the alloy solidifies, the heater winding is fixed into the piezometer surface, and is electrically insulated. According to calculations, the temperature difference between the piezometer ends, not covered by the winding, and the remaining portion of the piezometer must not exceed thousandths of a degree under the worst conditions. The heater is connected across mains through a step-down transformer and diode rectifier and has a rating of 10 W. Electrical leads at the temperature of surrounding environment are extracted through ISSh glass beads soldered into the head of the tube (18).

Temperature sensors are inserted through two holes of 5 mm diameter and 75 mm length, drilled symmetrically with respect to the piezometer axis. One hole is used for installing the TSPN-1 standard platinum resistance thermometer connected to the R308 potentiometer, and the other hole is used for secondary TSP-0.37K platinum thermometer, providing a monitor in the temperature-control circuit.　Proper thermal contact of resistance thermometers with the body of the piezometer is ensured by using a packing mixture of vacuum paste and fine copper powder in the gap between the holes and thermometer sheaths.　Leads from the thermometers are extracted without affecting the hermetic sealing of the system through two pairs of glass insulators (11) soldered in bushings into the flanges of the cup (2) and the inner vessel (3).　To reduce the heat flow from leads to the platinum spiral of the thermometer, the leads are arranged so that most of their length is in contact with the piezometer body.

The piezometer is suspended on a steel cable from the lid of the cup (2) with support on three wire stays.　The general view of the assembled

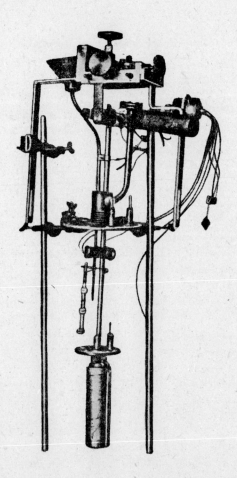

Fig. 3.　General view of assembled piezometer.

piezometer is shown in Fig. 3. The accuracy of experimentally determined values of the compressibilities considerably depends on the determination of the ballast volume; the volume coupled by the gas at the experimental pressure but at a temperature differing from that of the piezometer. The volume includes part of the supply lines for gas to the piezometer. In the present design of the cryostat, a supplementary soldered capillary is used for the determination of error introduced by the ballast volume [1]. The functional and supplementary capillaries, possessing an inner diameter of 0.35 mm, are soldered to the same depth into the stopper of the piezometer, and are then soldered together along their entire length, ensuring identical temperature distribution.

The hot ends of the capillaries are connected to the composite cross-shaped valve (14). Following simultaneous introduction of gas into the piezometer and the soldered capillary, and after pressure measurement, the valve allows by-pass of the gas into the gasometer, enabling measurement of the amount of gas contained in the ballast volume of the piezometer.

The actual piezometer volume is measured (with an accuracy of $\pm 0.03\%$) by calibration with liquid benzene.

It has already been noted that a given temperature of the piezometer

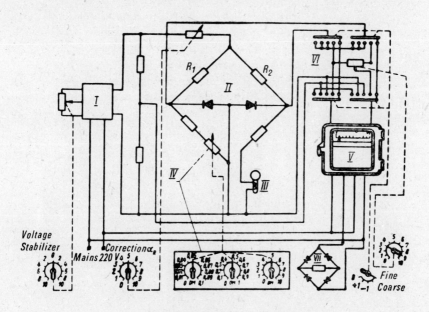

Fig. 4. Temperature-controller circuit.

I—dc voltage stabilizer ; II—measuring bridge ; III—TSP-0.37K resistance thermometer ;
IV—resistance box ; V—PSR-1-0.3 potentiometer ; VI—change over switch ;
VII—electromagnetic relay.

in the cryostat is maintained with an electric heater which is automatically switched on and off by temperature controller.   Circuit of the temperature controller [9] is shown in Fig. 4.

One of the arms of the measuring bridge (II) contains the secondary platinum resistance thermometer (III), which acts as the monitor for temperature control.   The other arm contains a resistance bow which regulates the resistance according to the required temperature level in the circuit.   Stable temperatures in the entire experimental temperature range are obtained by resistances R_1 and R_2, which considerably exceed the resistances of the other two arms.   The measuring bridge receives its electrical supply from the balancing-type dc electronic voltage stabilizer (I).

An ordinary potentiometer (V) is used as the controlling-recording instrument in the temperature-controller circuit.   The scale of the potentiometer is adjusted within limits of ± 1 mV, corresponding to a maximum change of $\pm 0.5°C$.   The circuit actuates the electromagnetic relay (VII) which opens or closes the circuit of heater winding.

Preliminary assay has demonstrated the recommended cryostat system, although simple, to ensure highly accurate control of the piezometer temperature, with temperature fluctuations within ± 0.02 deg.

The system possesses low thermal inertia; on attaining the desired temperature, the piezometer almost immediately becomes "operative".

The cryostat can be applied for temperatures exceeding that of the thermostatting liquid by 100 or more degrees.

Processing and analysis of these experimental results reveal satisfactory accuracy and applicability of these results to experimental investigation.

REFERENCES

1. KIRILLIN, V. A. and A. E. SHEINDLIN. *Issledovanie termodinamicheskikh svoistv veshchestv (Investigation of thermodynamic properties of substances).* Gosénergoizdat, Moscow, 1963.
2. ROGOVAYA, I. A.   Abstract of Kandidat's dissertation.   VNIIKImash, 1955.
3. TULYAKOV, A. P. *Khimicheskoe Mashinostroenie*, No. 2, 1935.
4. ZHOKHOVSKII, M. K. *Izmeritel'naya Tekhnika*, No. 7, 1959.
5. ZHOKHOVSKII, M. K. *Tekhnika izmereniya davleniya i razrezheniya (Measurement of pressure and vacuum).* Mashgiz, Moscow, 1952.
6. SAMOILOV, V. N.   Abstract of Kandidat's dissertation.   ÉNIN AN SSSR, 1952.

7. FEODOS'EV, V. I. *Soprotivlenie materialov (Strength of materials).* Mashgiz, Moscow, 1960.

8. WHITEHOUSE, I. E., T. A. CALLCOTT, I. A. NABER and I. S. RABY. *RSI,* **36** (86), 1965.

9. DAVYDOV, V. D. and S. L. FIL'TSER. *Trudy VNIIKImash,* No. 9, 1965.

UDC 541.27

REVIEW AND COMPILATION OF DATA ON THE VISCOSITY OF RAREFIED GASES OF THE HELIUM GROUP

V. A. Rabinovich and *V. A. Kryuchkov*

The systematic experimental study of the temperature dependence of the viscosity of inert gases, initiated during the 1920's, has resulted in the accumulation of considerable data. However, these data have generally pertained to a limited temperature range and have shown disagreement, complicating their practical application (see Table 1). The objectives of the present study are analysis, selection, and adjustment of the most reliable data for tabulation of the viscosity of neon, argon, krypton, and xenon from their triple points to 1300°K.

Schultze's viscosity measurements [1] at three temperatures and at atmospheric pressure constituted one of the first reports for argon. This study employed a glass viscometer consisting of a capillary with a diameter of 0.01514 mm and length of $\approx$52.54 cm, and two measuring cylinders through which gas displaced by mercury entered the capillary. Symmetry of the apparatus allowed the gas to pass through the capillary in both forward and reverse directions. Pressure at ends of the capillary was maintained nearly constant. The vessels were thermostatted at room temperature. Boiling water or aniline was circulated in the thermostat for obtaining experimental temperatures. Duration of the passage of a given quantity of gas through the capillary was fixed with a stopwatch of $\pm$0.5 sec accuracy. Nitrogen content of the investigated gas varied from 2.3% in the first series of experiments to 0.5% in the second. The data of the two series agree within $\pm$0.6% [1].

The relative viscosity of gases of the helium group was determined by Rankine [2], using the data on the viscosity of air by placing the viscometer

Table 1. List of studies reporting experimental determination of temperature-dependence of the viscosity of inert gases

Author(s), year of publication, and reference number	Temperature, °K	Method of determination
NEON		
Rankine, 1910 [2]	283–373	Capillary
Edwards, 1928 [3]	195–718	,,
Trautz et al, 1929-35 [5]	90–1100	,,
Van Itterbeek and Van Paemel, 1940 [6]	20–293	Oscillating disk
Wobser and Müller, 1941 [7]	293–371	Falling ball
Johnston and Grilly, 1942 [8]	80–300	Oscillating disk
Kestin and Leidenfrost*, 1959 [14]	293	,,
Thornton, 1960 [15]	~291	Capillary
Kestin and Whitelow*, 1963 [16]	296–519	Oscillating disk
ARGON		
Schultze, 1901 [1]	291–457	Capillary
Rankine, 1910 [2]	285–373	,,
Trautz et al, 1929-35 [5]	293–1100	,,
Van Itterbeek and Van Paemel, 1940 [6]	55–90	Oscillating disk
Wobser and Müller, 1941 [7]	293–371	Falling ball
Johnston and Grilly, 1942 [8]	80–300	Oscillating disk
Vasilesco, 1938 [10]	273–1868	Capillary
Bonilla, Wang and Weiner, 1956 [11]	273–2073	,,
Rocco and Halford, 1958 [12]	211–471	,,
Kestin and Leidenfrost*, 1959 [14]	293	Oscillating disk
Thornton, 1960 [15]	~291	Capillary
Kestin and Whitelow*, 1963 [16]	298–538	Oscillating disk
Cronin, 1965 [18]	140–293	Capillary
Rigby and Smith, 1966 [19]	293–972	,,
KRYPTON		
Rankine, 1910 [2]	284–373	Capillary
Nasini and Rossi, 1928 [4]	288–373	,,
Trautz et al, 1929-35 [5]	273–373	,,
Kestin and Leidenfrost*, 1959 [14]	293	Oscillating disk
Thornton, 1960 [15]	~291	Capillary
Clifton, 1963 [17]	297–666	Oscillating disk
Rigby and Smith, 1966 [19]	293–972	Capillary
XENON		
Rankine, 1910 [2]	284–373	Capillary
Nasini and Rossi, 1928 [4]	290–373	,,
Trautz et al, 1929-35 [5]	293–550	,,
Kestin and Leidenfrost*, 1959 [14]	298	Oscillating disk
Thornton, 1960 [15]	~291	Capillary
Rigby and Smith, 1966 [19]	293–972	,,

*These investigations will be considered subsequently in the present work during analysis of pressure-dependence of viscosity.

in a wide tube filled with thermostatted liquid. A mercury drop falling inside the tube of ≈ 3.5 mm diameter created pressure at the capillary tube in the closed system of the tube and capillary. A constant temperature, established with 0.2-0.4 deg accuracy prior to the experiment, was maintained during the passage of gas along the capillary. Rankine studied the effect of surface tension of mercury on velocity and demonstrated, on the basis of data on the viscosity of air, that by increasing the temperature from 15°C to 100°C, surface tension of mercury decreases by 6%. Additional corrections during the calculation of viscosities were made for slip and expansion of gases. Rankine does not mention the content of impurities in the gas or mercury, although he states that "very high purity" specimens were used.

Edwards [3] determined the viscosity of neon using a capillary ($d=0.026$ cm, $L=76.7$ cm) at six temperatures. At $t>15$°C, the capillary was placed in a thermostat, and at $t=-78.4$°C, constant temperature was maintained using a Dewar flask filled with solid carbon dioxide and alcohol. Temperatures were measured with a platinum resistance thermometer. Each of the six values reported in the work represents the average of numerous measurements. Neon of 98% purity was used. Edwards used vacuum liquefaction for removal of helium from the gas. Purified neon was collected in a sufficiently large vessel and passed through the capillary at constant temperature and pressure. The level of mercury in the manometer was determined with a catherometer with accuracy upto 0.1 mm. Determination of absolute viscosities was not attempted. The instrument constant was, therefore, selected from standard viscosity of $\eta_{15}=1784.6 \cdot 10^7$ g/cm . sec. Corrections were made for slipping of the gas and difference in levels of mercury meniscus. Edwards calculated the error in individual measurements to be 0.8%.

Nasini and Rossi [4] used Rankine's method to determine the viscosity of helium krypton and xenon at room temperature and normal boiling point of water. The capillary measured $d=0.016$ cm and $L=55$ cm, and the outer enclosing tube was of 0.2 cm diameter. Temperature was regulated along the height of the viscometer and measured with an accuracy of 0.1 deg. Operation of the apparatus was assayed by measuring air viscosity at 17.6°C and 99.6°C and by comparing the results with those of other authors for similar parameters. Disagreement did not exceed 0.5%. Apparently, this value gives the chance error in the data of Nasini and Rossi [4] on the viscosities of krypton and xenon. Purity of the gases was determined spectroscopically and was observed to be 99.99%.

Around 1925, detailed investigations of the temperature-dependence of the viscosity of various gases and gas mixtures were initiated at the Physicotechnical Laboratory of Heidelberg University under the guidance of Trautz. A number of reports published by Trautz and colleagues [5] contain data on the viscosity of the four inert gases, of which argon and neon were most thoroughly studied. The viscometer constructed by Trautz and Weizel consisted of two measuring vessels of 200 and 250 cm^3 filled with a given quantity of mercury and interconnected with a U-shaped tube. During any given experiment, the pressure drop and the gas volume flowing through the capillary in a given time interval remain constant and are entirely dependent on the design of the apparatus, considerably simplifying measurement of the relative values of viscosities. The authors were particularly interested in the selection of capillaries. Preliminary experiments showed the pressure ions at the capillary extremities to be directly proportional to the density of the gas under study, and inversely proportional to the length of the capillary and fourth power of its radius. Trautz and Zink used two capillaries for measuring viscosity of neon and argon by the relative method (data on viscosity of air were used). The first capillary possessed measurements of $L=2200$ mm and $d=0.5$-0.6 mm, and the second possessed diverging ends and dimensions of $L=2300$ mm and $d=0.6$ mm. Duration of gas passage through both capillaries was nearly consistent. Under steady-state conditions, furnace temperature along the length of the capillaries was measured with $Pt/Pt.Rh$ thermocouples separated by a distance of ~ 10 cm. According to the authors, the error in temperature measurements was within ± 3 deg.

Zimmerman and Trautz measured the viscosity of neon at low temperatures and reported viscosities at 273.1, 194.6 and 90°K. These temperatures were respectively obtained by using water, solid carbon dioxide with benzene, and liquid oxygen as the thermostatting liquids. Air was used as the standard at the first temperature, and hydrogen at the second and third temperatures. Temperature could be maintained constant within ± 0.1 deg, measured with a platinum resistance thermometer with the same error. The time of passage of gas through the capillary was varied over the range of 200-900 sec. Due to the small size of the cryostat, two- and three-way capillaries were used. Corrections were made during viscosity calculations for the kinetic energy and expansion of the gas within the capillary, as well as variation in capillary dimensions with temperature, slipping of gas, and barometric pressure. The effect of the error in temperature measurement was also calculated. Neon and argon of over 99% purity were used. Percentage impurities in krypton and xenon were not indicated. The authors estimate values to have an error of less than 1%.

Van Itterbeek and Van Paemel [6] determined viscosity of argon at 55-90°K and also at 293.5°K. The results of measurements were processed using the well-known formula in which the instrument constant is determined by measuring the viscosity of hydrogen, for which reliable data are available over the investigated temperature range. The log decrement and period of disk oscillation were measured under vacuum of below 10^{-5} mm Hg and at investigated pressures (0.22-10.4 cm Hg). The authors report twelve values of viscosity for argon, each value being the average of three to four measurements. Within experimental error the log-log plot of experimental values was shown to yield a straight line. The same authors later studied pressure-dependence of viscosity of neon at normal boiling points of oxygen and hydrogen. Pressure was varied from 300 to 0.00120 mm Hg and was measured with two McLeod gauges with an accuracy of upto 10^{-4} mm Hg. The results showed viscosity to be pressure-sensitive only below 3 mm Hg, at which point it declined rapidly.

Wobser and Müller [7] studied temperature-dependence for a number of substances, including neon and argon, using the falling-ball method. Their viscometer consisted of a cylindrical glass tube ($d=15.936$ mm) and hollow glass ball ($d=15.880$ mm). Inclination of the viscometer axis with the vertical axis could be changed within 3-87°, depending on the substance to be studied and pressure in the apparatus. The ball could be propelled in the reverse direction by rotating the viscometer around its horizontal axis. The viscometer was placed in a water bath, wherein the desired temperature could be maintained with an accuracy of ±0.02 deg. Duration of fall of the ball between two markings was measured with two stopwatches with divisions of 0.02 sec. The effect of various factors on the accuracy of measurements was considered in [7], including (1) the effect of the expansion coefficient of the glass of both tube and ball at varying sizes of the gap, and (2) the degree of rarefaction and mean free path of gas molecules affecting the duration of fall. As it is difficult to ensure coaxility between tube and ball, data on viscosity of air were used for calculation. Reported viscosities for argon and neon represent averages of seven to ten measurements. Spectrally pure gases were used. The authors estimated accuracy of their results at $\pm(0.1-0.15)\%$.

Johnston and Grilly [8] used the oscillating-disk method for determining viscosity of argon and neon, on an apparatus previously used for other substances [9]. Temperatures were measured with two thermocouples with an accuracy of ±0.05 deg. One thermocouple was fixed to the lower, rigid disk, and the other was immersed into cryostat bath for thermostatting the apparatus. A special component ensured constant distance between the rigid and movable disks during heating or cooling. An illuminated scale, maintained at a distance of 3048 mm from the apparatus, was used for measuring the amplitude of the consecutive oscillations. Log decrement and oscillation period were observed for 500-600 sec and measured with a stopwatch of ±0.2 sec accuracy. The energy loss in the suspension wire was more accurately determined in reference [8] than in reference [9]. The authors observed that annealing of the wire under high vacuum (upto 10^{-8} mm Hg) to slight redness by passing an electrical current through it reduces this loss from 7.10^{-4} to 2.10^{-4}. The apparatus constant was determined on air (at $T=296.1°K$; $\eta_{air}=1833 . 10^{-7}$poise). Experiments were performed at 34 cm Hg. The authors estimated the maximum possible error of their viscosities for argon and neon at 0.54 and 0.62%, respectively. Argon was spectrally pure, and neon contained less than 0.25% impurities.

Vasilesco [10] measured by the relative method the viscosities of argon, carbon dioxide, air, and nitrogen. The capillary ($L=100$ cm, $d_{inner}=0.5$ mm, $d_{outer}=1$ mm) and the tube for preliminary heating of gas ($L=80$ cm; $d=2$ mm), both of platinum, had a spiral form. Capillary was heated in two ways, directly by electric current and indirectly in electrically heated graphite tubular furnaces. In the first case, temperature was measured with a Pt . Rh/Pt thermocouple, and with an optical pyrometer in the second case. Both methods yielded indentical results. A special controller was used to maintain the pressure gradient across the ends of the capillary constant within $\pm 1.0\%$. While using the results of measurements for calculating viscosity of argon, corrections were made for kinetic energy, nonstable laminar flow at capillary inlet, acceleration, gas slipping, compression of gas in the capillary, changes in the pressure gradient across the capillary, expansion, and curvature of the capillary and contamination of gas. Argon was 99.69% pure. The error in measurement of η_T/η_0 depended on temperature-measuring instruments and, according to the authors, could be within 0.014-0.001.

Bonilla, Wang, and Weiner [11], measured the viscosity of normal- and heavy-water vapor and argon. Viscosity of argon was studied, as there was some doubt regarding the reliability of Vasilesco's values. Their capillary was 90% Pt and 10% Rh alloy, approximately 72.5 cm in length, with an internal diameter of about 0.0635 cm. Argon was 99.9% pure. The deviation between the data of references [11] and [10] does not exceed 1%.

Rocco and Holford [12] measured viscosity of argon, metnane, and ethane to verify the agreement between experimental values and those obtained from some concepts based on structural models. These authors do not describe in detail the particular apparatus, purity of substances, or experimental conditions, except they state that they employed the standard capillary method described by Partington [13]. Their 20 values of the viscosity of argon agree with those obtained in previous investigations within $\pm 0.5\%$, according to estimation.

Thornton [15] measured the viscosity of binary mixtures of monatomic gases as a function of the composition using a modified Rankine viscometer. Corrections were made for surface tension of the falling drop. The instrument constant was determined using the value $(1740 . 10^{-7}$ g/cm.sec) of viscosity of nitrogen at 18°C. Spectrally pure neon, argon containing 0.2% impurities, krypton containing 1% xenon, and xenon containing 1% krypton were used.   According to [15] the possible error was below ±1.0%.

Clifton [17] used the oscillating-disk method for investigating the viscosity of krypton at various temperatures.   A molybdenum disk ($d=$ 3.096 cm, $\rho = 0.076$ cm) was fixed to a molybdenum rod ($d = 0.15$ cm, $L=36.20$ cm).   The suspension system weighed 12.175 g.   Two iron-constantan thermocouples calibrated with respect to Pt . Rh/Pt thermocouples were used for measuring temperatures and temperature field. Tabulated values of temperature represent the average of readings of the two thermocouples.   The authors estimate the error in their temperature measurement to be 2-3 deg.   The instrument constant was determined using helium.   Log decrement and the period of oscillation were measured with a stopwatch of 0.2 sec error.   To reduce convective effect, measurements were performed in the pressure range of 3.7-23.8 cm Hg.   Viscosity was observed to be independent of pressure within the same range.   Most of the reported viscosities are the average of three to four measurements with an error of ±1.0%.   Mass spectroscopy showed that the krypton contained 0.04% by volume of nitrogen.

Cronin [18] used the absolute method to determine the viscosities of six gases including argon.   As the instrument constant was calculated from geometrical dimensions of the capillary, these were carefully measured. The glass capillary possessed dimensions of $d=0.254 \pm 0.00508$ mm, $L=$ 845 mm.   Additional calibration of the capillary with mercury allowed two-fold reduction in the indicated error.   Both room and bath temperatures could be measured on the apparatus.   The bath was filled with different liquids.   The volume of gas passing through the capillary was measured at pressure gradients of 15 to 10 cm Hg.   The time of passage was varied between 8 to 200 sec.   Corrections were made for slipping and expansion of gas in the capillary.   Cronin, however, reported his values only graphically.   His comparison with the data of other authors showed a deviation of 2-3%.   Argon was 99.9% pure.

Rigby and Smith [19] measured viscosities of argon, krypton, and xenon by the relative method, using reliable data on viscosity of nitrogen. Two spiral-shaped glass capillaries were used.   One possessed dimensions of $d=0.04$ em and $L=150$ cm, and the other, $d=0.04$ cm and $L=2000$ cm.   Both capillaries were placed in a thermostat.   The thermostat temperature was measured with a Pt . Rh/Pt thermocouple with ±1 deg accuracy.   A standard sphere of one liter capacity, filled with the gas under study, was placed in a water thermostet of 25±0.1°C temperature. Pressure decrease inside the standard sphere on passing the gas through the capillary was measured with a mercury manometer.   The positions of three platinum contacts in the manometer corresponded to pressures of 26, 19 and 12 cm Hg respectively.   Two values of viscosity were obtained in most of the experiments, one in the pressure range of 26-19 cm Hg and the other at 26-12 cm Hg. Gas was passed for durations varying from 30 min to 4 hr and was reproduced with less than ±1% error. Viscosity values obtained at different pressure gradients agreed within ±0.3%. In calculating viscosities from experimental results, corrections were made for slipping and expansion of gas in the capillary. Corrections were not made for curvature of the capillary, as the correction required was negligible. Gases used were over 99.0% pure. The authors consider the error in reference values of viscosity of nitrogen to be the source of greatest error and the average error in their values to be less than 1%.

All these data on viscosity of the helium group gases at different temperatures were evaluated, analyzed, and graphically and analytically processed. Curves of η against T were plotted for each substance and average curves were plotted along the most reliable of the data over the entire temperature range of experiments. Viscosity values for rounded temperature values were determined from averaged curves and reveal error of under ±0.2%.

Neon. The temperature range of 273-373°K is the most frequently investigated range for this gas, and the results of six studies [2, 3, 5, 7, 8, 16] agree within±0.5%. Johnston and Grilly's [8] values dominate at lower temperatures and the values of Trautz and Zimmerman [5] and Edwards [3] at $T=195$°K are respectively 1 and 1.4% higher. On approaching normal boiling point of oxygen. The results of [5, 6] are averaged by results of [8]. Further, there is a systematic deviation between the values of Johnston and Grilly [8] and Van Itterbeek and Van Paemel [6] (the latter are higher), the deviation being nearly 3% at $T=$ 77.4°K. There is only one reported value for the viscosity of neon at normal boiling point of hydrogen [6].

Medium and high temperature ranges have been investigated [2, 5, 16], and all the data agree, with the average common deviation in the overlapping range of temperatures not exceeding ±0.6%.

Argon. In comparison with other gases, argon has been subjected to considerably more thorough investigation, covering a wider temperature range. The majority of the available data agree within ±1%. Schultze's [1] values are slightly higher (upto 1.6%). Kestin and Whitelow's [16] values show systematic deviation. The deviation increases with temperature increase, attaining 2.5% at $T=538$°K.

Below room temperature, the values of Johnston and Grilly [8], as in the case of neon, form a reliable basis, showing agreement with the values of works [5, 6]. A single curve can be drawn over the temperature range from triple point to 2000°K to express the most reliable experimental data, coinciding with the curve previously drawn by the present authors [20].

Krypton. Viscosity of krypton was determined at two main temperature levels, room temperature and normal boiling point of water. In this range, the data of various authors [2, 4, 5, 14, 15] agree within ±1%. For higher temperatures, Clifton's [17] and Rigby and Smith's [19] values are available. Analysis of these data showed considerable discrepancy, increasing with increased temperature and attaining 4% at certain points. The experimental temperatures were apparently not measured with sufficient accuracy in work [17]. However, their low values were not due to this fact, as in this temperature range the viscosity is not so temperature-dependent as to induce such a high error. Apparently, the main reason for the discrepancy is the considerable difference between the instrument constants as calculated from geometric dimensions and those obtained by calibration with helium. The present authors have concluded this on the basis of Clifton's statement [17] that his calibration curve for helium was below that obtained from the data of Trautz and Binkele [5]. It is interesting to note that, similar to Kestin and Whitelow [16], Clifton [17] used the oscillating-disk method, and whereas Kestin and Whitelow's values for argon are too high, Clifton's values for krypton are too low. Considering these points, the reference curve of $\eta_T = f(T)$ for krypton was drawn close to the values of work [19], which we consider sufficiently reliable.

Xenon. There are no data on the viscosity of xenon below room temperature. In the temperature range of 284-298°K, results of four authors [2, 4, 14, 15] agree within ±0.7%. Rigby and Smith's [19] and Trautz and Heberling's [5] values are for $T > 373°$K and agree closely in the common temperature range, indicating high reliability. The reference curve for $T = 293$-550°K thus yields the averages of the two sets of data [5, 19] and, at higher temperatures, the averages of the data of work [19].

It is generally established that with monatomic gases of the helium group, the experimental data entirely confirm the molecular-kinetic theory. This assumption has been firmly accepted because of the close agreement obtained by various authors, within narrow temperature ranges, between the calculated and experimental results. Such comparison is generally made only in that temperature range in which the experiments are actually performed; hence, those reference curves are used which are obtained from viscosity data for four gases over a wide temperature range, to check the accuracy of calculations based on models and to establish the nature of the $\eta_T = f(T)$ relationship. Besides, it was necessary to select a method allowing extrapolation to temperatures not covered by experimentation.

The molecular-kinetic theory of rarefied gases [21] leads to the following equation for calculation of viscosity :

$$\eta_T \cdot 10^8 = 266.93 f_n \frac{\sqrt{M\,T}}{\sigma^2 \Omega^{(2,2)}(T^*)}, \quad \text{n} \cdot \text{sec/m}^2 \tag{1}$$

where M=molecular weight; T=absolute temperature; σ=diameter of collision; $\Omega^{(2,2)}$ = reduced collision integral, depending on reduced temperature $T^* = kT/\varepsilon$ (k= Boltzmann constant, ε=depth of potential well) : f_n=also a function of reduced temperature with values between 1-1.008 (we assume f_n=1).

The reduced integral of collisions depends on the choice of the function of molecular interaction and is usually tabulated. Since tabulated values are available for the more common potentials (Lennard-Jones 12-6, Buckingham, Chihara, Morse, etc.) along with experimentally obtained viscosities of various substances, it is possible to determine the parameters of the function of molecular interaction and estimate degree of accordance between theoretical and experimental relationships.

Application of the Lennard-Jones 12-6 potential to monatomic gases is fully justified (in fact, the model was suggested for this purpose) :

$$U(r)=4\varepsilon\left[\left(\frac{\sigma}{r}\right)^{12}-\left(\frac{\sigma}{r}\right)^{6}\right] \qquad (2)$$

To determine constants ε and σ, viscosities should be determined at two values of the temperature following the method described in work [21]. However, this method presents disadvantages of complicated calculation of ε/k by consecutive approximations, different parameters given by two different and sufficiently separated pairs of reference points, and by the fact that the parameter range in which satisfactory agreement between experimental and theoretical data exists cannot be readily established. The application of equation (1) has been facilitated by a method utilizing all of the viscosity data for the four gases for the determination of parameters of the potential and enhancing determination of the range of applicability of this equation.

If equation (1) is rearranged to the form

$$\Upsilon=\frac{266.93\sqrt{MT}}{\eta_T \cdot 10^3}=\sigma^2\,\Omega^{(2,2)}\,(T^*) \qquad (3)$$

and then presented in logarithmic form, we obtain

$$log\ \Upsilon=log\ \sigma^2+log\,\Omega^{(2,2)}(T^*). \qquad (4)$$

However,

$$log\ T^*= -log\frac{\varepsilon}{k} +log\ T. \qquad (5)$$

From tabulated [21] values of the reduced collision integral, the plot of $\Omega^{(2,2)}$ (T^*) versus T^* is obtained on log-log graph paper. On the same scale, a reference curve of log Y versus log T is plotted on tracing paper. The experimental reference curve is then arranged parallel to the coordinates to coincide with the theoretical curve. The results obtained by this method are shown in Fig. 1, indicating that the curves cannot be completely fitted within limits of experimental error over the temperature range of the experiment. Hence we attempted to obtain satisfactory agreement over as wide a temperature range as possible.

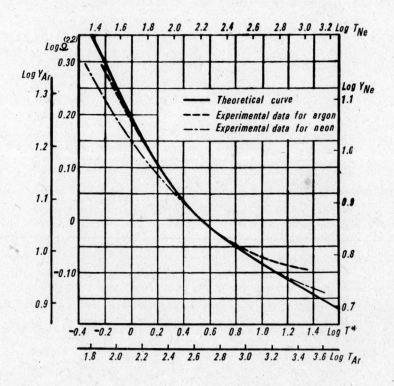

Fig. 1. Joint plots of experimental $Y= \dfrac{266.93\sqrt{MT}}{\eta_T \cdot 10^3}$ curves for neon and argon with theoretical curve of reduced collision integral Ω (2.2).

Theoretical and experimental curves for neon coincide almost entirely in the reduced-temperature range of $T^*=2.78$–12.8 (120-550°K). Considerable deviation is observed at low and high temperatures. Similar deviations are observed for argon, krypton, and xenon. Experimental curves for krypton and xenon are not shown in Fig. 1, as they completely coincide with the argon curve. Attempts to reduce the deviation at low temperatures resulted in increased deviation at moderate and high temperatures.

The large deviations of dissimilar signs beyond the temperature range with close agreement can be slightly reduced by certain other functions (e.g., the Morse function) of molecular interaction. However, it is impossible to reduce the deviation to values compatible with the possible experimental error, as has been confirmed by the detailed calculations in references [22, 23]. It was, therefore, decided to limit the calculations of parameters (see Table 2) only to the Lennard-Jones potential.

Table 2. Parameters of Lennard-Jones potential

Substance	ε/k, °K	σ, Å	Temperature range, °K
Neon	43.15	2.7450	120-550
Argon	130.00	3.3910	190-650
Krypton	193.31	3.5994	300-700
Xenon	261.79	3.9422	350-620

Tabulated values of reduced collision integral and values of potential 2 given in Table 2 can be applied to determine viscosity of the four gases only in the given temperature ranges. However, analytical relationships describing viscosities from the triple points to 1300°K (2000°K for argon) are more convenient for use. To obtain such relationships, functions $\Upsilon = \sigma^2 \Omega^{(2,2)} (T^*)$ were considered in which reduced collision integral for argon and neon was based on experimental data. Analysis of these functions and preliminary calculations showed that a corrected collision integral can be expressed with the desired accuracy by an expression of the form :

$$\sigma^2 \, \Omega^{(2,2)} \, (T^*) = \sum_{i=0}^{n} A_i/(T^*)^i. \tag{6}$$

Coefficients A_i in equation (6) were determined using a standard program on a digital computer. Reference Υ/σ^2 curves for neon and argon were approximated with polynomials of three to nine terms. The polynomial for final calculation was selected in such a way that the reference curves were represented with an error of below $\pm0.3\%$ with the least number of terms. Comparison of experimental and calculated values showed the fifth-order polynomial to satisfy the condition for neon, and a fourth-order polynomial, for argon. Higher-order polynomials generally did not yield significantly close agreement, and considerably increased the values of coefficients.

The log-log plots of reference curves for argon, krypton, and xenon were observed to almost completely coincide (Fig. 2). Analytical relationships for krypton and xenon could therefore be obtained by recalculating the coefficients of the polynomial for argon based on its experimental values of viscosities in the temperature range of 83.81-2000°K. The apparent relationship between coefficients of polynomials for the three gases was determined by parameters from Table 2. This method of recalculating the coefficients simplifies the derivation of analytical expressions for reference

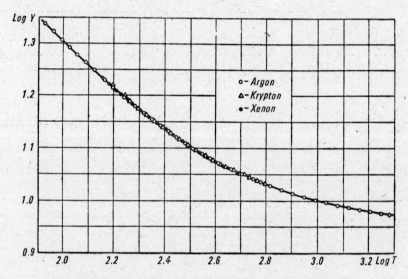

Fig. 2.   Averaged curve of temperature-dependence of viscosities of argon, krypton and xenon.

Table 3.   Coefficients A_i for different values of i

i	A_i values for			
	Neon	Argon	Krypton	Xenon
0	5.013630	8.803180	9.918459	11.897653
1	13.374926	9.280277	10.456000	12.542459
2	—21.876442	0.759863	0.856131	—1.026969
3	25.709742	—1.088008	—1.225848	—1.470462
4	—14.283153	0.139682	0.157378	0.188783
5	2.949252	—	—	—

curves for krypton and xenon and permits extrapolation of the viscosity data for these gases to high and low temperature regions. Table 3 gives values of coefficients A_i in equation (6) for the four gases.

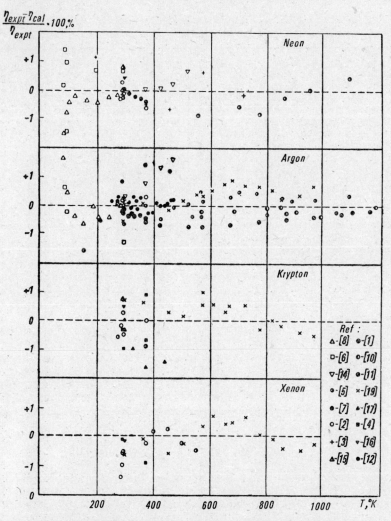

Fig. 3. Discrepancy between experimental and calculated from equations (1) and (6) viscosities.

Equation (1), with reduced collision integral replaced by the proper polynomials of form (6) for each of the gases, was used to calculate viscosities which were compared with a majority of the experimental values analysed. Fig. 3 shows the deviation between the experimental and calculated values,

Table 4. Recommended viscosities for argon, neon, krypton, and xenon at atmospheric pressure

T, °K	$\eta_T \cdot 10^8$ n . sec/m²				T, °K	$\eta_T \cdot 10^8$ n . sec/m²			
	Neon	Argon	Krypton	Xenon		Neon	Argon	Krypton	Xenon
24.54	434	—	—	—	430	4037	3003	3450	3235
30	525	—	—	—	440	4098	3055	3516	3301
40	676	—	—	—	450	4159	3106	3581	3367
50	825	—	—	—	460	4219	3157	3645	3432
60	965	—	—	—	470	4279	3207	3709	3496
70	1094	—	—	—	480	4338	3256	3772	3560
80	1216	—	—	—	490	4396	3305	3835	3624
83.81	—	709	—	—	500	4454	3354	3897	3687
90	1330	758	—	—	510	4511	3402	3958	3750
100	1440	837	—	—	520	4568	3449	4019	3812
110	1546	916	—	—	530	4624	3496	4080	3874
115.76	—	—	1040	—	540	4679	3543	4140	3935
120	1648	996	1074	—	550	4734	3589	4199	3996
130	1748	1075	1156	—	560	4789	3635	4258	4056
140	1845	1153	1239	—	570	4843	3680	4316	4116
150	1940	1230	1323	—	580	4897	3725	4374	4176
160	2033	1307	1407	—	590	4950	3769	4431	4235
161.36	—	—	—	1296	600	5003	3813	4488	4294
170	2124	1383	1490	1359	610	5055	3857	4544	4352
180	2213	1458	1574	1433	620	5107	3900	4600	4410
190	2300	1531	1658	1508	630	5158	3943	4656	4467
200	2385	1603	1741	1583	640	5209	3985	4711	4524
210	2469	1674	1823	1658	650	5260	4027	4766	4581
220	2552	1744	1905	1733	660	5310	4069	4820	4637
230	2634	1813	1986	1808	670	5360	4110	4874	4693
240	2714	1881	2066	1883	680	5410	4151	4927	4748
250	2793	1948	2146	1958	690	5459	4152	4980	4803
260	2871	2014	2225	2033	700	5508	4233	5033	4858
270	2947	2079	2303	2107	710	5556	4273	5085	4912
280	3022	2143	2380	2181	720	5604	4313	5137	4966
290	3096	2206	2457	2255	730	5652	4352	5188	5020
300	3169	2268	2533	2328	740	5699	4391	5239	5073
310	3241	2329	2608	2401	750	5746	4430	5290	5126
320	3312	2389	2682	2473	760	5793	4469	5340	5179
330	3382	2449	2755	2545	770	5839	4507	5390	5231
340	3451	2508	2828	2616	780	5885	4545	5440	5283
350	3519	2566	2900	2687	790	5931	4583	5490	5335
360	3586	2623	2971	2757	800	5976	4621	5539	5386
370	3653	2679	3042	2827	810	6021	4658	5588	5437
380	3719	2735	3112	2896	820	6066	4695	5636	5488
390	3784	2790	3181	2965	830	6111	4732	5684	5538
400	3848	2844	3249	3033	840	6155	4769	5732	5588
410	3912	2898	3317	3101	850	6199	4805	5780	5638
420	3975	2951	3384	3168	860	6243	4841	5827	5688

Table 4—*Continued*

$T, °K$	$\eta_T . 10^8$ n . sec/m^2				$T, °K$	$\eta_T . 10^8$ n . sec/m^2			
	Neon	Argon	Krypton	Xenon		Neon	Argon	Krypton	Xenon
870	6287	4877	5874	5737	1090	7185	5616	6841	6755
880	6330	4913	5921	5786	1100	7224	5648	6882	6799
890	6373	4948	5967	5835	1110	7262	5679	6923	6842
900	6416	4983	6013	5883	1120	7300	5710	6964	6885
910	6459	5018	6059	5931	1130	7338	5741	7005	6928
920	6501	5053	6104	5979	1140	7376	5772	7046	6971
930	6543	5088	6149	6027	1150	7413	5803	7086	7014
940	6585	5122	6194	6074	1160	7450	5834	7126	7056
950	6626	5156	6239	6121	1170	7487	5864	7166	7098
960	6667	5190	6284	6168	1180	7524	5894	7206	7140
970	6708	5224	6328	6215	1190	7561	5924	7246	7182
980	6749	5258	6372	6261	1200	7598	5954	7285	7224
990	6790	5291	6416	6307	1210	7635	5984	7324	7265
1000	6830	5324	6459	6353	1220	7671	6014	7363	7306
1010	6870	5357	6502	6399	1230	7707	6044	7402	7347
1020	6910	5390	6545	6444	1240	7743	6073	7441	7388
1030	6950	5423	6588	6489	1250	7779	6102	7479	7429
1040	6990	5456	6631	6534	1260	7815	6131	7517	7470
1050	7029	5488	6673	6579	1270	7851	6160	7555	7510
1060	7068	5520	6715	6623	1280	7886	6189	7593	7550
1070	7107	5552	6757	6667	1290	7921	6218	7631	7590
1080	7146	5584	6799	6711	1300	7956	6247	7669	7630

with the average relative deviation within $\pm 0.6\%$. This agreement enables calculation and tabulation of the most probable values of viscosity of the four gases at atmospheric pressure and at temperatures varying from the triple point to 1300°K in steps of 10 deg (see Table 4). In our opinion, the maximum error in these values should not exceed $\pm 1\%$ within the experimental range of temperature, but may be slightly higher beyond this range.

References

1. SCHULTZE, N. *Annalen der Physik,* No. 5, 140, 1901.
2. RANKINE, A. *Proc. Roy. Soc., London,* **A83**, 516, 1910; *Phys. Z.,* **11**, 497, 1910; **11**, 745, 1910.
3. EDWARDS, R. *Proc. Roy. Soc., London,* **119**, 578, 1928.
4. NASINI, A. and C. ROSSI. *Gaz. Chem.,* **58**, 433, 1928.
5. TRAUTZ, M. and BAUMANN. *Annalen der Physik,* No. 2, 733, 1929.

TRAUTZ, M. and K. KIPPHAN. *Annalen der Physik*, No. 2, 743, 1929.

TRAUTZ, M. and LUDEWIGS. *Annalen der Physik*, No. 3, 409, 1929.

TRAUTZ, M. and H. BINKELE. *Annalen der Physik*, No. 5, 561, 1930.

TRAUTZ, M. and MELSTER. *Annalen der Physik*, No. 7, 409, 1930.

TRAUTZ, M. and R. ZINK. *Annalen der Physik*, No. 7, 427, 1931.

TRAUTZ, M. and R. HEBERLING. *Annalen der Physik*, No. 10, 155, 1931; No. 20, 118, 1934.

TRAUTZ, M. and H. ZIMMERMAN. *Annalen der Physik*, No. 22, 189, 1935.

6. VAN ITTERBEEK, A. and O. VAN PAEMEL. *Physica*, **5**, 1009, 1938; **7**, 273, 1940.

7. WOBSER, R. and F. MÜLLER. *Kollid-Beih*, No. 52, 165, 1941.

8. JOHNSTON, H. and E. GRILLY. *J. Phys. Chem.*, **46**, 948, 1942.

9. JOHNSTON, H. and K. McCLOSKEY. *J. Phys. Chem.*, **44**, 1038, 1938.

10. VASILESCO, V. *Annalen Phys. (Paris)*, **20**, 137-176; 292-334, 1938.

11. BONILLA, C., S. WANG and H. WEINER. *Trans. ASME*, **78**, 1285, 1956.

12. ROCCO, O. and J. HALFORD, *J. Chem. Phys.*, **28**, (6), 1958.

13. PARTINGTON, J. *An advanced treatise on physical chemistry*, London, 1949.

14. KESTIN, J. and W. LEIDENFROST. *Physica*, **25**, 1033, 1959.

15. THORNTON, E. *Proc. Phys. Soc.*, **76**, 104, 1960; **77**, 1166, 1960.

16. KESTIN, J. and J. WHITELOW. *Physica*, **29**, 335, 1963.

17. CLIFTON, D. *J. Chem. Phys.*, **38**, 1123, 1963.

18. CRONIN, D. *Am. J. Phys.*, **33**, 835, 1965.

19. RIGBY, M. and E. SMITH. *Trans. Farad. Soc.*, **62**, 54, 1966.

20. VASSERMAN, A. A., YA. Z. KAZAVCHINSKII and V. A. RABINOVICH. *Teplofizicheskie svoistv vozdukha i ego komponentov (Thermophysical properties of air and its components)*. Nauka, Moscow, 1966.

21. HIRSCHFELDER, D., C. KERTISS and R. BERD. *Molekulyarnaya teoriya gazov i zhidkostei (Molecular theory of gases and liquids)*. Izd. Inn. Lit., Moscow, 1961.

22. HANLEY, H. *NBS Tech. Note*, 333, 1966.

23. HANLEY, H. and G. CHILDS. *NBS Tech. Note*, 352, 1967.

III. HYDROCARBONS AND THEIR DERIVATIVES

UDC 541.11

REFERENCE SPECIFIC VOLUMES FOR METHANE

V. A. Zagoruchenko and *A. M. Zhuravlev*

Hydrocarbon gases constitute the most extensively studied group of substances. The compilation of reliable thermodynamic tables must follow the development of reference values. Analysis of available p-v-T data on liquid and gaseous methane has been undertaken, as this is one of the most investigated hydrocarbons. The predominant use of methane in the chemical industry requires an evaluation of the thermal properties which is too complex and detailed to be accomplished in an ordinary isolated, individual experimental study.

A reference skeleton of specific volumes of methane at pressures of 1-1000 bar and temperatures of 100-800°K was obtained in the present work on a graphical analysis of the experimentally obtained p-v-T data from the available literature. These references are listed in Table 1.

Only measurements in the single-phase region have been included, excluding those on the saturation curve. Parameter ranges are mainly indicated as reported in the original work (along isochores or isotherms). The work of Ol'shevskii, Leduce, and Amagi, prior to 1900, is not included. Many investigations, for instance [1, 2, 11, 12, 16, 17], were repeated in wider parameter ranges. In such cases, all reported works have been included. Tomaes and Van Steenwinkel determined the second virial coefficient, and Table 1 lists the temperature range.

For obtaining reference specific volumes, the experimental data were graphically tabulated for consistency along isotherms and isochores, in respect to the purity of the methane used in each previous investigation and analytical study [14, 15]. The experimental data were converted into dimensionless coordinates:

$$\sigma = \frac{p\,v}{R\,T_{cr}}, \tau = \frac{T}{T_{cr}} \text{ and } \omega = \frac{v_{cr}}{v},$$

and isotherms of $\sigma - \tau = f(\omega)$ were plotted.   The following critical constants were accepted : $p_{cr} = 46.41$ bar ; $T_{cr} = 190.55°K$; and $v_{cr} = 0.006161$ m³/kg.   Molecular weight of methane $= 16.043$ and universal gas constant $= 8.3143$ kJ/mole.

Table 1.   List of studies on *p-v-T* values of liquid and gaseous methane

Author(s), year of publication, reference	Measurement ranges		
	p, bar	T, °K	ρ, kg/m³
Barell and Robertson, 1917 [5]	1.0-40.5	288.2	–
Keyes, Smith and Joubert, 1922 [12]	–	273.2-473.2	28-125
Keyes and Burks, 1927 [11]	–	273.2-473.2	25-100
Kvalnes and Gaddy, 1931 [13]	0-1013.3	203.2-473.2	–
Freeth and Verschoyle, 1931 [9]	17.4-218.0	273.2-293.2	–
Michels and Nederbragt, 1935 [16]	–	273.2-423.2	13.7-38.0
Michels and Nederbragt, 1936 [17]	–	273.2-423.2	13.7-161.3
Olds, Reamer, Sage and Lacey, 1943 [19]	0-689.5	294.3-510.9	–
Schamp, Mason, Richardson and Altman, 1958 [20]	20.3-233.1	273.2-423.2	–
Pavlovich and Timrot, 1958 [4]	9.8-196.1	111.8-333.2	–
Thomaes and Van Steenwinkel, 1960 [21]	–	108.4-249.3	–
Müller, Leland and Kobayashi, 1961 [18]	2.8-482.6	144.3-283.2	–
Douslin*, 1962 [7]	–	273.2-623.2	12-200
Van Itterbeek, Verbeke and Staes 1963 [10]	6.9-316.9	114.5-188.2	–
Dobrovol'skii, Belyaeva and Golubev, 1964 [2]	49.0-490.3	112.2-191.1	–
Deffet, Lialine and Ficks, 1964 [6]	0-3040.0	323.8-425.0	–
Golubev, Dobrovol'skii and Belyaeva, 1965 [1]	1.0-500.0	110-570	–

*Douslin's data [7] are cited in reference [8].

After averaging $\sigma - \tau$ isotherms, values were obtained from isochores at intervals of 0.05 ω and then $\sigma - \tau = f(\tau)$, isochores were averaged in respect to the corresponding values at saturation.

Common consistency in the experimental data provided a skeleton of σ values on 50 isochores, the skeleton covering 15 isotherms at steps of 50°K.

The next stage of matching the data consisted of calculating on isochores the values of $\varphi = \dfrac{\sigma - \sigma_{cr}}{\tau - 1}$, where σ_{cr} is the value of σ on the critical isotherm for a given value of ω. The obtained values of φ were then averaged along isochores and isotherms.

After reconverting σ, ω and τ values into the corresponding p, v, T values, the data were finally corrected from the equation of state reported in work [3] in respect to the derivatives. Deviations $p_{cal} - p_{exp}$ [3] were averaged along two sections ($t = $const and $v = $const), allowing incorporation of the final corrections. Reference-specific volumes of methane thus obtained are shown in Table 2.

Tables 3 through 7 compare reference values of $z = \dfrac{pv}{RT}$ with the experimentally obtained data of various authors. Müller and colleagues [18] determined the compressibility of pure methane while studying the H_2-CH_4 system. Table 3 shows comparison between these data and evidence of disagreement between reference and experimentally-obtained values, increasing inversely with decreasing temperature values.

Table 2. Reference specific volumes for methane, m³/kg

p, bar	v at T, °K						
	100	125	150	175	200	225	250
1	0.002271	0.6322	0.7662	0.8986	1.030	1.161	1.292
2	0.002270	0.3078	0.3774	0.4451	0.5118	0.5779	0.6437
5	0.002269	0.002471	0.1437	0.1726	0.2007	0.2280	0.2550
10	0.002267	0.002468	0.06478	0.08168	0.09691	0.1114	0.1254
15	0.002266	0.002464	0.002761	0.05098	0.06219	0.07244	0.08221
20	0.002264	0.002461	0.002753	0.03525	0.04472	0.05294	0.06061
30	0.002260	0.002454	0.002737	0.003372	0.02700	0.03337	0.03898
40	0.002256	0.002448	0.002722	0.003281	0.01777	0.02352	0.02816
50	0.002252	0.002442	0.002708	0.003213	0.01169	0.01754	0.02167
60	0.002249	0.002436	0.002692	0.003159	0.006487	0.01352	0.01735
80	0.002241	0.002424	0.002670	0.003074	0.004169	0.008527	0.01199
100	0.002235	0.002413	0.002647	0.003008	0.003791	0.006028	0.008925
150	0.002218	0.002387	0.002597	0.002890	0.003373	0.004250	0.005587
200	0.002202	0.002363	0.002555	0.002805	0.003186	0.003740	0.004504
300	0.002174	0.002322	0.002488	0.002686	0.002959	0.003300	0.003711
400	0.002148	0.002285	0.002433	0.002602	0.002823	0.003075	0.003363
500	0.002124	0.002254	0.002388	0.002537	0.002725	0.002928	0.003154
600	—	—	—	—	0.002654	0.002820	0.003008
700	—	—	—	—	0.002591	0.002736	0.002899
800	—	—	—	—	0.002539	0.002668	0.002812
900	—	—	—	—	0.002493	0.002610	0.002740
1000	—	—	—	—	0.005454	0.002561	0.002680

Table 2—*Continued*

p, bar	v at T, °K					
	275	300	325	350	375	400
1	1.422	1.552	1.682	1.812	1.942	2.072
2	0.7093	0.7747	0.8400	0.9053	0.9704	1.036
5	0.2817	0.3083	0.3347	0.3611	0.3874	0.4136
10	0.1392	0.1528	0.1663	0.1797	0.1931	0.2064
15	0.09171	0.1010	0.1102	0.1193	0.1283	0.1373
20	0.06796	0.07512	0.08214	0.08907	0.09593	0.1027
30	0.04422	0.04923	0.05410	0.05887	0.06357	0.06821
40	0.03236	0.03631	0.04010	0.04379	0.04741	0.05096
50	0.02526	0.02857	0.03172	0.03476	0.03773	0.04063
60	0.02054	0.02343	0.02615	0.02876	0.03129	0.03376
80	0.01469	0.01705	0.01923	0.02129	0.02327	0.02519
100	0.01127	0.01329	0.01513	0.01686	0.01850	0.02009
150	0.007096	0.008528	0.009352	0.01109	0.01226	0.01339
200	0.005439	0.006437	0.007422	0.008367	0.009273	0.01014
300	0.004197	0.004737	0.005316	0.005910	0.006503	0.00788
400	0.008689	0.004049	0.004435	0.004842	0.005261	0.005684
500	0.003403	0.003673	0.003960	0.004263	0.004578	0.004901
600	0.003213	0.003430	0.003659	0.003900	0.004149	0.004407
700	0.003073	0.003257	0.003449	0.003649	0.003855	0.004068
800	0.002965	0.003126	0.003292	0.003463	0.003640	0.003821
900	0.002878	0.003021	0.003168	0.003319	0.003474	0.003632
1000	0.002805	0.002936	0.003068	0.003203	0.003341	0.003482

p, bar	v at T, °K					
	450	500	550	600	700	800
1	2.332	2.591	2.851	3.110	3.629	4.147
2	1.166	1.296	1.426	1.555	1.815	2.074
5	0.4660	0.5183	0.5704	0.6225	0.7266	0.8306
10	0.2330	0.2591	0.2854	0.3116	0.3638	0.4160
15	0.1551	0.1728	0.1904	0.2079	0.2429	0.2778
20	0.1162	0.1296	0.1429	0.1561	0.1825	0.2087
30	0.07737	0.08641	0.09538	0.1043	0.1220	0.1396
40	0.05796	0.06484	0.07164	0.07838	0.09175	0.1050
50	0.04632	0.05190	0.05740	0.06284	0.07362	0.08429
60	0.03857	0.04328	0.04791	0.05249	0.06153	0.07047
80	0.02891	0.03253	0.03607	0.03955	0.04642	0.05319
100	0.02314	0.02609	0.02897	0.03180	0.03736	0.04283
150	0.01553	0.01758	0.01957	0.02151	0.02531	0.02902
200	0.01181	0.01339	0.01492	0.01641	0.01931	0.02214
300	0.008222	0.009311	0.01036	0.01139	0.01337	0.01580
400	0.006527	0.007351	0.008153	0.008936	0.01045	0.01192
500	0.005558	0.006214	0.006860	0.007493	0.008723	0.009914

Table 2—*Continued*

p, bar	v at T, °K					
	450	500	550	600	700	800
600	0.004938	0.005477	0.006015	0.006545	0.007581	0.008586
700	0.004510	0.004964	0.005421	0.005876	0.006771	0.007642
800	0.004197	0.004587	0.004982	0.005380	0.006166	0.006935
900	0.003959	0.004299	0.004646	0.004997	0.005697	0.006385
1000	0.003772	0.004072	0.004380	0.004693	0.005322	0.005945

Table 3. Comparison of reference values of z (Top line) with experimentally obtained values (Bottom line) [18]

p, bar	z at T, °K			
	199.82	227.57	255.37	283.15
13.79	0.9082	0.9400	0.9587	0.9712
	0.9076	0.9395	0.9581	0.9706
27.58	0.8019	0.8759	0.9170	0.9429
	0.7996	0.8760	0.9162	0.9434
41.37	0.6699	0.8078	0.8750	0.9148
	0.6627	0.8091	0.8751	0.9160
68.95	0.3090	0.6627	0.7930	0.8630
	0.3017	0.6593	0.7908	0.8639
124.11	0.4260	0.5264	0.6794	0.7887
	0.4325	0.5237	0.6725	0.7881
179.26	0.5660	0.6060	0.6860	0.7760
	0.5667	0.6147	0.6844	0.7781
206.84	0.6332	0.6593	0.7170	0.7898
	0.6331	0.6640	0.7150	0.7923
262.00	0.7692	0.7718	0.8003	0.8448
	0.7682	0.7690	0.7992	0.8430
317.16	0.9000	0.8847	0.8932	0.9162
	0.9021	0.8820	0.8913	0.9163
372.32	—	0.9965	0.9886	0.9960
		1.0043	0.9879	0.9950
482.64	—	—	—	1.1610
				1.1450
δ_{av}, %	0.61	0.41	0.39	0.36
δ_{max}, %	2.41	0.77	1.03	1.39

Table 4. Comparison of reference values of z (Top line) with experimentally obtained values (Bottom line) [19]

p, bar	z at T, °K					
	294.26	327.59	394.26	444.26	477.59	510.93
13.79	0.9751	0.9833	0.9932	0.9972	0.9988	1.0004
	0.9749	0.9833	0.9932	0.9972	0.9989	1.0002
27.58	0.9506	0.9676	0.9869	0.9948	0.9984	1.0010
	0.9503	0.9673	0.9869	0.9948	0.9982	1.0007
55.16	0.9043	0.9388	0.9764	0.9916	0.9982	1.0033
	0.9037	0.9383	0.9766	0.9916	0.9981	1.0028
86.18	0.8592	0.9118	0.9682	0.9903	1.0001	1.0074
	0.8582	0.9119	0.9685	0.9905	1.0000	1.0069
120.66	0.8228	0.8908	0.9637	0.9922	1.0048	1.0140
	0.8222	0.8913	0.9641	0.9927	1.0047	1.0135
172.37	0.8056	0.8805	0.9668	1.0013	1.0166	1.0278
	0.8059	0.8809	0.9671	1.0020	1.0164	1.0272
206.84	0.8169	0.8879	0.9753	1.0117	1.0276	1.0395
	0.8163	0.8886	0.9752	1.0120	1.0273	1.0385
310.26	0.9154	0.9593	1.0270	1.0593	1.0743	1.0851
	0.9191	0.9622	1.0271	1.0587	1.0728	1.0829
413.68	1.0551	1.0704	1.1054	1.1263	1.1358	1.1431
	1.0610	1.0761	1.1069	1.1253	1.1335	1.1402
551.58	1.2584	1.2399	1.2319	1.2325	1.2332	1.2328
	1.2664	1.2480	1.2341	1.2315	1.2307	1.2296
689.48	1.4634	1.4185	1.3692	1.3476	1.3362	1.3290
	1.4713	1.4259	1.3722	1.3490	1.3375	1.3290
δ_{av}, %	0.29	0.19	0.06	0.04	0.05	0.11
δ_{max}, %	0.63	0.64	0.22	0.10	0.20	0.26

Table 5. Comparison of reference values of z (Top line) with experimentally obtained values (Bottom line) [13]

p, bar	z at T, °K					
	203.15	223.15	273.15	323.15	373.15	473.15
1.01	0.9941	0.9954	0.9976	0.9988	0.9993	1.0000
	0.9940	0.9952	0.9976	0.9988	0.9993	0.9999
30.40	0.7910	0.8521	0.9282	0.9623	0.9806	0.9978
	0.7928	0.8537	0.9281	0.9623	0.9793	0.9969
60.80	0.4480	0.6797	0.8594	0.9293	0.9649	0.9975
	0.4515	0.6779	0.8590	0.9292	—	0.9966
101.32	0.3789	0.4998	0.7827	0.8949	0.9503	1.0004
	0.3766	0.5000	0.7834	0.8969	—	
141.86	0.4756	0.5269	0.7427	0.8755	0.9444	1.0073
	0.4752	0.5256	0.7439	0.8776	—	
202.65	0.6248	0.6438	0.7604	0.8782	0.9525	1.0243
	0.6245	0.6434	0.7613	0.8801	0.9548	1.0227

Table 5—*Continued*

P, bar	z at T, °K					
	203.15	223.15	273.15	323.15	373.15	473.15
303.98	0.8667	0.8573	0.8870	0.9482	1.0046	1.0695
	0.8663	0.8578	0.8865	0.9517	1.0066	1.0673
405.30	1.0980	1.0674	1.0436	1.0586	1.0864	1.1301
	1.0980	1.0685	1.0443	1.0632	1.0901	1.1279
607.95	1.5358	1.4720	1.3713	1.3151	1.2901	1.2752
	1.5408	1.4740	1.3676	1.3199	1.2946	1.2745
810.60	1.9606	1.8565	1.6855	1.5803	1.5118	1.4363
	1.9626	1.8618	1.6854	1.5837	1.5147	1.4367
1013.25	2.3688	2.2302	1.9951	1.8433	1.7382	1.6056
	2.3683	2.2331	1.9952	1.8420	1.7347	1.6044
δ_{av}, %	0.15	0.12	0.07	0.20	0.20	0.10
δ_{max}, %	0.78	0.28	0.27	0.43	0.35	0.21

Table 6. Comparison of reference values of z (Top line) with experimentally calculated values (Bottom line) [9]

ρ, kmol/m²	z at T, °K					
	273.15	323.15	373.15	473.15	573.15	623.15
1	0.9491	0.9675	0.9806	0.9975	1.0081	1.0120
	0.9492	0.9680	0.9809	0.9974	1.0074	1.0111
1.5	0.9256	0.9533	0.9724	0.9975	1.0132	1.0190
	0.9258	0.9535	0.9727	0.9973	1.0121	1.0176
2	0.9035	0.9400	0.9652	0.9984	1.0193	1.0271
	0.9038	0.9404	0.9657	0.9981	1.0178	1.0251
3	0.8638	0.9163	0.9539	1.0029	1.0338	1.0450
	0.8636	0.9172	0.9544	1.0025	1.0316	1.0424
4	0.8291	0.8982	0.9469	1.0113	1.0521	1.0672
	0.8290	0.8987	0.9474	1.0105	1.0492	1.0636
5	0.7999	0.8843	0.9443	1.0239	1.0746	1.0937
	0.7996	0.8852	0.9450	1.0228	1.0712	1.0888
6	0.7760	0.8756	0.9465	1.0412	1.1018	1.1242
	0.7755	0.8763	0.9471	1.0396	1.0973	1.1182
7	0.7579	0.8721	0.9538	1.0637	1.1340	—
	0.7579	0.8731	0.9547	1.0616	1.1281	—
8	0.7459	0.8742	0.9669	1.0916	—	—
	0.7453	0.8754	0.9673	1.0894	—	—
10	0.7407	0.8976	1.0117	—	—	—
	0.7396	0.8990	1.0129	—	—	—
12	0.6749	0.9504	1.0862	—	—	—
	0.6740	0.9539	1.0903	—	—	—
δ_{av}, %	0.05	0.11	0.09	0.10	0.24	0.28
δ_{max}, %	0.16	0.37	0.38	0.25	0.52	0.55

Table 7. Comparison of reference values of z (Top line) with experimentally calculated values (Bottom line) [6]

p, bar	z at T, °K					
	323.78		374.49		425.03	
	ref	exp	ref	exp	ref	exp
10.13	0.9872	0.9874	0.9933	0.9933	0.9969	0.9970
20.26	0.9747	0.9750	0.9869	0.9868	0.9940	0.9942
30.40	0.9626	0.9629	0.9808	0.9807	0.9915	0.9917
40.53	0.9511	0.9512	0.9752	0.9752	0.9892	0.9894
50.66	0.9400	0.9402	0.9701	0.9701	0.9873	0.9873
60.80	0.9297	0.9300	0.9652	0.9654	0.9855	0.9856
81.06	0.9110	0.9117	0.9572	0.9575	0.9830	0.9834
101.3	0.8958	0.8968	0.9511	0.9515	0.9821	0.9826
152.0	0.8749	0.8750	0.9459	0.9459	0.9859	0.9858
202.6	0.8799	0.8796	0.9546	0.9544	0.9988	0.9975
253.3	0.908	0.907	0.976	0.975	1.020	1.017
304.0	0.949	0.951	1.007	1.006	1.047	1.044
354.6	1.002	1.004	1.045	1.045	1.079	1.076
405.3	1.058	1.062	1.091	1.089	1.114	1.112
506.6	1.189	1.188	1.188	1.188	1.194	1.193
608.0	1.322	1.319	1.289	1.294	1.279	1.282
709.3	1.442	1.450	1.398	1.404	1.372	1.375
810.6	1.578	1.580	1.511	1.515	1.460	1.470
911.9	1.713	1.710	1.627	1.626	1.564	1.566
1013.2	1.845	1.838	1.733	1.736	1.657	1.662
δ_{av}, %	0.14		0.09		0.15	
δ_{max}, %	0.38		0.39		0.68	

Olds and colleagues [19] determined the properties of methane over a wide temperature range. The methane they used contained less than 0.001 mole-fraction of impurities. Their results are expressed in the form of the compressibility factor, with average deviation not exceeding 0.3% (Table 4).

Kvalnes and Gaddy [13] studied compressibility of methane on nine isotherms. Table 5 shows these experimentally obtained values to agree with the reference values.

Douslin [7] studied the properties of methane at high temperatures (Table 6), with the average deviation not exceeding 0.3%.

The work of Deffet and colleagues [6] is one of the most recent studies of the thermal properties of methane. These values agree closely with the reference values (Table 7).

Comparisons with reference values of Michels and colleagues [17], and Schamp and colleagues [20] in the temperature range of 273.2-423.2°K were also performed. Reference values agree with these data within ±0.1% (at identical pressures).

The data of references [1] and [10] were used for liquid methane. The agreement was within ±0.3% (at identical pressures).

REFERENCES

1. GOLUBEV, I. F., O. A. DOBROVOL'SKII and T. N. BELYAEVA. *Trudy GIAP,* No. 16, 20, 1965.
2. DOBROVOL'SKII, O. A., T. N. BELYAEVA and I. F. GOLUBEV. *Gazovaya Promyshlennost'*, No. 11, 1964.
3. ZAGORUCHENKO, V. A. *Trudy Konferentsii po Perspektivam Razvitiya i Vnedreniya Kholodil'noi Tekhniki v Narodnoe Khozyaistvo SSSR (Transactions of the Conference on Scope for Development and Introduction of Refrigeration Techniques in the State Economy of USSR)*. Gostorgizdat, Moscow, 1963.
4. PAVLOVICH, N. V. and D. L. TIMROT. *Teploenergetika,* No. 4, 1958.
5. BARELL, H. and R. ROBERTSON, *Bureau of Mines Tech. Paper,* No. 158, 1917.
6. DEFFET, L., L. LIALINE and F. FICKS. *Ind. Chem. Belge,* **29**, 879, 1964.
7. DOUSLIN, D. R. *Second Symposium on Thermophysical Properties,* U.S.A., 1962.
8. DOUSLIN, D. R., R. H. HARRISCH, R. T. MOORE and I. P. MOCULLOUGH. *J. Chem. Eng. Data,* **9**, 358, 1964.
9. FREETH, F. and T. VERSCHOYLE. *Proc. Roy. Soc., London,* **A130**, 453, 1931.
10. VAN ITTERBEEK, A., O. VERBEKE and K. STAES. *Physica,* **29**, 742, 1963.
11. KEYES, F. and H. BURKS. *J. Am. Chem. Soc.,* **49**, 1403, 1927.
12. KEYES, F., L. SMITH and D. JOUBERT. *J. Math. Phys.,* **1**, 191, 1922.
13. KVALNES, H. and V. GADDY. *J. Chem. Soc.,* **53**, 394, 1931.
14. MATSCHKE, D. and G. THODOS. *J. Petrol. Tech.,* **21**, October, 67, 1960.
15. MATHEWS, C. and C. HURD. *J. AIChE,* **42**, 55, 1946.
16. MICHELS, A. and G. NEDERBRAGT. *Physica,* **2**, 1000, 1935.
17. MICHELS, A. and G. NEDERBRAGT. *Physica,* **3**, 569, 1936.
18. MÜLLER, W., T. LELAND and R. KOBAYASHI. *AIChE Journal,* **7**, 267, 1961.
19. OLDS, R., H. REAMER, B. SAGE and W. LACEY. *Ind. Eng. Chem.,* **35**, 922, 1943.
20. SCHAMP, H., E. MASON, A. RICHARDSON and A. ALTMAN. *Physics of Fluids,* **1**, 329, 1958.
21. THOMAES, G. and R. VAN STEENWINKEL. *Nature,* **187** (4733), 229, 1960.

UDC 541.11

INVESTIGATION OF THE SHAPE OF THE TWO-PHASE CURVE FOR ETHANE NEAR THE CRITICAL POINT BY THE METHOD OF QUASISTATIC THERMOGRAMS

Yu. R. Chashkin, V. A. Smirnov and *A. V. Voronel'*

According to the classical Gibbs-Van der Waals-Landau theory, the liquid-vapor boundary curve should be represented as a second-order parabola near the critical point when plotted with temperature T and specific volume v as coordinates [1]. The phenomenological theory of Azbel', Voronel', and Giterman [2], relating to the peculiar behavior of specific heat C_V at the critical point, also assumes the same shape for the boundary curve. However, Mayer's statistical theory [3] presupposes a flat horizontal section at the top of the two-phase curve near the critical point. All investigators unanimously agree, however, that beyond the critical point, the boundary curve on T-v coordinates is close to cubic.

The present investigation explores the possibilities of the method of quasistatic thermograms [4]. The two-phase boundary near the critical point, the subject of this investigation, is at present attracting the attention of many physicists, theoretical as well as experimental, rendering the present problem all the more interesting and topical.

Clarification of the shape of the boundary is required for two important reasons. (1) Variations in the T-v relationship for the boundary leads to different thermodynamic results. As shown by Krichevskii and Khazanova [5], increase in specific heat ΔC_V at the critical point basically depends on the order of the two-phase parabolic curve; with a cubic relationship, ΔC_V has a finite value at the critical point and at higher orders, its value becomes infinite. (2) The problem of proving or disproving the applicability of the Ising model to the critical point becomes important. Studies

[6, 7] using the Ising model to interpret this phenomenon at the critical point also apply the Guggenheim equation [8].

$$t \sim \tilde{v}^3, \tag{1}$$

where $t = \dfrac{T_{cr} - T}{T_{cr}}, \quad \tilde{v} = \left(\dfrac{v - v_{cr}}{v_{cr}} \right).$

If the two-phase curve is a second-order parabola, the Ising model cannot be used for investigating the liquid-vapor critical point.

A short survey of experimental studies

The empirical Guggenheim equation was later confirmed by Lorentzen [9], Rice [10, 11], and Zimm [12]. All these works, however, did not consider a number of factors (hydrostatic effect, nonequilibrium during measurement, etc.), contraindicating the reliability of the results.

There are also a few studies in which $\left(\dfrac{\partial^3 p}{\partial v^3} \right) T_{cr}$ is determined by triple differentiation of p-v-T data, considerably diminishing the accuracy of results. For a majority of substances, the value of $\left(\dfrac{\partial^3 p}{\partial v^3} \right) T_{cr}$ is known to be exceedingly small (of the order of $1 . 10^{-5}$ atm . mole^3 . cm^{-9}) and to range within the limits of accuracy for calculations from p-v-T data. Authors of these computations (e.g., [13]), using zero value of this quantity, naturally obtained cubic relationships (1).

Weinberger and Schneider [14] established applicability of the Guggenheim equation upto $(\rho_{liq} - \rho_{gas}) \rho_{liq} \geqslant 10$, where ρ_{liq} and ρ_{gas} are the respective densities of the substances in liquid and gaseous states. $T_{cr} - T \geqslant 0.030$ deg.

Atack and Schneider [15] studied the two-phase boundary of SF$_6$ near the critical point (at $T_{cr} - T \leqslant 0.030$ deg, $\tilde{v} < 0.05$), and we consider these results to clearly indicate a quadratic two-phase curve in this region, although Atack and Schneider did not reach this conclusion. Using their data, we plotted log $\tilde{v}$ as a function of log t (see Fig. 1) (parameters T_{cr} and v_{cr} in accordance with reference [15]). This relationship is close to linear with a gradient of about 0.5, indicating a quadratic relationship.

$$t \sim \tilde{v}^2 \tag{2}$$

Recently published studies confirm the opinion that equation (1) applies for the two-phase curve only beyond the critical point, whereas near the curve the relationship is quadratic [16-18]. Makarevich and Sokolova [17] express the region of quadratic relationship for SF_6 as $t \leqslant 2 \cdot 10^{-4}$, $\tilde{v} < 0.1$.

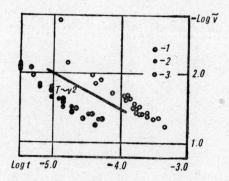

Fig. 1.   Boundary curve on log-log scale.

1—*for pure* SF_6;   2—*for* SF_6 *with air as impurity;*   3—*for chlorine* [18].

Methods of measurement

The most widely applied method for experimental determination of the liquid-vapor boundary is the measurement of temperature at which the meniscus disappears. The point of disappearance is fixed visually. The method yields favorable results, distant to the critical point. As the critical point approaches, the difference between liquid and vapor phases diminishes, and the visual determination of the point of phase transition becomes increasingly unreliable, and the observations are further complicated by critical opalescence. Therefore, the temperature region of $T_{cr} \pm$ 0.005 deg remains practically inaccesible for investigation. The method of quasistatic thermograms previously recommended by the present authors [4] proved extremely useful in the case of ethane and, we believe, yielded reliable data upto temperatures differing from the critical temperature by approximately 0.0003 deg.

The well-known method of thermograms (in which, at a constant rate of heat removal, specimen temperature is measured as a function of time) provides phase transitions in the specimen from the shape of the thermograms. Actually, the temperature-time relationship at constant rate of heat removal shows the dependence of temperature on energy. Thus, flat regions (T=const) on thermograms indicate evolution or absorption of the latent heat of transition; discontinuities, sudden increase in derivatives (specific heat), and lags indicate increase in specific heat. The common thermograms, however, are unsuitable near the critical point because of their inadequate sensitivity and lack of equilibrium conditions. Thermograms should satisfy the following conditions : (1) the amount of heat removed per unit time should be less than the heat effect under study, to allow observation, and (2) the rate of heating or cooling should be sufficiently small and should satisfy the relation

$$\frac{dT}{d\tau} < \frac{\Delta T}{\tau_B}, \tag{3}$$

where $\dfrac{\tau_B}{\Delta T}$ is the relative relaxation time of the system (see, for example, reference [19]). Taking the value of $T_{cr} - T \approx 0.0003$ deg from study [19], we obtain $\dfrac{\tau_B}{\Delta T} \sim 10^4$ min/deg and, consequently, the allowable rates of change of temperature in this case must be $\dfrac{dT}{d\tau} < 6 \cdot 10^{-3}$ deg/h. If the heat capacity of the specimen is 40 J/deg, the allowable heat flow is approximately $7 \cdot 10^{-5}$ J/sec.

Our measurements were performed in a KU-300/70 adiabatic calorimeter (Fig. 2). According to calculations, the total maximum stray heat flow in the system did not exceed $7 \cdot 10^{-5}$ J/sec. The actual value was less by one order and the required temperature rate could be obtained by an artificial heat flow of the order of $5 \cdot 10^{-5}$ J/sec. The calorimeter was filled with ethane to the maximum required density (exceeding the critical density by about 10%). The temperature of the apparatus was adjusted

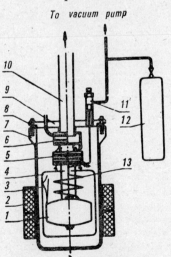

To vacuum pump

Fig. 2. Schematic diagram of calorimetric apparatus.
1—*Calorimeter;* 2—*Magnetic coil;* 3—*Thermocouples;* 4—*Screen;* 5—*"Hot" ring;* 6—*"Cold" ring;* 7—*Vacuum casing;* 8—*Packing ring;* 9—*Flange;* 10—*Vacuum Communication;* 11—*Valve;* 12—*Gas Cylinder;* 13—*Capillary.*

to the working temperature region and was maintained for a sufficiently long time under adiabatic conditions. Recording of the thermograms was then initiated.

Locating the first point on the boundary curve is somewhat difficult, as its temperature is not usually determined with high accuracy. The first measurement was, therefore, performed at high rates of temperature variation. After this coarse location of the required temperature range, subsequent measurements were performed at low equilibrium rates of heating or cooling ($\sim$0.003 deg/hr). Thermograms were frequently obtained (two to five times) in either direction and at each density. Fig. 3 shows one such thermogram. Temperature $T_{c\max}$ of the log in the curve path corresponds to maximum heat capacity. The discontinuity at T_{cr} occurs on transgression of the boundary curve, when there is a sudden variation in heat capacity. For transition to another isochore, part of the substance in the calorimeter was passed into a measuring cylinder (see Fig. 2) and the amount of this gas was measured.

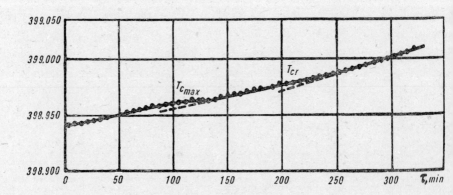

Fig. 3.   A typical thermogram obtained on KU-300/70 (values on ordinates are in arbitrary units).

After completing a series of experiments covering the density range of interest to us, the remaining gas was collected in the gas cylinder for measurement.

Results of measurements

Three general series of measurements were obtained; the results are given in Figs. 4 and 5 and Table 1. Fig. 5 also gives the data of work [20] for densities quite remote from the critical point. At $\tilde{v} < 0.07$ (log $\tilde{v} < 1.2$), the experimentally obtained relationship of log $\tilde{v}$ versus log t obviously close to linear with a gradient of 0.5 (broken line with dots).

Much of the above data confirms equation (2). In the interval of $-1.2 < \log \tilde{v} \leqslant -0.8$, the curve is close to linear with a gradient of ~ 0.33, confirming equation (1). The deviation of the data of work [20] from the dotted straight line (Fig. 5) corresponding to the cubic relationship is caused by the asymmetry of the boundary curve at large v and t.

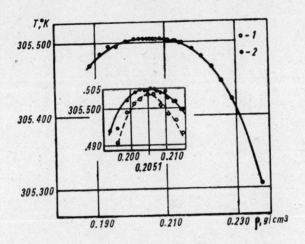

Fig. 4. Boundary curve for ethane in T-ρ coordinates.
1—*curve of maximum heat capacities;* 2—*boundary curve.*

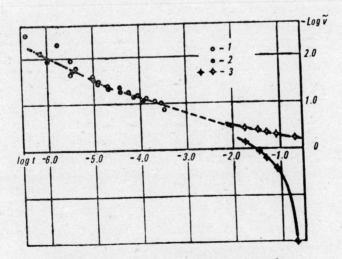

Fig. 5. Boundary curve for ethane on log scale.
1—*at* $p > p_{cr}$; 2—*at* $p < p_{cr}$; 3—*data of work* [20].

Table 1.   Results of temperature measurements

ρ, g/cm³	T_{cr}, °K	$T_{c_{max}}$	Transition temperature without stirring, T'_{cr}, °K
0.2370	305.3069	—	—
0.2290	305.4220	—	—
0.2262	305.4452	—	—
0.2234	305.4646	—	—
0.2206	305.4790	—	—
0.2179	304.4896	—	—
0.2149	305.4995	305.4929	—
0.2145	305.4994	—	—
0.2129	305.5018	305.4964	305.5057
0.2126	305.5017	—	—
0.2108	305.5026	305.4981	305.5056
0.2100	305.5045	—	—
0.2088	305.5042	305.5007	—
0.2075	305.5046	—	—
0.2068	305.5052	305.5037	—
0.2058	305.5053	—	—
0.2051	305.5049	305.5038	—
0.2040	305.5049	—	—
0.2027	305.5051	305.502	—
0.2012	305.5044	305.5014	—
0.1990	305.5023	305.49882	—
0.1961	305.4947	305.4905	—
0.1939	305.4938	—	—
0.1916	305.4843	—	—
0.1884	305.4690	—	—

We determined the critical temperature and density of ethane as :

$$T_{cr} = 305.5054°K \pm 0.01 \text{ deg};*$$
$$\rho_{cr} = 0.2051 \text{ g/cm}^3 \pm 0.3\%.$$

Table 1 gives the coordinates of the boundary curve, temperatures $T_{c_{max}}$ corresponding to the maximum heat capacities (which had been previously observed in works [4, 21]), and temperatures T_{cr} of transition across the boundary curve when the substance is poorly stirred. The latter feature serves only as an illustration, since the concept of "poor stirring" is not properly defined. The irregularities in heat capacity cannot

---

*The accuracy of measurement of the absolute temperature depends on the accuracy of the primary instrument, a gas thermometer in our case, and is 0.01 deg. The accuracy of determination of the relative temperature depends on the stability and sensitivity of the sensor (resistance thermometer) and measuring instruments; this is about 0.0002 deg in our case.

be observed without stirring, and the transition temperature is difficult to determine from the thermograms. The substance must, therefore, be stirred occasionally.

It is appropriate to briefly mention the geometric location of T_{cmax} points. Following our experiments on ethane and argon [21], the curve of heat capacity maxima has been adequately determined on the T–ρ space and is enclosed by the boundary curve (Fig. 4), with only one common point at $t=0$, $v=0$ (critical point).*

The existence of one such curve, the spinoidal, inside a heterogeneous region with a single common point within a two-phase boundary, is known in thermodynamics. The spinoidal is the line of limiting metastable states along isotherms and isobars and satisfies the condition

$$\left(\frac{\partial p}{\partial v} \right)_{\mathrm{T}} = 0, \tag{4}$$

characterizing infinitely large compressibility.

There is no basis for assumption regarding the existence of a supernumerary thermodynamically possible curve inside a heterogeneous region. However, the concept that the spinoidal and the curve of maxima of heat capacity are identical can be substantiated only by less convincing qualitative concepts, such as the theories that an increase in heat capacity implies increase in density fluctuations (the appearance of additional freedom degrees) and that density fluctuations increase with compressibility. Nonetheless, the problem is of considerable interest and, in our opinion, could be clarified by compressibility experiments.

The authors express their gratitude to N. E. Khazanova and I. S. Lesnevskaya for useful discussions.

REFERENCES

1. LANDAU, L. D. and E. M. LIFSHITS. *Statisticheskaya fizika (Statistical physics)*. Nauka, Moscow, 1964.
2. AZBEL', M. YA., A. V. VORONEL' and M. SH. GITERMAN. *Zh. Eksper. i Teoret. Fiz.*, **46**, 673, 1963.
3. MAYER, J. and M. HEPPERT-MAYER. *Statisticheskaya mekhanika (Statistical mechanics)*. IIL, Moscow, 1952.
4. VORONEL', A. V., V. G. GORBUNOVA, YU. R. CHASHKIN and V. V. SHCHEKONCHIKHINA. *Zh. Eksper. i Teoret. Fiz.*, **50**, 897, 1966.

* We believe that the noncoincidence of these curves at the critical point of ethane indicates the presence of a small amount of impurities [14].

5. KRICHEVSKII, I. R. and N. E. KHAZAROVA. *Zh. Fiz. Khim.*, **29**, 1087, 1955.
6. LEE, T. D. and C. N. YANG. *Phys. Rev.*, **87**, 410, 1952.
7. FISHER, M. E. *Crit. Phen.*, **21**, Washington D. C., 1965.
8. GUGGENHEIM, E. A. *J. Chem. Phys.*, **13**, 253, 1945.
9. LORENTZEN, H. L. *Acta Chem. Scand.*, **7**, 1335, 1953.
10. RICE, O. K. *J. Chem. Phys.*, **23**, 164, 1955.
11. RICE, O. K. *J. Chem. Phys.*, **23**, 169, 1955.
12. ZIMM, B. H. *J. Chem. Phys.*, **20**, 538, 1952.
13. HABGOOD, H. W. and W. G. SCHNEIDER. *Canad. J. Chem.*, **32**, 164, 1954.
14. WEINBERGER, M. A. and W. G. SCHNEIDER. *Canad. J. Chem.*, **30**, 422, 1952.
15. ATACK, D. and W. G. SCHNEIDER. *J. Phys. Coll. Chem.*, **55**, 532, 1951.
16. SHERMAN, R. H. *Phys. Rev. Let.*, **15**, 141, 1965.
17. MAKAREVICH, L. A. and E. S. SOKOLOVA. Pis'ma v Redaktsiyu. (Letters to the Editor). *Zh. Eksper. i Teoret. Fiz.* **4**, 408, 1966.
18. TSEKHANSKAYA, YU. V., V. A. POLYAKOVA and G. M. KOZLOVSKAYA. *Zh. Fiz. Khim.*, **41**, 501, 1967.
19. CHASHKIN, YU. R., A. V. VORONEL', V. A. SMIRNOV and V. G. GORBUNOVA. *Zh. Eksper. i Teoret., Fiz.*, **52**, 112, 1967.
20. VORONEL', A. V. and YU. R. CHASHKIN. *Zh. Eksper. i Teoret. Fiz.*, **51**, 394, 1966.

UDC 541.11

MEASUREMENT OF DENSITY OF NORMAL HEXANE AND DISTILLED WATER AT PRESSURES UPTO 10,000 kg/cm²

V. A. Borzunov, V. N. Razumikhin and *V. A. Stekol'nikov*

For studies at high pressures, the values of compressibility of liquids serving as working fluids are necessary. Such information is partly available in the present literature, but the number of liquids investigated and the maximum values of applied pressures are insufficient, and the available data are not sufficiently accurate. Bridgeman [2] has investigated the largest number of liquids by using a movable sealed piston and bellows-type piezometer. Such methods, however, presumably cannot ensure accuracy of compressibility measurement (by density values) higher than 2-3%.

The hydrostatic method developed in the Institute of VNIIFTRI enables direct determination of the density of a liquid under pressure, and hence of the compressibility with greater accuracy and reliability.

Earlier investigations [1] show the maximum error at pressures upto 10,000 kg/cm² obtained by this method not to exceed $\pm\,0.5 \times 10^{-4}$ g/cm³. Such high accuracy can be ensured only when the viscosity of the liquid, at the given temperature and pressure, does not exceed 0.4 poise.

The hydrostatic method of measurement of density under pressure basically involves determination of the equilibrium position of a balance beam with hydrostatic loads at the given pressure and temperature.

The arrangement of hydrostatic balance used by the present authors for determination of density of a liquid under pressure is shown in Fig. 1.

A nickel-plated brass balance beam, 200 mm in length, has an angle prism (3) at the center, which is supported by an agate bearing (13) fixed in the bracket (12) of the base of the balance.   Prisms with loading pans (9, 14) are fixed to the ends of the balance-beam.   The functioning bodies of materials with different densities are placed in these pans.   The pointer (1) is fixed to the end of the beam while another pointer (15) is attached to the base of the balance.   When pointers (1, 15) coincide, an equilibrium position is indicated which is necessary for the determination of balance. These pointers are not used in ordinary measurements of density of liquids under pressure.

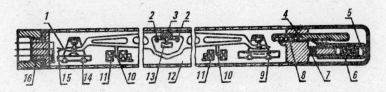

Fig. 1.   Arrangement of hydrostatic balance.

At about two-thirds of the length of the arm from the fulcrum (3), ferrite rods (10) are fixed to the beam.   These provide cores for the coils (11) mounted on the base of the balance.   The lead wires from these coils are extracted through special seals (16), and the lead wires from the compression chamber are correspondingly extracted through special conical seals.

For initial balancing of the beam, small weights (2) are provided when the liquid under investigation is at atmospheric pressure.   The weights are of the same material (brass) and have identical masses. Additional weights balancing the beam under pressure are deposited on the loading pan by a special loading device (4), located on the right-hand side of the balance.   The loading device contains a rod and small weights are placed in the holes (8) provided on one end, and on the other end exists a ratchet arrangement.   The weights are constructed in the form of small spherical steel balls and possess identical masses.

When the push-button (5) is pressed the lever attached to it displaces the rod to the left by one tooth.   One ball is released from the hole and falls into the right-hand pan.   A special valve is used for this operation. After the push-button has been pressed once, the spring (7) returns it to the initial position and the next ball is released.   The spring (6), having a much greater stiffness than that of the other spring (7), protects the pushing device from accidental overloading.

The equilibrium position of the beam is determined by electronic indicators for which the symmetrically placed induction coils serve as sensor elements.   The ferrite rods, fixed to the beam of the balance, are able to move freely inside the induction coils.

For studying the relationship between the density of a liquid and the applied pressure, the hydrostatic balance initially placed in the liquid is transferred to the compression chamber (Fig. 2).

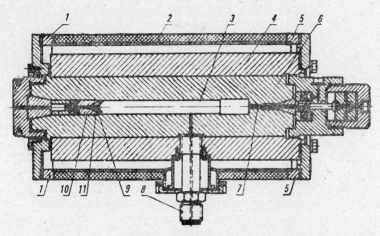

Fig. 2. Schematic arrangement of compression chamber.

The chamber consists of a double-walled steel cylinder. The inner part of the chamber is constructed of alloy steel 50 KhFA, while the outer portion is of steel 45. The bore (3) in the cylinder (6) is connected to the intensifier by means of a nipple (8) through a high-pressure valve.

The hydraulic balance is placed inside the bore (3) of the chamber and is then closed by the metallic plug (10). There are three electrodes (9) in the plug to which lead wires from the coils are connected. The electrodes used are conical metal rods insulated by either mica or iron oxide. Inside the plug (10) is a blind passage (11) designed for introducing thermocouples. The thermocouple placed in the passage measures the temperature of the working liquid. The thermocouple is protected from the action of the high pressure and it is, therefore, not necessary to apply correction due to the variation in electromotive force under the influence of pressure.

In order to heat the liquid, the entire compression chamber is placed in a bath (2) which is fed through holes in the rings (1, 5) with the working liquid from a thermostat by forced circulation. A hydraulic valve located in the right-hand side of the compression chamber is used for dropping the balancing small balls onto the balance under pressure. A movement of the needle (7) of this valve activates the pushing device of the balance cassette.

The direct determination of density of a liquid under pressure consists of the following procedure. (1) The balance-beam, possessing two equal arms, loaded by two bodies of different densities and volumes, is adjusted to equilibrium in the liquid at atmospheric pressure. (2) With a change in the density of the liquid due to pressure, the initially balanced beam loses its equilibrium, and must be compensated by additional weight supplemented on the body of larger volume. This supplementary weight provides a mass which is an indirect measurement of the change in liquid density occurring due to the application of pressure.

The numerical value of density is determined by calculation from the following equations :

$$\rho_p = \frac{q - M - B \, \rho_4}{v_3 - \Delta v - Ap - B(1 - k_4 p)} , \tag{1}$$

where ρ_p=the density of the liquid at pressure p, under which the balance attains equilibrium; q=the mass of the supplementary weights to restore equilibrium under pressure; $\Delta v = v_1 - v_2$=the difference in the volumes of the two bodies with which the balance is in equilibrium at atmospheric pressure; v_3=the volume of the weights of mass q ; $M = v_2 \rho_2 - v_1 \rho_1$= the difference in the masses due to which equilibrium is lost; ρ_1 and ρ_2= densities of the bodies which restore the balance to equilibrium; $B = -\dfrac{M + (v_1 - v_2) \, \rho_0}{\rho_4 - \rho_0}$; ρ_0=the density of the liquid at atmospheric pressure; ρ_4=the density of the small weights (riders) balancing the beam at atmospheric pressures; k_4=the coefficient of volumetric compressibility of the body with density ρ_4; Ap=a term accounting for the deformation of the volumes of the balancing bodies.

All the quantities occurring on the right-hand side of the computation equation (1) were determined experimentally, with the exception of the coefficient of volumetric deformation of bodies, obtained from the data of Bridgeman [2].

The pressure corresponding to the density calculated by equation (1) was measured by a manganin (manganese-nickel-copper alloy) manometer. The objective of the present work is the determination of density of normal hexane and water by the hydrostatic method at pressures upto 10,000 kg/cm^2 and temperatures of 20, 35, 50, and 65°C respectively. The experimental results are presented in Tables 1 and 2. The relative decrements of volumes calculated from the relationship

$$C = \frac{\Delta v}{v_0} = 1 - \frac{\rho_0}{\rho_p} , \tag{2}$$

were processed on an electronic computer and approximated by Tait's empirical equation of the type

$$C = A \ln\left(1 + \frac{p}{B} \right) \qquad (3)$$

where C is the compressibility expressed in terms of volume decrements, A, B are constants for a given temperature, and p is the pressure.

The coefficients A and B for $H-C_6H_{14}$ and H_2O are given in Table 1.

Table 1. Tait's coefficients for normal hexane and distilled water

t, °C	A		B	
	$H-C_4H_{14}$	H_2O	$H-C_4H_{14}$	H_2O
20	0.09769	0.12677	675	2720
35	0.09616	0.12917	573	2940
50	0.09504	0.13263	481	3001
65	0.09644	0.12952	437	2826

Table 2. Density and relative volume decrement of normal hexane

p, kg/cm²	ρ, g/cm³	C_{cal}	C_{exp}	ΔC, %
		$t = 20\ °C$		
1	0.659_4	0.0000	0.0000	0.00
1165	0.731_6	0.098_1	0.098_7	—0.61
1630	0.749_6	0.119_9	0.120_3	—0.33
3300	0.797_2	0.173_2	0.172_9	0.17
4160	0.815_6	0.192_3	0.191_5	0.42
5125	0.834_1	0.210_1	0.209_4	0.33
5140	0.834_2	0.210_3	0.209_5	0.38
6250	0.852_8	0.227_4	0.226_8	0.26
7725	0.871_6	0.243_9	0.243_5	0.16
9010	0.890_6	0.260_2	0.259_6	0.23
		$t = 35\ °C$		
1	0.645_6	0.0000	0.0000	0.00
1060	0.717_8	0.100_1	0.100_6	—0.50
1480	0.735_8	0.122_7	0.122_6	0.08
2340	0.764_8	0.156_0	0.155_9	0.06
2975	0.783_0	0.175_3	0.175_5	—0.11
2995	0.783_1	0.175_9	0.175_6	0.23
3740	0.801_1	0.194_2	0.194_4	—0.10
3750	0.801_4	0.194_3	0.194_4	—0.05
4640	0.819_8	0.212_4	0.212_5	—0.05

Table 2—*Continued*

p, kg/cm^2	ρ, g/cm^3	C_{cal}	C_{exp}	$\triangle C$, %
		$t=35°$C		
5670	0.838$_3$	0.229$_7$	0.229$_9$	—0.09
6070	0.844$_6$	0.235$_7$	0.235$_6$	0.04
6850	0.857$_0$	0.246$_3$	0.246$_7$	—0.16
7320	0.863$_4$	0.252$_2$	0.252$_2$	0.00
8840	0.882$_6$	0.269$_2$	0.268$_5$	0.26
		$t=50°$C		
1	0.631$_5$	0.0000	0.0000	0.00
930	0.703$_6$	0.102$_2$	0.102$_5$	—0.29
1310	0.721$_3$	0.124$_3$	0.124$_5$	—0.16
1755	0.739$_5$	0.146$_0$	0.146$_0$	0.00
2075	0.750$_3$	0.158$_7$	0.158$_5$	0.25
2080	0.750$_3$	0.158$_9$	0.158$_3$	0.38
2295	0.757$_5$	0.166$_5$	0.166$_3$	0.12
2680	0.768$_5$	0.179$_0$	0.178$_3$	0.39
2895	0.775$_5$	0.185$_2$	0.185$_7$	—0.27
3355	0.786$_7$	0.197$_4$	0.197$_3$	0.05
3370	0.786$_8$	0.197$_7$	0.197$_4$	0.15
4170	0.805$_1$	0.215$_6$	0.215$_6$	0.00
4195	0.805$_1$	0.216$_1$	0.215$_6$	0.23
5105	0.823$_2$	0.233$_0$	0.233$_2$	—0.08
6170	0.842$_0$	0.249$_6$	0.250$_0$	—0.16
6180	0.842$_1$	0.249$_8$	0.250$_1$	—0.12
6215	0.842$_1$	0.250$_3$	0.250$_1$	0.08
6610	0.848$_3$	0.255$_7$	0.255$_6$	0.04
7380	0.860$_7$	0.265$_5$	0.266$_3$	—0.30
7450	0.860$_8$	0.266$_3$	0.266$_4$	—0.04
7930	0.867$_2$	0.271$_9$	0.271$_6$	0.04
8755	0.879$_5$	0.280$_8$	0.282$_0$	—0.40
9410	0.886$_2$	0.287$_3$	0.287$_4$	—0.04
		$t=65°$C		
1	0.617$_2$	0.0000	0.0000	0.00
1910	0.735$_9$	0.162$_0$	0.161$_3$	0.43
2070	0.743$_3$	0.168$_5$	0.169$_6$	—0.65
2440	0.754$_1$	0.181$_8$	0.181$_5$	0.16
3065	0.772$_3$	0.200$_6$	0.200$_8$	0.10
3300	0.779$_3$	0.206$_9$	0.208$_0$	—0.53
3795	0.790$_6$	0.219$_0$	0.219$_3$	—0.14

Table 2—*Continued*

p, kg/cm^2	ρ, g/cm^3	C_{cal}	C_{exp}	ΔC, %
		$t=65°C$		
4685	0.809_0	0.237_3	0.237_2	0.08
4890	0.814_8	0.241_2	0.242_5	—0.54
5710	0.827_5	0.255_0	0.254_1	0.35
5920	0.833_4	0.258_2	0.259_4	—0.46
6845	0.846_1	0.271_3	0.270_5	0.29
7115	0.852_2	0.274_8	0.275_8	—0.36
8160	0.864_4	0.287_3	0.286_4	0.31
8475	0.871_1	0.290_8	0.291_5	—0.24
9650	0.883_8	0.302_7	0.301_7	0.33
10,070	0.890_6	0.306_7	0.307_0	—0.03

Table 3. Density and relative volume decrement for distilled water

p, kg/cm^2	ρ, g/cm^3	C_{cal}	C_{exp}	ΔC, %
		$t=20°C$		
0	0.9982	0.0000	0.0000	0.00
840	1.032_8	0.034_1	0.033_5	1.80
1310	1.050_1	0.049_7	0.049_4	0.61
1825	1.067_4	0.065_1	0.064_8	0.46
2385	1.084_7	0.079_8	0.079_7	0.13
2995	1.102_0	0.094_1	0.094_1	0.00
3530	1.116_2	0.105_4	0.105_7	—0.28
3665	1.119_3	0.108_2	0.108_2	0.00
4245	1.133_7	0.119_2	0.119_5	—0.25
4380	1.136_7	0.121_6	0.121_8	—0.16
5000	1.151_2	0.132_2	0.132_9	—0.53
5170	1.154_1	0.135_0	0.135_0	0.00
5890	1.170_1	0.146_1	0.146_9	—0.54
6020	1.171_6	0.147_9	0.147_9	0.00
6795	1.186_8	0.158_7	0.158_9	—0.12
6810	1.186_8	0.159_0	0.158_9	0.06
7800	1.204_6	0.171_5	0.171_3	0.12
7815	1.204_6	0.171_7	0.171_3	0.23
8900	1.222_4	0.184_1	0.183_4	0.38

Table 3—*Continued*

p, kg/cm^2	ρ, g/cm^3	C_{cal}	C_{exp}	$\triangle C$, %
		$t=35°C$		
1	0.9940_6	0.0000	0.0000	0.00
1630	1.054_4	0.057_5	0.057_2	0.52
2215	1.071_9	0.073_2	0.072_6	0.83
2805	1.089_3	0.087_3	0.087_4	0.11
3470	1.106_7	0.101_5	0.101_8	-0.29
3705	1.111_8	0.106_2	0.105_9	0.28
4185	1.124_2	0.115_3	0.115_8	-0.43
4455	1.129_8	0.120_1	0.120_2	-0.08
5030	1.141_8	0.129_8	0.129_4	0.31
5250	1.147_4	0.133_3	0.133_7	-0.30
5260	1.147_4	0.133_5	0.133_7	-0.15
6140	1.165_2	0.146_7	0.146_8	-0.07
7085	1.182_9	0.159_6	0.159_7	-0.06
8105	1.200_8	0.172_1	0.172_1	0.00
9225	1.218_7	0.184_6	0.184_3	0.16
		$t=50°C$		
1	0.9880_8	0.0000	0.0000	0.00
1620	1.048_0	0.057_3	0.057_2	0.17
2200	1.065_4	0.072_8	0.072_6	0.27
2820	1.082_9	0.087_9	0.087_6	0.34
3490	1.100_3	0.102_3	0.102_0	0.29
3715	1.106_1	0.106_8	0.106_7	0.09
4220	1.117_8	0.116_4	0.116_0	0.34
4470	1.123_7	0.120_9	0.120_7	0.16
5135	1.139_5	0.132_3	0.132_9	-0.45
5300	1.141_4	0.135_0	0.134_3	0.52
6000	1.157_2	0.145_7	0.146_1	-0.27
6190	1.159_1	0.148_5	0.147_5	0.68
6935	1.175_0	0.158_8	0.159_1	-0.19
7965	1.192_9	0.171_9	0.171_7	0.12
8970	1.210_7	0.183_5	0.183_9	-0.22
		$t=65°C$		
1	0.98059	0.0000	0.0000	0.00
1573	1.040_4	0.057_3	0.057_5	0.3
2057	1.055_5	0.070_8	0.071_0	0.3
2127	1.057_8	0.072_7	0.073_0	0.4

Table 3—*Continued*

p, kg/cm²	ρ, g/cm³	C_{cal}	C_{exp}	ΔC, %
		$t=65°C$		
2684	1.072_9	0.086_5	0.086_0	0.5
2746	1.075_2	0.087_9	0.088_0	0.1
3340	1.090_4	0.101_1	0.100_7	0.4
3414	1.092_7	0.102_6	0.102_6	0.0
4045	1.107_9	0.115_1	0.114_9	0.2
4132	1.110_2	0.116_7	0.116_7	0.0
4835	1.125_4	0.129_2	0.128_7	0.4
5148	1.131_9	0.134_4	0.133_7	0.5
5663	1.143_0	0.142_4	0.142_1	0.3
6023	1.149_9	0.147_8	0.147_0	0.5
6547	1.160_6	0.155_3	0.155_1	0.1
6938	1.167_4	0.160_5	0.160_0	0.3
7975	1.185_3	0.173_7	0.172_7	0.5
9008	1.203_4	0.185_5	0.185_2	0.2

The experimental values of C and those values calculated by equation (3) for the above-mentioned compounds are given in Tables 2 and 3.

REFERENCES

1. BORZUNOV, V. A. and V. A. RAZUMIKHIN. Investigations in the field of measurement of high pressures. *Trudy VNIIFTRI*, No. 75, (135), 1964.
2. BRIDGEMAN, P. *Fizika vysokikh davlenii (Physics of high pressures)*. Moscow-Leningrad, 1935.

UDC 541.27

ENTHALPY OF FORMATION OF ALKYL BENZENES

E. A. Smolenskii and *L. V. Kocharova*

The method of calculating the thermochemical properties of normal and isomeric paraffinic hydrocarbons in respect to the interaction of carbon-carbon bonds has been described in detail [1]. The present paper describes the use of this method for calculating the enthalpy of formation $\triangle H_f^0$ of this class of compounds.

One modification of the method [2] consists of the following. The energy of formation of alkyl derivatives of benzene differs from the energy of formation of benzene itself and from the energies of formation of substitutional alkanes. This difference is due to the energies of interaction between radicals and the benzene ring, and to the energy of interaction between radicals. The contributions of the following interactions are accounted for as :

The interaction of bonds in respective ortho, meta, and para positions is expressed as :

If i is the number of interactions of type a_i, the following formula may be applied for calculating the energies of formation of alkyl benzenes :

$$\triangle H_f^0(C_{n+6} H_{2n+6}) - \triangle H_f^0(C_6H_6) = \sum_{R_i} \triangle H_f^0(R_iH) + \sum_{i=1}^{12} n_i a_i.$$

Using the least-square method for processing the available experimental data [2], coefficients were observed to possess the following values :

$$a_1 = 10.020; \quad a_2 = -2.480; \quad a_3 = -2.079; \quad a_4 = -1.037;$$

$$a_5 = -0.568; \quad a_6 = 0.059; \quad a_7 = 0.593; \quad a_8 = -0.072; \quad a_9 = -0.200;$$

$$a_{10} = 0.204; \quad a_{11} = 0.202; \quad a_{12} = 0.209 \quad \text{kcal/mole}.$$

The following table compares experimental and calculated values of $\triangle H_f^0$ for alkyl benzenes (in gaseous state). The average deviation for 41 compounds is 0.12 kcal/mole.

Comparison of experimental and calculated $\triangle H_f{}^0$ values for alkyl benzenes

Alkyl benzene	$\triangle H_f{}^0$, kcal/mole	
	Experimental	Calculated
Methylbenzene	11.95	11.95
Ethylbenzene	7.12	7.12
1, 2-dimethylbenzene	4.54	4.67
1, 3-dimethylbenzene	4.12	4.01
1, 4-dimethylbenzene	4.29	3.88
H-propylbenzene	1.87	1.97
Isopropylbenzene	0.94	0.86
1-methyl-2-ethylbenzene	0.29	0.04
1-methyl-3-ethylbenzene	—0.46	—0.62
1-methyl-4-ethylbenzene	—0.73	—0.74
1, 2, 3-trimethylbenzene	—2.29	—2.68
1, 2, 4-trimethylbenzene	—3.33	—3.47
1, 3, 5-trimethylbenzene	—3.84	—4.00
H-butylbenzene	—3.30	—3.36
Isobutylbenzene	—5.15	—4.67
F-butylbenzene	—4.17	—4.41
Tetrabutylbenzene	—5.42	—5.42
1, 2-diethylbenzene	—4.53	—4.58
1, 3-diethylbenzene	—5.22	—5.25
1, 4-diethylbenzene	—5.32	—5.37
1-methyl-2-propylbenzene	—5.17	—5.10
1-methyl-3-propylbenzene	—5.86	—5.77
1-methyl-4-propylbenzene	—5.97	—5.91
1-methyl-2-isopropylbenzene	—6.10	—6.01
1-methyl-3-isopropylbenzene	—6.79	—6.68
1-methyl-4-isopropylbenzene	—6.90	—6.79
1, 2-dimethyl-3-ethylbenzene	—7.11	—7.11
1, 2-dimethyl-4-ethylbenzene	—7.61	—7.89
1, 3-dimethyl-2-ethylbenzene	—7.11	—7.10
1, 3-dimethyl-4-ethylbenzene	—7.91	—7.89
1, 3-dimethyl-5-ethylbenzene	—8.50	—8.43
1, 4-dimethyl-2-ethylbenzene	—7.91	—7.89
1, 2, 3, 4-tetramethylbenzene	—10.02	—10.23
1, 2, 3, 5-tetramethylbenzene	—10.71	—10.89
1, 2, 4, 5-tetramethylbenzene	—10.82	—11.82
H-pentylbenzene	—8.23	—8.21
H-hexylbenzene	—13.15	—13.17
H-heptylbenzene	—18.08	—18.09
H-octylbenzene	—23.00	—23.03
1, 2, 3, 4, 5-pentamethylbenzene	—17.80	—17.25
1, 2, 3, 4, 5, 6-hexamethylbenzene	—25.26	—24.88

There is virtually no experimental information on $C_{11}H_{16}$ and higher alkyl benzenes. Using our formula, the energy of formation ΔH_f^0 was calculated for all $C_{11}H_{16}$ isomers in gaseous state.

Alkyl benzene	H_f^0, kcal/mole
H-pentylbenzene	—8.21
(2-methylbutyl) benzene	—9.501
Isopentylbenzene	—10.128
Tetrapentylbenzene	—10.131
Neopentylbenzene	—12.133
(1, 2-dimethylpropyl) benzene	—11.120
(1-ethylpropyl) benzene	—9.200
(1-methylbutyl) benzene	—9.259
1-methyl-4-butylbenzene	—11.219
1-methyl-3-butylbenzene	—11.098
1-methyl-2-butylbenzene	—10.431
1-methyl-4-tetrabutylbenzene	—13.072
1-methyl-3-tetrabutylbenzene	—12.958
1-methyl-2-tetrabutylbenzene	—12.289
1-methyl-4-sec-butylbenzene	—12.061
1-methyl-3-sec-butylbenzene	—11.947
1-methyl-2-sec-butylbenzene	—11.278
1-methyl-4-isobutylbenzene	—12.533
1-methyl-3-isobutylbenzene	—12.412
1-methyl-2-isobutylbenzene	—11.742
1-ethyl-2-propylbenzene	—9.727
1-ethyl-3-propylbenzene	—10.396
1-ethyl-4-propylbenzene	—10.510
1-ethyl-2-isopropylbenzene	—10.633
1-ethyl-3-isopropylbenzene	—11.304
1-ethyl-4-isopropylbenzene	—11.411
1, 4-dimethyl-5-propylbenzene	—13.041
1, 3-dimethyl-5-propylbenzene	—13.580
1, 3-dimethyl-6-propylbenzene	—13.034
1, 2-dimethyl-5-propylbenzene	—13.036
1, 2-dimethyl-6-propylbenzene	—12.248
1, 5-dimethyl-6-propylbenzene	—13.745
1, 3-dimethyl-5-isopropylbenzene	—14.286
1, 3-dimethyl-6-isopropylbenzene	—13.731
1, 2-dimethyl-5-isopropylbenzene	—13.435
1, 5-dimethyl-6-isopropylbenzene	—13.356
1, 2-dimethyl-3-isopropylbenzene	—12.958

Continued

Alkyl benzene	H_f^0, kcal/mole
1-methyl-2, 5-diethylbenzene	—12.858
1-methyl-2, 4-diethylbenzene	—12.312
1-methyl-2, 6-diethylbenzene	—11.524
1-methyl-4, 5-diethylbenzene	—12.310
1-methyl-5, 5-diethylbenzene	—11.522
1, 3, 4-trimethyl-5-ethylbenzene	—15.112
1, 2, 3-trimethyl-5-ethylbenzene	—15.107
1, 2, 4-trimethyl-3-ethylbenzene	—14.445
1, 3, 5-trimethyl-6-ethylbenzene	—15.103
1, 2, 4-trimethyl-5-ethylbenzene	—15.233
1, 2, 3-trimethyl-4-ethylbenzene	—14.440
1, 2, 3, 4, 5-pentamethylbenzene	—17.850

The agreement between experimentally obtained and calculated values confirms the negligible difference of calculated results from true values.

REFERENCES

1. SEIFER, A. L., E. A. SMOLENSKII and L. V. KOCHAROVA. In : *Teplofizicheskie kharakteristiki veshchestv* (*Thermophysical characteristics of substances*). Seriya Fizicheskie Konstanty i svoistva Veshchestv, No. 1, Izd, Standartov, Moscow, 1968.
2. SMOLENSKII, E. A. and L. V. KOCHAROVA. *Zh. Fiz. Khim.* **39**, 1969.

UDC 541.27

CRITICAL AND BOILING TEMPERATURES OF BENZENE AND ITS FLUORODERIVATIVES

P. A. Kotlyarevskii and *V. B. Derman*

The objective of the present work is the determination of the critical temperature of benzene and its fluoroderivatives of the C_6H_6-C_6F_6 series on the basis of available experimental data and analysis of theoretical methods for the determination of T_{cr}.

The C_6H_6-C_6F_6 series contains 13 substances : benzene C_6H_6, fluorobenzene C_6H_5F, 1, 2-; 1, 3-; 1, 4-difluorobenzene $C_6H_4F_2$, 1, 2, 3-; 1, 2, 4-; 1, 3, 5-trifluorobenzenes $C_6H_3F_3$, 1, 2, 3, 4-, 1, 2, 4, 5-; 1, 2, 3, 5-tetrafluorobenzenes $C_6H_2F_4$, pentafluorobenzene C_6HF_5, and hexafluorobenzene C_6F_6.

Critical temperatures of benzene and fluorobenzene are the most widely studied, and sufficiently reliable data [1-12] are available, showing agreement within $\pm0.5\%$. There are also available data on the critical temperatures of pentafluorobenzene [9] and hexafluorobenzene [9, 12] with accuracy upto $\pm0.5\%$. The available data obtained from experiments on the critical temperatures of the substances under study are given in Fig. 1. There are no data on other substances.

Boiling temperatures have been investigated for all 13 substances except 1, 2, 3-trifluorobenzene [1, 3, 6-9, 12-32]. Results of analysis and compilation of these data are given in Fig. 2, which shows a definite relationship between the boiling point and the number of fluorine atoms in the benzene ring. The accuracy of $t_{boiling}$ values accepted in the present work is within experimental error. The value of the boiling temperature accepted for 1, 2, 3-$C_6H_3F_3$ is tentative and based on the observed relationships.

A number of authors [7, 8, 33-35] base calculations of T_{cr} on additive

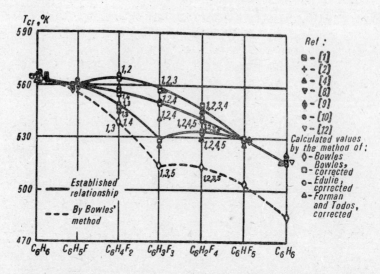

Fig. 1. Critical temperatures of benzene and its fluoroderivatives as functions of number of fluorine atoms in the compound (1, 2; 1, 3;...1, 2, 3, 5 indicate isomers).

properties of quantity $\dfrac{T_{boil}}{T_{cr}} = \Theta$ for molecules of different structures and recommend formulae and tables for calculating Θ from contributions of atoms and groups.

On the basis of accepted values of $T_{boiling}$, we have calculated critical temperatures for a number of substances using four methods, suggested by Riede, Edulie, Liederson, and Bowles, and, according to Bretsch-

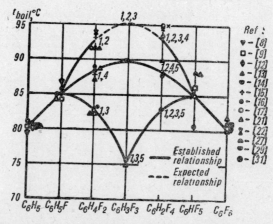

Fig. 2. Boiling temperatures for benzene and fluoroderivatives as functions of number of fluorine atoms in the compounds (1, 2; 1, 3;...1, 2, 3, 5 indicate isomers).

neider's classification [7], these belong to the "second" group of methods, allowing calculation of substance properties on the basis of experimental data (in the present case, T_{boiling}). The accepted values of T_{boiling} and T_{cr} for the C_6H_6-C_6F_6 series are given in the table below :

	$T_{\text{boil}}^{\circ}K$	$T_{\text{cr}}^{\circ}K$
C_6H_6	353.25	562.6
C_6H_5F	358.15	560.0
$1, 2\text{-}C_6H_4F_2$	366.15	563.3
$1, 3\text{-}C_6H_4F_2$	356.05	548.4
$1, 4\text{-}C_6H_4F_2$	361.55	556.6
$1, 2, 3\text{-}C_6H_3F_3$	368.35*	558.4
$1, 2, 4\text{-}C_6H_3F_3$	362.95	550.4
$1, 3, 5\text{-}C_6H_3F_3$	348.65	528.8
$1, 2, 3, 4\text{-}C_6H_2F_4$	366.15	547.6
$1, 2, 4, 5\text{-}C_6H_2F_4$	361.75	541.1
$1, 2, 3, 5\text{-}C_6H_2F_4$	356.15	532.8
C_6HF_5	358.15	529.15
C_6F_6	553.45	516.7

*Value obtained by interpretation.

Analysis proves methods of the "second" group to be quite reliable for many compounds including those of the benzene series.*

According to Riedl, the value Θ is calculated as :

$$\Theta = 0.574 + \Sigma \Delta \Theta_1, \tag{1}$$

The formulae of Edulie, Liederson, and Bowles are respectively

$$\Theta = \frac{\Sigma \Delta \Theta_2}{100}, \tag{2}$$

$$\Theta = 0.567 + \Sigma \Delta \Theta_3 - (\Sigma \Delta \Theta_3)^2, \tag{3}$$

$$\Theta = \Sigma \Delta \Theta_4, \tag{4}$$

and methods are given to calculate $\Delta \Theta_1$, $\Delta \Theta_2$, $\Delta \Theta_3$ and $\Delta \Theta_4$.

Results of calculations show Riedl's method to yield inaccurate results for the substances under investigation (deviations $\pm 20\%$).

*Unfortunately, other well-known methods based on the use of experimental data on various thermophysical properties cannot be used, as such data are not available for the compounds under study.

Liederson, Edulie, and Bowles's methods agree with experimental values of T_{cr} only for benzene and C_6H_5F ; however, with the increasing number of flourine atoms, the error in determination of T_{cr} increases to 7% (30°) in the case of C_6F_6 (see Fig. 1, which illustrates values calculated from Bowles's method).

The deviations may be explained by the fact that the authors used only the data on C_6H_5F for obtaining the contribution of fluorine for benzene compounds. The methods should therefore be corrected for higher fluoroderivatives of benzene. Hence, we have used experimental data on critical temperature of C_6F_6. Assuming the contribution of fluorine atoms to the value of Θ to increase linearly with the number of fluorine atoms, Θ values have been calculated for the compounds in the C_6H_5F-C_6F_6 series (see table below). A check on C_6H_5F showed calculated values of T_{cr} obtained by corrected methods of Bowles and Edulie to be 529.02 and 529.49°K, respectively, and the experimentally obtained value to be 529.15$\pm$1°K [9], indicating that the assumed linear relationship yields reliable results for the series under investigation.

The calculated data were checked by Forman and Thodos's method [36], since it allows calculation of T_{cr} in respect to differences between isomers. Results of these calculations also confirmed the assumption regarding the effect on critical temperature of the number of fluorine atoms (the error in T_{cr} was $\sim$8% for C_6H_6).

The deviation is, however, considerable. Therefore, as previously, the contribution of fluorine atoms to the Van der Waals constants a and b was calculated and T_{cr} was determined for all compounds.

Corrected additive contributions of fluorine atoms for determination of T_{cr} for C_6H_6F-C_6F_6 series

Substance	$\triangle \Theta_2$	$\triangle \Theta_4$	$\triangle a^2/_3$	$\triangle b^3/_4$
		For calculation methods of :		
	Edulie	Bowles	Forman and	Thodos
C_6H_5F	29.75	0.2987	4210	7.2200
$C_6H_4F_2$	29.70	0.2983	4022	7.3345
$C_6H_3F_3$	29.65	0.2979	3833	7.4495
$C_6H_2F_4$	29.60	0.2975	3645	7.5650
C_6HF_5	29.55	0.2971	3455	7.6810
C_6F_6	29.50	0.2968	3265	7.7963

Analysis of all results obtained shows that for compounds 1, 2-; 1, 2, 3-; 1, 2, 3, 4-*x*; and 1, 3-; 1, 3, 5-; 1, 2, 3, 5-*x* all corrected methods yield results within $\pm$0.6%. Forman and Thodos's method [36] gives slightly differing values for 1, 4-; 1, 2, 4; and 1, 2, 4, 5-*x*. It must be noted that this method, belonging to the "first" group according to Bretschneider's classification, considers only the structural formula, and thus yields identical values of T_{cr} for some isomers of large substitution (e.g., 1, 2, 4, 5- and 1, 2, 3, 5-*x*).

The finally accepted values of T_{cr} (see table above) are calculated from corrected methods of Edulie and Bowles, since these mutually independent methods are based on experimental values of $T_{boiling}$ and yield results agreeing both commonly and with values obtained by the corrected method of Forman and Thodos. The error in the accepted values of T_{cr} obtained by the two methods does not exceed 1%.

REFERENCES

1. VARGAFTIK, N. B. *Spravochnik po teplofizicheskim svoistvam gazov i zhidkostei* (*Handbook on thermophysical properties of fluids*). Fizmatgiz, Moscow, 1963.

2. KOBE, K. A. and R. E. LYNN. *Chem. Rev.*, **52**, 117, 1953.

3. *Handbook of Chemistry and Physics*. Chem. Rubber Publ. Co., Cleveland, Ohio, 1956.

4. CONNOLLY, J. F. and G. A. KANDALIC. *J. Chem. and Eng. Data*, **7** (1), 137, 1962.

5. CHANG, D. C. H., J. C. McCOUBREY and D. C. PHILLIPS. *Trans. Farad. Soc.*, **58** (2), 224, 1962.

6. BARON, N. M., E. I. KYVAT and E. A. PODGORNAYA. *Kratkii spravochnik fizikokhimicheskikh velichin* (*A short handbook of physicochemical values*). Khimiya, Moscow, 1965.

7. BRETSCHNEIDER, S. *Svoistva gazov i zhidkostei* (*Properties of gases and fluids*). Khimiya, Moscow, 1966.

8. RIED, R. K. and T. R. SHERWOOD. *Svoistva gazov i zhidkostei* (*Properties of gases and fluids*). Goztekhizdat, Moscow, 1964.

9. PATRICK, C. P. and G. S. PROSSER. *Trans. Farad. Soc.*, **60**, (4), 700, 1964.

10. DOUSLIN, D. R., R. T. MOORE, J. R. DAWSON and G. WADDINGTON. *J. Am. Chem. Soc.*, **80** (9), 2031, 1958.

11. MELVINE HUGHES, E. A. *Fizicheskaya khimiya* (*Physical chemistry*), Vols. **I** and **II**. IIL, Moscow, 1962.

12. COUNSELL, J. F., J. H. S. GREEND and H. MARTIN. *Trans. Farad. Soc.*, **61** (2), 212, 1965.

13. GUDITSKII, M. *Khimiya organicheskikh soedinenii bora* (*Chemistry of organic compounds of boron*). Gozkhimizdat, Moscow, 1961.

14. KAPPER, P. *Kurs organicheskoi khimii (A course in organic chemistry)*. Goztekhizdat, Moscow, 1960.

15. SHIMANN, G. *Oganische fluorrerbindungen, ihrer bedutung fur die technik*. Steinkopff, Darmstadt, 1951.

16. *Spravochnik khimika (A Chemist's handbook)*. Vol. **II**. Gozkhimizdat, Moscow, 1951.

17. PAVLATH, A. E. and A. J. LEFFLER. *Aromatic fluorine compounds*. New York, 1964.

18. JORDAN, T. E. *Vapor pressures of organic compounds*, Interscience, New York, 1954.

19. DRISBACH, R. R. Physical properties of chemical compounds. *Advances in Chemistry*, Series 15, 1955.

20. SIMONS, J. Fluorine and its compounds, Vol. **I**, 1953; Vol. **II**, 1956.

21. KENICHI, F., K. HISAO, O. TAICHIRO, I. YOSHIAKI and S. SAMON. *J. Chem. Soc. Japan, Pure Chem. Series*, **29** (9), 1120, 1958.

22. SCOTT, D. W., J. E. MESSERLY and S. P. McCULLOUGH. *J. Chem. Phys.*, **38** (2), 532, 1963.

23. FINGER, G. C. and R. E. OESTERLING. *J. Am. Chem. Soc.*, **78**, (11), 2593, 1956.

24. FLORIN, E. E., W. J. PUMMER and L. A. WALL. *J. Res. Nat. Bur. Standards*, **62** (3), 119, 1959.

25. PUMMER, W. J., R. E. FLORIN and L. A. WALL. *J. Res. Nat. Bur. Standards*, **62** (3), 113, 1959.

26. NIELD, E., R. STEPHENS and J. C. TATLOW. *J. Chem. Soc.*, **166** (1), 1959.

27. STEPHENS, R. and J. C. TATLOW. *Chem. and Ind.*, No. 25, 821, 1957.

28. NIELD, E., R. STEPHENS and J. TATLOW. *J. Chem. Soc.*, 3800, Oct., 1960.

29. PUMMER, W. J. and L. A. WALL. U. S. Patent, 260-650, No. 3046313, Publication 24/7/62.

30. DESIRANT, Y. *Bull. Soc. Chim. Belges*, **67**, Nos. 11-12, 676, 1958.

31. DESIRANT, Y. *Bull. Cl. Soc. Acad. Roy. Belgique*, **41** (7), 759, 1955.

32. GOUDSELL, J. A., M. STASEY and J. C. TATLOW. *Nature*, **178** (4526), 1956.

33. RIEDEL, L. *Z. Electrochem.*, **53**, 222, 1949.

34. RIEDEL, L. *Chem. Ing. Techn.*, **24**, 353, 1952; **26**, 259, 1954; **28**, 419, 1956.

35. GAMBILL, W. R. *Chem. Eng.*, **66** (12), 181, 1959; (14) 157, 1959.

36. FORMAN, J. C. and G. THODOS. *AIChE Journal*, **4**, 356, 1958; **6**, 206, 1960.

UDC 541.27

THERMODYNAMIC FUNCTIONS OF FLUORINATED BENZENE COMPOUNDS IN IDEAL-GAS STATE

V. P. Onishchenko and *V. A. Abovskii*

The present work analyzes the investigations of various authors and assigns vibration frequencies after adjustment for consistency, both internally and corresponding to vibrations in other halogenoaromatic molecules. The assignment obtained is described below and in Table 1.

Vibrations not observed in spectra are assigned tentative values of frequency and are indicated in parentheses in Table 1. These values were obtained using the inequality rule [1], law of additions, and Maslov's procedure for approximate frequency calculations [2]. Data on structures of the molecules under study were taken from references [3, 4].

Thermodynamic functions $H_T^0-H_0^0$, s_T^0 and c_p^0 were calculated in the approximation of "harmonic vibrator-rigid rotator" [5, 6] for temperatures of 200-1200°K at intervals of 10 deg. The results are presented for 100° increments in Table 2 and as polynomials

$$A(x)=a_0+a_1x+\ldots+a_8x^8 \qquad \text{at} \quad x=10^{-30}K.$$

Coefficients of polynomials are given in Table 3.

Assignment of frequencies

Benzene. Symmetry is D_{6h}; $I = I_A I_B I_C \cdot 10^{-112} = 0.0644$ g³ · cm⁶. Assignments in vibration spectra of benzene were considered to be final except for forbidden frequencies of B_{2v} and A_{2g} types, regarding which there was disagreement. Detailed investigation of second-order lines [7] enables assignment of these vibrations to values of 1309 and 1150 cm⁻¹. We could, therefore, compute more exhaustive values of thermodynamic functions than those obtained earlier [8].

Table 1. Vibration spectra of fluorinated benzenes

C₆H₆	C₆H₅F	o-C₆H₄F₂	m-C₆H₄F₂	p-C₆H₄F₂	1,2,4-C₆H₃F₃	1,3,5-C₆H₃F₃	1,2,3,4-C₆H₂F₄	1,2,5-C₆H₂F₄	C₆H₂F₄	C₆HF₅	C₆F₆
a_1 3062	a_1 3101	a_1 3092	a_1 3096	a_1 3084	a_1 3094	a_1 3111	a_1 3090	a_1 3090	a_1 3097	a_1 3105	a_1 1655
3060	3067	3053	3086	3050	3094	3081	1032	1631	3088	1648	1530
3054	3044	1610	3087	1617	3062	1620	1522	1523	1643	1514	1490
1596	1596	1514	1608	1511	1628	1471	1328	1405	1439	1410	1323
1480	1499	1200	1456	1245	1518	1350	1211	1200	1374	1286	1157
1309	1220	1277	1286	1225	1441	1122	1162	1124	1225	1075	1006
1177	1157	1152	1066	1142	1376	1010	1048	997	748	718	640
1150	1022	1024	1008	1012	1308	993	682	786	700	578	559
1037	1008	762	735	859	1250	578	460	580	487	470	443
992	808	567	524	740	1204	502	325	(450)	(384)	325	315
606	519	295	331	451	1143	326	268	310	280	272	264
b_2 3054	b_2 3091	b_2 3070	b_2 3096	b_2 3084	1098	b_2 3111	b_2 3070	b_2 3080	b_2 1643	b_2 1648	b_2 1655
3047	3058	3060	1621	3077	964	1620	1607	1631	1534	1540	1530
3047	1603	1625	1493	1617	835	1471	1515	1455	1277	1268	1253
1596	1460	1464	1290	1437	781	1400	1402	1240	1196	1182	1157
1480	1323	1294	1265	1285	728	1122	1239	1176	1164	1138	1006
1346	1236	1212	1158	1285	586	1000	988	1050	1125	953	691
1177	1157	1103	1123	1085	503	993	747	641	853	688	443

Table 1—*Continued*

C₆H₆	C₆H₅F	o-C₆H₄F₂	m-C₆H₄F₂	p-C₆H₄F₂	1, 2, 4-C₆H₃F₃	1, 3, 5-C₆H₃F₃	1, 2, 3, 4-C₆H₂F₄	1, 2, 5-C₆H₂F₄	C₆H₂F₄	C₆HF₅	C₆F₆
1037	1066	857	954	635	441	502	489	510	635	436	315
1010	614	547	514	427	341	500	310	334	(375)	304	264
606	405	437	478	350	288	326	291	258	(284)	247	208
$b_1$970	$b_1$997	$b_1$929	$b_1$978	$b_1$928	$a_2$932	$b_1$1191	$b_1$803	$b_1$840	$b_1$871	$b_1$838	$b_1$714
849	894	750	853	833	856	845	597	702	869	697	595
676	754	450	770	692	808	665	374	606	669	556	370
405	685	240	672	508	688	595	170	368	461	(310)	249
$a_2$985	500	$a_2$982	458	375	602	253	$a_2$922	(240)	295	217	215
970	242	843	235	163	456	214	(720)	(144)	140	(132)	125
849	$a_2$970	703	$a_2$879	$a_2$943	327	$a_2$845	(540)	$a_2$845	$a_2$600	a_2(600)	$a_2$595
703	826	590	599	800	238	665	(420)	645	417	391	370
405	405	197	251	405	161	214	(160)	205	202	171	125

Table 2. Thermodynamic functions for fluorinated benzenes

Substance	Thermodynamic Function	T, °K										
		200	300	400	500	600	700	800	900	1000	1100	1200
C_6H_6	$h_T^0 - h_0^0$, cal/mole	1824.02	3434.91	5777.74	8793.81	12363.9	16379.8	20758.5	25437.1	30367.1	35510.0	40834.1
	s_T^0, cal/mole·deg	57.9653	64.4001	71.0900	77.7946	84.2899	90.4726	96.3146	101.822	107.014	111.914	116.546
	c_P^0, cal/mole·deg	12.6937	19.7496	26.9812	33.1307	38.0893	42.0925	45.3771	48.1146	50.4221	52.3826	54.0577
C_6H_5F	$h_T^0 - h_0^0$, cal/mole	2022.61	3906.79	6542.23	9840.94	13675.8	17936.7	22540.0	27423.3	32539.2	37850.3	43326.8
	s_T^0, cal/mole·deg	64.8721	72.4084	79.9402	87.2761	94.2547	100.815	106.958	112.706	118.095	123.155	127.919
	c_P^0, cal/mole·deg	15.1156	22.6602	29.8802	35.8737	40.6394	44.4401	47.5228	50.0656	52.1903	53.9826	55.5052
$o\text{-}C_6H_4F_2$	$h_T^0 - h_0^0$, cal/mole	2279.23	4444.29	7365.25	10933.3	15018.3	19510.6	24327.3	29406.5	34701.5	40175.8	45800.9
	s_T^0, cal/mole·deg	68.4635	77.1348	85.4888	93.4265	100.862	107.779	114.207	120.187	125.764	130.980	135.874
	c_P^0, cal/mole·deg	17.7313	25.5552	32.6664	38.4708	43.0464	46.6636	49.5680	51.9387	53.9001	55.5399	56.9224

Table 2—*Continued*

Substance	Thermodynamic Function	$T, °K$										
		200	300	400	500	600	700	800	900	1000	1100	1200
m-$C_6H_4F_2$	$h_T^0 - h_0^0$, cal/mole	2226.84	4382.02	7304.08	10877.1	14967.7	19464.9	24285.2	29366.7	34662.9	40137.6	45762.4
	s_T^0, cal/mole·deg	68.1418	76.7707	85.1274	93.0761	100.522	107.447	113.879	119.862	125.440	130.657	135.550
	c_P^0, cal/mole·deg	17.5351	25.5282	32.7043	38.5272	43.1002	46.7063	49.5976	51.9562	53.9075	55.5396	56.9164
p-$C_6H_4F_2$	$h_T^0 - h_0^0$, cal/mole	2253.83	4423.68	7354.96	10933.0	15026.5	19525.8	24348.0	29431.7	34730.2	40207.4	45834.8
	s_T^0, cal/mole·deg	66.8985	75.5875	83.9711	91.9311	99.3818	106.310	112.745	118.730	124.311	129.530	134.426
	c_P^0, cal/mole·deg	17.6990	25.6484	32.7717	38.5638	43.1234	46.7258	49.6178	51.9785	53.9319	55.5654	56.9430
1, 2, 4-$C_6H_3F_4$	$h_T^0 - h_0^0$, cal/mole	2491.51	4967.95	8242.14	12160.8	16576.6	21374.0	26468.8	31799.8	37322.0	43001.1	48224.5
	s_T^0, cal/mole·deg	71.4603	81.3834	90.7526	99.4733	107.512	114.901	121.700	127.977	133.793	139.205	144.259
	c_P^0, cal/mole·deg	20.3770	28.9861	36.2302	41.8938	46.2304	49.5794	52.2154	54.3308	56.0562	57.4822	58.6731

Table 2—*Continued*

Substance	Thermodynamic Function	T, °K										
		200	300	400	500	600	700	800	900	1000	1100	1200
1, 3, 5-C$_6$H$_3$F$_3$	$h_T^0 - h_0^0$, cal/mole	2485.79	4914.80	8105.53	11929.6	16254.1	20968.8	25990.6	31257.9	36724.4	42354.8	48121.5
	s_T^0, cal/mole . deg	69.4615	79.1990	88.3296	96.8395	104.712	101.973	118.674	124.876	230.633	135.999	141.016
	c_P^0, cal/mole . deg	20.1616	28.2851	35.3064	40.9494	45.3555	48.8011	51.5335	53.7357	55.5363	57.0262	58.2713
1, 2, 3, 4-C$_6$H$_2$F$_4$	$h_T^0 - h_0^0$, cal/mole	2797.82	5561.89	9073.75	13187.3	16663.1	22726.0	27965.7	33432.2	39080.7	44877.1	50794.9
	s_T^0, cal/mole . deg	74.8732	85.9673	96.0239	105.181	113.530	121.159	128.153	134.588	140.538	146.061	151.210
	c_P^0, cal/mole . deg	23.3633	31.6357	38.3589	43.6941	47.8472	51.0779	53.6169	55.6399	57.2736	58.6092	59.7129
1, 2, 3, 5-C$_6$H$_2$F$_4$	$h_T^0 - h_0^0$, cal/mole	2771.02	5492.85	8983.57	13092.7	17682.5	22942.8	27890.9	33365.6	39021.7	44824.9	50748.9
	s_T^0, cal/mole . deg	74.9244	85.8451	95.8394	104.986	113.343	120.953	127.987	134.433	140.390	145.920	151.074
	c_P^0, cal/mole . deg	22.8905	31.3119	38.2469	43.7032	47.9100	51.1594	53.7009	55.7194	57.3462	58.6744	59.7711

Table 2—*Continued*

Substance	Thermodynamic Function	$T, °K$										
		200	300	400	500	600	700	800	900	1000	1100	1200
1, 2, 4, 5-$C_6H_2F_4$	$h_T^0 - h_0^0$, cal/mole	2760.62	5503.42	9010.67	13128.7	17722.3	22683.7	27931.2	33404.7	39059.1	44860.4	50782.5
	s_T^0, cal/mole . deg	73.3562	84.3615	94.4039	103.570	111.934	119.576	126.579	133.024	138.980	144.508	149.660
	c_P^0, cal/mole . deg	23.0590	31.5171	39.3705	43.7623	47.9315	51.1604	53.6910	55.7040	57.3283	58.6556	59.7523
C_6HF_5	$h_T^0 - h_0^0$, cal/mole	3088.72	6134.83	9925.91	14301.9	19132.1	24311.5	29760.2	35418.7	41242.8	47199.1	53262.5
	s_T^0, cal/mole . deg	78.3262	90.5620	101.423	111.166	119.962	127.940	135.212	141.875	148.009	153.685	158.450
	c_P^0, cal/mole . deg	26.0721	34.4860	41.0746	46.2275	50.2004	53.2552	55.6213	57.4761	58.9500	60.1354	61.1013
C_6F_6	$h_T^0 - h_0^0$, cal/mole	3429.47	6786.63	10869.2	15509.9	20582.2	25984.7	31639.3	37487.0	43484.5	49599.3	55807.3
	s_T^0, cal/mole . deg	78.4994	91.9968	103.698	114.033	123.272	131.593	139.140	146.026	152.344	158.171	163.572
	c_P^0, cal/mole . deg	29.1493	37.5353	43.8497	48.7542	52.5234	55.3982	57.5952	59.2880	60.6074	61.6488	62.4812

Table 3. Thermodynamic functions for fluorinated benzenes and polynomial coefficients

Substance	Thermo-dynamic Function	a_0	a_1	a_2	a_3	a_4	a_5	a_6	a_7	a_8
C_6H_6	$h_T^0 - h_0^0$, cal/mole	−429.015	+17634.8	−91125.7	+424244	−789894	+857303	−558475	+202657	−31548.2
	s_T^0, cal/mole.deg	+47.9696	+34.5330	+103.350	−142.777	+82.1419	−18.2064	—	—	—
	c_P^0, cal/mole.deg	+17.4874	−179.544	+1234.17	−3096.03	+4166.83	−3224.99	+1349.41	−236.911	—
C_6H_5F	$h_T^0 - h_0^0$, cal/mole	+168.475	+6657.22	−10447.2	+166889	−290925	+253507	−114303	+21193.2	—
	s_T^0, cal/mole.deg	+50.1031	+69.9028	+26.7909	−43.2531	+14.5392	—	—	—	—
	c_P^0, cal/mole.deg	+13.2691	−107.506	+959.337	−2447.21	+3318.92	−2569.67	+1072.80	−187.746	—
$C_6H_4F_2$	$h_T^0 - h_0^0$, cal/mole	−150.336	+10518.6	−23664.6	+235210	−472335	+521004	−339531	+122612	−18962.6
	s_T^0, cal/mole.deg	+48.8977	+117.973	−186.946	+648.658	−1381.83	+1707.35	−1233.88	+486.642	−81.1015
	c_P^0, cal/mole.deg	+11.2999	−59.9269	+789.872	−2195.11	+3265.93	−2911.29	+1551.62	−454.311	+55.8442

Table 3—*Continued*

Substance	Thermo-dynamic Function	a_0	a_1	a_2	a_3	a_4	a_5	a_6	a_7	a_8
$C_6H_4F_2$	$h_T^0 - h_0^0$, cal/mole	−74.1898	+9149.89	−18154.3	+222809	−454214	+503354	−328516	+118648	−18339.6
	s_T^0, cal/mole.deg	+49.4314	+107.479	−135.285	+506.376	−1139.16	+1445.16	−1059.17	+421.142	−70.5364
	c_P^0, cal/mole.deg	+9.76974	−46.4752	+73.7449	−2070.73	+3071.84	−2712.57	+1423.78	−407.613	+48.4568
$C_6H_4F_2$	$h_T^0 - h_0^0$, cal/mole	−61.4836	+8912.58	−14964.7	+210793	−430497	+475786	−309447	+111362	−17153.4
	s_T^0, cal/mole.deg	+47.8680	+109.973	−140.140	+505.741	−1120.77	+1411.60	−1030.06	+408.326	−68.2340
	c_P^0, cal/mole.deg	+9.12692	−34.0231	+663.600	−1847.71	+2674.23	−2274.50	+1129.85	−297.359	+30.7174
1, 2, 4-$C_6H_3F_3$	$h_T^0 - h_0^0$, cal/mole	+71.7306	+5898.08	+11942.8	+151348	−351706	+408611	−273644	+100543	−15742.5
	s_T^0, cal/mole.deg	+49.9362	+116.949	−78.0186	+256.116	−646.016	+878.420	−670.513	+273.531	−46.6117
	c_P^0, cal/mole.deg	+7.18972	+3.90277	+582.577	−1856.95	+2984.79	−2851.32	+1638.14	−524.226	+71.9464

Table 3—*Continued*

Substance	Thermo-dynamic Function	a_0	a_1	a_2	a_3	a_4	a_5	a_6	a_7	a_8
1, 3, 5-$C_6H_3F_3$	$h_T^0 - h_0^0$, cal/mole	−55.4766	+7295.16	+9037.12	+138933	−303318	+335334	−214938	+75893.6	−11457.8
	s_T^0, cal/mole.deg	+46.9868	+132.132	−162.215	+469.377	−964.576	+1175.90	−841.767	+329.262	−54.4678
	c_P^0, cal/mole.deg	+6.43844	+30.2091	+345.786	−988.173	+1252.21	−800.068	+192.734	+37.0789	−20.6748
1, 2, 3, 4-$C_6H_2F_4$	$h_T^0 - h_0^0$, cal/mole	+77.1032	+3174.35	+53991.5	−898.195	−52274.8	+57757.5	−28639.2	+6181.12	−288.642
	s_T^0, cal/mole.deg	+48.1282	+156.452	−155.220	+285.063	−477.848	+524.434	−348.772	+128.476	−20.1758
	c_P^0, cal/mole.deg	+0.13998	+153.087	−281.234	+727.551	−1594.36	+2155.19	−1689.13	+710.557	−124.524
1, 2, 3, 5-$C_6H_2F_4$	$h_T^0 - h_0^0$, cal/mole	+36.8947	+4888.94	+37577.1	+59009.8	−172414	+199.335	−128054	+44695.1	−6633.85
	s_T^0, cal/mole.deg	+49.0273	+151.107	−156.848	+349.544	−666.671	+793.674	−561.544	+217.932	−35.8317
	c_P^0, cal/mole.deg	+4.00887	+87.6424	+103.648	−443.612	+515.902	−191.520	−103.712	+113.121	−28.1327

Table 3—*Continued*

Substance	Thermodynamic Function	a_0	a_1	a_2	a_3	a_4	a_5	a_6	a_7	a_8
1, 2, 4, 5-$C_6H_2F_4$	$h_T^0 - h_0^0$, cal/mole	+127.788	+2831.15	+51557.9	+14598.2	−89060.3	+105097	−63647.8	+20210.6	−2655.52
	s_T^0, cal/mole.deg	+47.5571	+146.647	−117.266	+204.296	−372.777	+438.979	−306.644	+117.101	−18.9134
	c_P^0, cal/mole.deg	+0.86626	+132.231	−135.410	+244.280	−677.569	+1099.38	−957.312	+429.275	−78.4185
C_6HF_5	$h_T^0 - h_0^0$, cal/mole	+86.5744	+1895.87	+77432.6	−70627.2	+69133.2	−74099.0	+58763.3	−26194.7	+4852.26
	s_T^0, cal/mole.deg	+47.6589	+182.944	−192.303	+284.994	−382.142	+355.500	−206.604	+67.3718	−9.41000
	c_P^0, cal/mole.deg	−1.86216	+211.007	−560.420	+1454.98	−2752.94	+3312.96	−2399.43	+955.650	−161.002
C_6F_6	$h_T^0 - h_0^0$, cal/mole	+69.8909	+629.538	+105737	−163455	+241308	−269183	+1921.45	−76822.2	+13054.8
	s_T^0, cal/mole.deg	+42.9334	+218.779	−261.002	+341.502	−342.070	+211.989	−63.1752	+0.38219	+3.00525
	c_P^0, cal/mole.deg	−5.25727	+299.650	−1039.30	+2826.53	−5119.61	+5855.32	−4067.73	+1568.85	−257.841

Hexafluorobenzene. Symmetry is D_{6h}, $I = 10.978$ g$^3 \cdot$ cm^6. Substitution with fluorine results in the appearance of fundamental bands in the "finger-print" region, presenting considerable difficulties in assigning lowest frequencies. Steele [1] assigns a value of 175 cm^{-1} to lowest nonplanar vibrations and his force-constant calculations [9] yield a frequency of 121 cm^{-1} for these vibrations. Similar calculations of Nonnenmacher [10] yield a value of 119 cm^{-1}. We have accepted the value of 125 cm^{-1} obtained calorimetrically [11].

Fluorobenzene. Symmetry is C_{2v}, $I = 0.233$ g$^3 \cdot$ cm^6. Scott's thorough investigation [12] gives assignments subsequently analyzed by Steele [13], whose interpretation we have accepted.

Orthodifluorobenzene. Symmetry is C_{2v}, $I = 0.619$ g$^3 \cdot$ cm^6. Vibration spectra of this compound were investigated in studies [14-16]. The fifth highest class a_1 frequency was assigned values of 1399 [16], 1313 [14], and 1200 cm^{-1} [15]. Force-constant calculations yield 1224 cm^{-1} [15], favoring the latter value. However, since the corresponding vibration in 1, 2, 3, 4-$C_6H_2F_4$ is assigned the 1211 cm^{-1} band [16], these assignments seem unreliable.

The fifth highest class b_2 frequency is assigned values of 1348 [16], 1294 [14], and 1252 cm^{-1} [15]. The force-constant value of 1280 cm^{-1} [15] proves the assignments [14-16] to possess frequencies of 450, 437, 597, 547, and 590 cm^{-1} (classes a_2 and b_1).

The interpretation of lowest frequencies of nonplanar vibrations requires special mention. In class a_2, the assignments are 196 [14] and 240 cm^{-1} [15], and in class b_1, 195 [16], 197 [15], and 298 cm^{-1} [14]. Force-constant calculations [10] yield 176 cm^{-1} for class a_2 and 254 cm^{-1} for class b_1, allowing a single-value assignment of vibrations (see Table 1).

$$\sum_{1}^{30} \nu^2_i = 63.60 \cdot 10^6$$

Metadifluorobenzene. Symmetry is C_{2v}, $I = 0.785$ g$^3 \cdot$ cm^6. Vibration A_{2g} (class b_2) is assigned by Ferguson [17] and Varsanyi [18] to the 1339 cm^{-1} band, but seems unreliable in terms of the inequality law. Further, this vibration is characteristic of disubstitutions in rings : p-C_6H_4FCl 1287 cm^{-1}, o-C_6H_4FCl 1288 cm^{-1}, o-$C_6H_4F_2$ 1294 cm^{-1}, m-$C_6H_4Cl_2$ 1295 cm^{-1}, and in m-$C_6H_4F_2$ the frequency of 1290 cm^{-1} seems probable.

The lowest class a_2 vibration was assigned the value of 271 cm^{-1} in study [14], and 251 cm^{-1} in works [17, 18]. Since force-constant calculations [10] yield the value of 231 cm^{-1}, we accepted the frequency of 251 cm^{-1}, Besides, in m-C_6H_4FCl this vibration is assigned the frequency of 245 cm^{-1} [18].

$$\sum_{1}^{30} \nu^2_i = 63.97 \cdot 10^6$$

Paradifluorobenzene. Symmetry is D_{2h}, $I=0.655$ g$^3 \cdot$ cm^6. This substance was most thoroughly investigated in studies [9, 14, 16, 18]; however, the assignments by these authors are somewhat inaccurate. The highest class b_1 frequency is assigned for 887 cm^{-1} in work [18], and 928 cm^{-1} in studies [9, 14, 16]. Since this vibration in p-C_6H_4FCl has a characteristic frequency of 936 cm^{-1}, the second assignment seems more correct. The value of 186 cm^{-1} assigned to the lowest class b_1 frequency [9, 16] appears unreliable. The band observed at 163 cm^{-1} [14] and the calculated frequency of 168 cm^{-1} [9] for this vibration seems more correct.

$$\sum_1^{30} \nu^2_i = 63.58 \cdot 10^6$$

1, 2, 3-*trifluorobenzene.* Symmetry is C_2, $I=1.478$ g$^3 \cdot$ cm^6. Spectral investigations have not been undertaken.

1, 2, 4-*trifluorobenzene.* Symmetry is C_2v, $I=1.711$ g$^3 \cdot$ cm^6. The assignment made in study [19] has been accepted.

$$\sum_1^{30} \nu^2_i = 51.96 \cdot 10^6$$

1, 3, 5-*trifluorobenzene.* Symmetry is D_{3h}, $I=2.267$ g$^3 \cdot$ cm^6. Steele's assignment [16] is accepted with values of inactive frequencies from study [20].

$$\sum_1^{30} \nu^2_i = 54.26 \cdot 10^6$$

1, 2, 3, 4-*tetrafluorobenzene.* Symmetry is C_2v, $I=3.174$ g$^3 \cdot$ cm^6. Vibration spectra were investigated only in work [16]. The only doubtful assignment is that of the second lowest class b_2 frequency to 310 cm^{-1}, since the corresponding vibration in C_6F_6 is 315 cm^{-1}. Unobserved class a_2 vibrations have been tentatively assigned by the present authors as frequency values :

$$\sum_1^{30} \nu^2_i = 43.85 \cdot 10^6$$

1, 2, 3, 5-*tetrafluorobenzene.* Symmetry is C_2v, $I=3.842$ g$^3 \cdot$ cm^6. According to the inequality rule, the lowest class b_1 frequencies should range within intervals of 249-215 cm^{-1} and 163-125 cm^{-1}. The latter value is assigned to 186 cm^{-1} in work [16]. We have assigned it to tentative values of 240 cm^{-1} and 144 cm^{-1}. Two unobserved class a_1 frequencies are assigned in a similar manner :

$$\sum_{1}^{30} \nu^2{}_i = 43.54 \cdot 10^6$$

1, 2, 4, 5-*tetrafluorobenzene*. Symmetry is D_{2h}, $I' = 3.637$ g$^3 \cdot$ cm^6. Spectral investigation results are given in work [17] and force-constant assignment is given in works [9, 21]. The assignment of lowest class a_2 frequency to the value of 140 cm^{-1} and exclusion of the frequency of 202 cm^{-1} from the list of fundamentals seem doubtful. Following the inequality rule, we interpret the bands of 202 and 140 cm^{-1} as minimum in classes a_2 and b_1, respectively.

$$\sum_{1}^{30} \nu^2{}_i = 43.77 \cdot 10^6$$

Pentafluorobenzene. Symmetry is C_{2v}, $I = 6.499$ g$^3 \cdot$ cm^6. The assignment of study [21] is accepted. Unobserved vibrations are assigned tentative values of frequencies.

Chemical equilibrium calculations

For complete investigation of thermodynamic functions in view of the isomerization reactions in di-, tri-, and tetrafluorobenzenes, calculation is required for fractions of position isomers in their respective mixtures. Calculations were performed according to the chemical equilibrium for reactions :

$$m\text{-}C_6H_4F_2 \rightleftharpoons o\text{-}C_6H_4F_2; \quad 1, 3, 5\text{-}C_6H_3F_3 \rightleftharpoons 1, 2, 3\text{-}C_6H_3F_3;$$
$$m\text{-}C_6H_4F_2 \rightleftharpoons p\text{-}C_6H_4F_2; \quad 1, 3, 5\text{-}C_6H_3F_3 \rightleftharpoons 1, 2, 4\text{-}C_6H_3F_3;$$
$$1, 2, 4, 5\text{-}C_6H_2F_4 \rightleftharpoons 1, 2, 3, 4\text{-}C_6H_2F_4;$$
$$1, 2, 4, 5\text{-}C_6H_2F_4 \rightleftharpoons 1, 2, 3, 5\text{-}C_6H_2F_4.$$

Experimental standard heats of formation are available in the literature [22] only for C_6H_6, C_6H_5F, o-, m-, p-$C_6H_4F_2$ and C_6F_6, indicating requirement for the calculation of the heats of formation of tri- and tetrafluorobenzenes. Variation in heats of formation for isomers is theoretically due mainly to the difference in the energy of dipole-dipole repulsion of C-F bonds, due to the large electronegativity of the F atom. However, analysis of force constants for fluorinated benzenes [23] shows strengthening of the C-F bond in C_6F_6 in comparison with other molecules. In fact, the C-F bond in C_6H_5F has an energy of 132.0 kcal/mole, and 145.0 kcal/mole in C_6F_6 [24]. Thus, if the increment of the contribution of fluorine

Table 4. Equilibrium molal fractions of place isomers

Equilibrium	T, °K										
	200	300	400	500	600	700	800	900	1000	1100	1200
x_o	0.00005	0.00102	0.00432	0.01016	0.01785	0.02658	0.03571	0.04479	0.05356	0.06186	0.06960
x_m	0.74955	0.62838	0.55952	0.51555	0.48459	0.46126	0.44285	0.42784	0.41531	0.40464	0.39540
x_p	0.25039	0.37060	0.43616	0.47428	0.49756	0.51215	0.52144	0.52737	0.53112	0.53350	0.53500
$x_{1,2,3}$	0.00002	0.00059	0.00295	0.00769	0.01447	0.02262	0.03151	0.04065	0.04972	0.05852	0.06693
$x_{1,2,4}$	0.00350	0.01603	0.03291	0.04904	0.06252	0.07320	0.08151	0.08796	0.09298	0.09691	0.10002
$x_{1,3,5}$	0.99648	0.98338	0.96414	0.94327	0.92301	0.90417	0.88608	0.87139	0.85730	0.084457	0.83306
$x_{1,2,4,5}$	0.76978	0.74097	0.72084	0.70580	0.69473	0.68690	0.68179	0.67895	0.67793	0.67843	0.68017
$x_{1,2,3,5}$	0.22888	0.25078	0.25901	0.25989	0.25640	0.25012	0.24189	0.23225	0.22162	0.21020	0.19824
$x_{1,2,3,4}$	0.00134	0.00825	0.02015	0.03431	0.04887	0.06298	0.07631	0.08880	0.10045	0.11136	0.12159

substitution is added to the heat of formation of fluorobenzene for calculating the heats of formation of subsequent substitutions, a result lower than the experimentally obtained value can be anticipated, at least for C_6H_5F and C_6F_6. Such calculations yield $\triangle h^0{}_{298.15}(C_6F_6) = -258.0$ kcal/mole, whereas the experimental value is -220.4 kcal/mole; the energy of dipole-dipole repulsion has been calculated [25] to be 22 kcal/mole for C_6F_6.

However, analysis of heats of formation for other benzene substitutions showed true values higher than the calculated values of heat of formation, not entirely explained by dipole-dipole repulsion, to evolve only on complete substitution in the ring, probably due to the abrupt change in the bond energy on complete substitution. In particular, the increment in $\triangle h^0$ with methyl substitution in benzene is about 7.00 kcal/mole for C_6H_5 (CH_3) and $C_6H_2(CH_3)_4$ and is much less for $C_6(CH_3)_6$. Thus, in isomers of fluorosubstitution, intramolecular repulsion will result, inducing different heats of formation. Using calculated values of the energy of dipole-dipole interaction [25], we determined the heats of formation of tri- and tetra-fluorobenzenes :

$\triangle h^0{}_{298.15}$	Heat of formation, kcal/mole
1, 2, 3-$C_6H_3F_3$	-112.98
1, 2, 4-$C_6H_3F_3$	-115.08
1, 3, 5-$C_6H_3F_3$	-116.88
1, 2, 3, 4-$C_6H_2F_4$	-155.280
1, 2, 3, 5-$C_6H_2F_4$	-157.280
1, 2, 4, 5-$C_6H_2F_4$	-157.480

Further verification of the heats of formation apparently requires more precise calculation of the energy of interaction in molecules, utilizing molecular orbital methods, and more precise data on the effect of substitution in the ring on the total bond energy.

The small difference in the contributions of vibration to thermodynamic functions of position isomers allow calculation of thermodynamic functions for 1, 2, 3-$C_6H_3F_3$ from the vibration spectra of 1, 3, 5-$C_6H_3F_3$. Results of calculations, performed on a Ural-2 computer, are given in Table 4.

REFERENCES

1. STEELE, D. and D. WHIFFEN. *Trans. Farad. Soc.*, **55** (3), 1959.
2. MASLOV, P. G. and YU. P. MASLOV. *Optika i Spektroskopiya*, **3** (1), 1957.

3. SUTTON. *Tables of interatomic distances.* Chem. Soc., London, Sp. Publ., 1958.

4. ALMENNINGEN, A. et al. *Acta Chem. Scand,* **18** (9), 1964.

5. VOL'KENSTEIN, M. V. et al. *Kolebaniya molekula (Molecular vibrations).* GITTL, Vols. **I-III**, 1949.

6. GODNEV, I. N. *Vychiclenie termodinamicheskikh funktsii molekulyarnym dannym (Calculation of thermodynamic functions from molecular data).* GITTL, 1956.

7. SUSHCHINSKII, M. M. and MUKHDAKHMETOV. *Optika, Spektroskopiya,* **16** (2), 1964.

8. VARGAFTIK, N. B. *Spravochnik teplofizicheskim svoistvam gazov i zhidkostei (Handbook of thermophysical properties of gases and liquids).* Fizmatgiz, Moscow, 1963.

9. STEELE, D. and D. WHIFFEN. *Trans. Farad. Soc.,* **56** (1, 8-12), 1960.

10. NONNENMACHER, G. and R. MECKE. *Spectrochim. Acta,* **17,** 1961.

11. COUNSELL, J. F. et al. *Trans. Farad. Soc.,* **61** (2), 212, 1965.

12. SCOTT, D. W. et al. *J. Am. Chem. Soc.,* **78,** 21, 5, 5457, 1956.

13. STEELE, D. et al. *J. Chem. Phys.,* **33** (4), 1242, 1960.

14. GREEN, KYNANSTON, et al. *J. Chem. Soc.,* No. 1, 473, 1963.

15. SCOTT, D. W. et al. *J. Chem. Phys.,* **38** (2), 532, 1963.

16. STEELE, D. *Spectrokhim. Acta,* **18** (7), 915, 1962.

17. FERGUSON, E. E. et al. *J. Chem. Phys.,* **21** (9), 1457-1470, 1953.

18. VARSANYI, G. *Advances Molec. Spectroscopy,* **2,** 939-953, 1962.

19. FERGUSON, E. E. et al. *J. Chem. Phys.,* **21** (10), 1727, 1953.

20. FERGUSON, E. E. et al. *J. Chem. Phys.,* **21** (5), 886, 1953.

21. STEELE, D. and D. WHIFFEN. *Spectrochim. Acta,* **16,** 368-375, 1960.

22. GOOD, W. D. and D. W. SCOTT. *Pure and App. Chem.,* **2,** 77-82, 1961.

23. DELBOUILLE, L. *J. Chem. Phys.,* **25** (1), 182, 1956.

24. DIBELER. et al. *J. Chem. Phys.,* **26** (2), 304-305, 1957.

25. COX, J. D. et al. *Trans. Farad. Soc.,* **60** (4), 653, 1964.

UDC 541.11

EXPERIMENTAL INVESTIGATION OF COMPRESSIBILITY OF FREON-12

I. I. Perel'shtein

Freon-12 is the most important refrigerating agent. The first experimental investigation of the compressibility of Freon-12 was undertaken in 1931 [1]. However, the range of measurement was limited to a pressure of 20 bar while the accuracy of measurement of specific volumes was 2-3%.

In 1955 two groups of American investigators [2, 3] experimentally attempted determination of thermal properties of Freon-12 over a wide range of the parameters of state. The measurements were obtained by a constant-volume piezometer [1, 2, 3] with the temperature-measurement instruments as described in works [2, 3] being the most accurate.

As noted by Tsoiman [4], the scatter of experimental points [2] at the isochoric and isothermal sections reaches 3%. These values were further used for formulating the equation of state, providing computation for the latest tables of thermodynamic functions of Freon-12 [5].

An analysis of work [3] indicated to the present author the favorable internal adjustment of these experimental data. As only the results of study [3] were considered reliable, additional experimental investigation of Freon-12 was undertaken with expedient variation in method from that described in work [3].

In 1964-65, in the VNI-Kh-I Institute, specific volumes of superheated vapor were measured in the positive temperature region upto 198°C and at pressures upto 85 bar. The superiority of the procedure employed, using a variable-volume piezometer, over the constant-volume piezometer procedure, is due to the possible simultaneous presentation of experimental isochoric and isothermal data, facilitating both regulation of the internal adjustment and correlation of the experimental data.

In October 1966, data of Michels and colleagues [6], obtained in the temperature range of 0-150°C, when compared to the compressibility data obtained in our laboratory, evinced agreement to within 0.12% except in the critical region, where the discrepancy is upto 0.2%.

Schematic arrangement of experimental apparatus

In our investigation, the compressibility of Freon-12 was analyzed by an apparatus which was a considerably improved version of the one described in works [7, 8] (see Figs. 1 and 2).

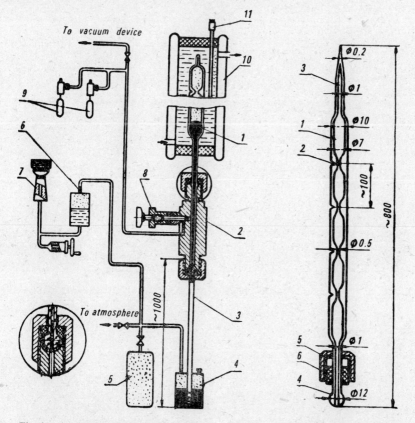

Fig. 1.   Arrangement of variable-volume piezometric apparatus.

Fig. 2.   Arrangement of piezometer.

DESCRIPTION OF FIG. 1.   The glass piezometer (1) is mounted inside the compression chamber (2).   To one side of the chamber, a flask (4), two-thirds filled with mercury, is connected through a tube (3) of length

1 m.   One end of the tube (3), which has a lateral hole, is placed in the lower portion of the flask, dipped inside mercury.

Pressure is created in the piezometer through mercury with compressed nitrogen in the cylinder (5).   Simultaneously the pressure of the compressed nitrogen is transmitted through an oil flask (6), to the standard piston manometer (7) of type MP-60, and with accuracy of class 0.05. On the other side the compression chamber is connected through a needle valve (8) to a vacuum device and to small cylinders (9), which are filled with the investigated substance.

The entire length of the piezometer is placed inside a 30-mm diameter glass tube (10) through which is pumped the thermostatting liquid (ethyl-alcohol, water, or glycerine).   Since the glass tube (10) contains a vaccum casing, the temperature variation along the tube does not exceed 0.005°C. A resistance type platinum thermometer (11) is provided inside the tube (10), at the level of the central portion of the piezometer, which is filled with the substance.

The position of the mercury meniscus inside the capillary was fixed by a cathetometer fabricated in our laboratory.   The cathetometer possesses a maximum value of 700 mm on the vertical scale.   Comparison of the cathetometer with a similar factory-produced instrument reveals its degree of accuracy to be at least 0.03 mm.   The cathetometer is directly fixed inside the compression chamber.

DESCRIPTION OF FIG. 2.   The piezometer is constructed of molybdenum glass and consists of five bulbs (1).   The volume of each bulb is approximately 5 cm^3.   The bulbs are connected through graduated capillaries (2) which assist in mercury volume determination during calibration and analysis of the substance.   The capillary (3) is soldered to the top bulb and the upper end of the capillary is extracted.   A glass ball (4), fixed to the lower end of the piezometer, is designed for hermetic sealing of the piezometer in the compression chamber.   Before fixing the ball, a protective nut (5) with a fluoroplast plug (6) is attached to the capillary of the piezometer.

For thermostatting at $T = -50$-200°C with an accuracy of 0.01 deg, a simple arrangement (see Fig. 3) was used.   The thermostatting liquid is circulated from the auxiliary thermostat (2) through a spiral of the main thermostat (1), in which the temperature is maintained constant.   The temperature of the liquid is measured by the mercury contact thermometer (3), but the contact thermometer and the heater of the main thermostat (1) are separated.   This method is used for obtaining constant temperature above room temperature.

DESCRIPTION OF FIG. 3.   For obtaining stable temperatures from room temperature upto -20°C, the thermostat (2) is cooled by refrigerating machine FAK-0.7.   Dry ice filled in the cooling bath (4) is also used (dotted line connections) to obtain temperatures upto -50°C.

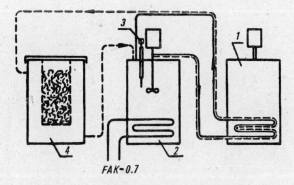

FAK-0.7

Fig. 3. Arrangement for thermostatting.

Measurement of the basic parameters

Standard platinum resistance thermometers, approved and calibrated by the Standard Committee, are used for temperature measurement. The resistance of the thermometers is measured during experimentation by the compensation method, using potentiometer PMS-48 of class A accuracy. Prior to the experiment, the resistance of the thermometer is measured at the melting point of ice on the same "compensation type" measuring apparatus on which actual measurements are subsequently performed. The deviations do not exceed 0.003 deg, indicating reliability of both the measuring device and the thermometer.

The acutal pressure p_{act} of the substance in the piezometer is determined as the algebraic sum of the pressure p_{man} measured by the piston manometer, the barometric pressure p_{bar}, the hydrostatic pressure of the oil p_{oil}, and the capillary dispersion p_d.

$$p_{act} = \left[p_{man} + p_{bar} + p_{oil} - p_{Hg} - p_d \right] \frac{g_{local}}{g_{normal}}$$

At temperatures above 150°C, the elasticity of mercury vapors is considered. The barometric pressure is read directly from the standard manometer with an accuracy of at least 0.2 mm Hg.

The influence of the hydrostatic oil pressure, calculated on the basis of the difference in level with an accuracy of 2 mm, is minimized by selection of a suitable layout of the manometer and the separating tank.

The hydrostatic pressure of mercury, p_{Hg}, is determined on the basis of difference in the levels of mercury in the piezometer and the opaque mercury tank. This level difference may be as high as 1.5-2 m; hence, measurement by a cathetometer may not be accurate.

The capillary dispersion p_d also possesses considerable magnitude due to the small cross-section of the intake (Fig. 2) (2).

The magnitude of the hydrostatic pressure of compressed nitrogen is negligibly small. A separate method was employed for accurate determination of the hydrostatic pressure of mercury and the capillary dispersion. This method is schematically presented in Fig. 4.

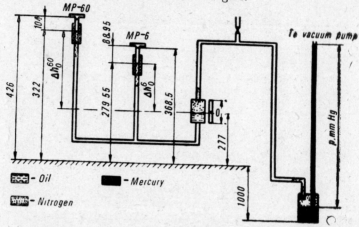

Fig. 4. Schematic arrangement of manometric graduations.

The vacuum created inside the piezometer is of the order of 10^{-3} mm Hg. By establishing the mercury meniscus in the piezometer at predetermined points, the hydrostatic pressure of mercury p_{Hg} and the capillary dispersion p_d are balanced by the pressure created by the weights on the piston manometer, together with the barometric pressure p_{bar} and the hydrostatic oil pressure p_{oil}. Hence,

$$p_{Hg}+p_d=p_{man}+p_{bar}+p_{oil}$$

Since the upper portion of the mercury column is at the experimental temperature and the lower portion is at room temperature, calibration is undertaken at different temperatures.

As an assay, the sum of the pressures $p_{Hg}+p_d$ is also determined when the piezometer is maintained exposed to atmosphere. Thus, for equilibrium,

$$p_{Hg}+p_d=p_{man}+p_{oil}$$

The values of p_{Hg} and p_d obtained by the two different methods agree well within the limits of accuracy of the manometers.

Location of the compression chamber at a height of about 1 m above the mercury tank facilitates measurement of the pressure of the substance in the piezometer of less than 1 atm by piston manometer.

The volume of the bulbs of the piezometer is determined by calibration with respect to mercury on a special apparatus described in study [8].

The quantity of the substance inside the piezometer is determined directly by weighing (on the analytical balance of the type ADV-200) the filling cylinder before and after filling the piezometer.

Experimental procedure

Calibration of the piezometer is repeated several times, and the volume of the bulbs is determined. The carefully calibrated piezometer is mounted inside the compression chamber.

Air is pumped from the mercury to be used for filling the intermediate cylinder. The mercury is periodically stirred during this procedure. After filling the intermediate cylinder with the degassed mercury, a vacuum of the order of 10^{-2} to 10^{-3} mm Hg is created in the piezometer; mercury is raised, creating a clearance separating the substance from the compressed gas.

The sum of the hydrostatic pressures of mercury and the capillary dispersion is then determined experimentally at various temperatures, and the piezometer is filled by an accurately measured quantity of the substance (see Fig. 5). A few grams of the substance are introduced into the

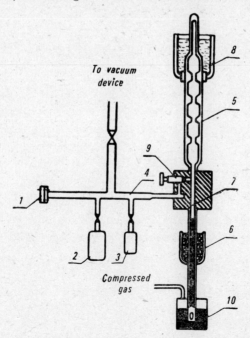

Fig. 5. Arrangement for filling the piezometer with the investigated substance.

cylinder (2) from a feeding cylinder (not shown in Fig. 5) through a connection (1) which is then closed. By repeated rotation of the substance from cylinder (2) into cylinder (3) and by simultaneous chilling, the substance is purified, liberated from the dissolved air, and is finally condensed in cylinder (2).

Following this procedure, a quantity of the substance sufficient to saturate the piezometer is condensed from cylinder (2) into cylinder (3). The saturated vapor in cylinder (2) is allowed to enter the pipe line (4), gradually at room temperature, and is then condensed in cylinder (3). Since the quantity of vapor released in each of these transfers is known, the operation is completed without loss of the substance.

Cylinder (3), thus filled by a known amount of the substance, is then disconnected and weighed on the balance several times during a 24-hr period to obtain stable data. Thereafter, cylinder (3) is connected to the charging device and the substance is transferred into the piezometer (5).

The piezometer (5) is first rinsed with freon. Then air is pumped out of it and by adding dry ice to the Dewar container (6), mercury in tube (7) is chilled. Liquid nitrogen is poured into the Dewar container (8), provided at the top of the piezometer, so that as soon as valve (9) is open, the substance in cylinder (3) is forcefully propelled into the piezometer. Following transfer of the entire substance into the piezometer, the valve (9) is closed. The substance inside the piezometer thus chilled, mercury in tube (7) is heated, thereby gradually increasing pressure, until mercury appears in the lower visible portion of the piezometer.

Liquid nitrogen from container (8) is then allowed to evaporate completely, while the temperature and pressure of the substance increase. Simultaneously, pressure of the gas in the intermediate container (10) is also increased to maintain the meniscus of mercury within the limits of the piezometer. When all portions of the piezometer attain room temperature, the pressure of the substance equals the saturation pressure. The quantity of noncondensed portions is visually estimated when condensation is completed. Since the upper portion of the piezometer consists of a capillary of 0.2 mm diameter, the volume of the noncondensed material can be estimated with sufficient accuracy.

The remainder of the substance in the charging pipe lines is recondensed into cylinder (3), which is again weighed. As the weight of the cylinder both before and after the charging operation is known, the amount of the substance in the piezometer can be calculated accurately. Repeating the operations described above in exactly reversed order following the experiment provides a double check on the readings for the weight of the substance in the piezometer.

Following this procedure, formal experimentation begins. Each reading is taken after establishment of a thermodynamic equilibrium, occurring within one or two minutes for the super-heated vapor; considerably more time is required to achieve a state of dry, saturated vapor. This state is signified by the appearance of the first drop of the condensate, as an ultrathin layer over the meniscus of mercury. With a 30-x telescopic microscope, it is possible to closely ascertain the appearance of this drop upon compression and its disappearance upon expansion. The pressure difference corresponding to the compression or expansion of the gas necessary for appearance or disappearance of the drop does not exceed 0.1%.

At each point, the excess pressure in the compression chamber is measured by the piston manometer. Simultaneous readings are taken for the barometric pressure, the height of mercury in the container, and the voltage drop over the ends of the platinum resistance thermometer. During experimentation, the meniscus of mercury is consistently maintained within the limits in the piezometer. Five isochores are obtained as a result of these measurements.

Following completion of the experiments, the upper contracted end of the piezometer is opened to check the calibration, and it is observed that even after three calibrations no residual deformation results in the piezometer.

In this procedure, it was possible to measure, with sufficient accuracy, the saturation pressure, specific volume of dry, saturated vapor, and specific volume of superheated vapor at $T = -35$ to $+200°C$ and at $p = 0.5\text{-}100$ kg/cm². Direct experimental data on the compressibility in the form of a network of isotherms and isochores were also obtained (see Table 1).

Table 1. Experimental data on compressibility

	First series of experiments				
	% at ρ, g/cm³				
t, °C	0.03890	0.04898	0.06552	0.09695	0.1889
67.47	0.8921	0.8649	0.8208	0.7396	—
78.295	0.8994	0.8740	0.8332	0.7579	—
98.42	0.9111	0.8890	0.8520	0.7871	0.6135
118.32	0.9210	0.9011	0.8690	0.8112	0.6587
134.41	0.9278	0.9098	0.8809	0.8281	0.6899
150.21	0.9339	0.9175	0.8910	0.8428	0.7169
160.35	0.9376	0.9220	0.8970	0.8515	0.7328
175.67	0.9427	0.9284	0.9055	0.8637	0.7547
197.85	0.9493	0.9365	0.9162	0.8796	0.7835

Table 1—*Continued*

t, °C	% at ρ, g/cm³				
	0.1312	0.1650	0.2206	0.3264	0.6363
88.15	0.6996	0.6321	—	—	—
98.16	0.7178	0.6548	0.5595	—	—
112.03	0.7417	0.6834	0.5969	0.4602	0.24516
112.49	0.7420	0.6842	0.5979	0.4616	—
118.575	0.7515	0.6964	0.6132	0.4830	0.27461
134.57	0.7731	0.7234	0.6486	0.5305	—
160.18	0.8041	0.7614	0.6974	0.5967	0.44833

In such an experiment, the critical parameters could be easily measured, the critical temperature determined by successive estimations along the isotherms [8], and the critical pressure simultaneously measured by determination of the critical temperature using isothermal compression and expansion, and by Al'stul's method [8].

Experimental results of analysis

According to the procedure in study [9], our experimental data and the data of study [3] are represented by the following equation of state :

$$\sigma = \alpha_0 + \alpha_1\, \tau + \beta\, \psi,$$

where $\sigma = \dfrac{p\, v}{R\, T_{cr}}$; $\alpha_0, \alpha_1, \beta$ are functions of $\omega = \dfrac{v_{cr}}{v}$; ψ is a function of $\tau = \dfrac{T}{T_{cr}}$.

The experimental data were initially averaged in terms of $\dfrac{\sigma - \tau}{\omega}$ and ω along the isotherms. The second and third virial coefficients, determined graphically, are presented in the table below :

t, °C	B	C	t, °C	B	C
112	−1.1409	0.4489	145	−1.0162	0.4039
115	−1.1278	0.4439	150	−0.998	0.3972
120	−1.1078	0.4364	155	−0.979	0.3900
125	−1.0885	0.4293	160	−0.961	0.3825
130	−1.0706	0.4230	165	−0.944	0.3750
135	−1.0525	0.4166	170	−0.927	0.3671
140	−1.0347	0.4104			

Values of the second and third virial coefficients were substituted in the equations of the basic isotherms : critical (112°C), 130°C and 155°C. The initial equation is :

$$\sigma = \tau + B\omega + C\omega^2 + D\omega^3 + E\omega^4.$$

Coefficients D and E were calculated from σ-τ-B_{av}-ω-$C_{av}\omega^2$ and ω, drawn from the graph (see Table 2).

Table 2. Coefficients of averaged basic isotherms

t, °C	τ	B	C	D	E
112	1.000	—1.14093	0.4489	0.01932	—0.028424
130	1.0467	—1.07061	0.422985	0.019455	—0.028126
155	1.1116	—0.979188	0.389998	0.014710	—0.021014

Using the equations of the basic isotherms, the elementary functions α_0, α_1, and β were determined at length $=1$, 2, 3, 4 in the temperature function $\psi = 1/\tau^1$.

Assuming that at $\omega = 1$ the value of β is minimum, it has been determined that $l = 4$. Hence, we may finally derive :

$$\alpha_0 = -2.110380\omega + 0.746074\omega^2 + 0.436271\omega^3 - 0.60400\omega^4;$$
$$\alpha_1 = 1 + 1.086724\omega - 0.353535\omega^2 - 0.325148\omega^3 + 0.451826\omega^4;$$
$$\beta = -0.117273\omega + 0.05636025\omega^2 - 0.0918033\omega^3 + 0.124660\omega^4;$$
$$\psi = 1/\tau^4$$

with $t_{cr} = 112$°C, $p_{cr} = 41.96$ kg/cm^2, and $\rho_{cr} = 0.52$ g/cm^3.

The equation of state formulated above, characteristic for densities less than critical (used in refrigeration industry), corresponds quite well (within $\pm 0.2\%$) with our experimental data upto a temperature of 160°C and with the data of work [3].

REFERENCES

1. BUFFINGTON, R. M. and W. K. GILKEY. *Ind. Eng. Chem.*, **23** (3), 1931.
2. McHARNESS, R. C., B. J. EISEMAN and J. J. MARTIN. *Refrig. Eng.*, **63** (9), 1955.
3. KELLS, L. F., S. F. ORLEO and W. H. MEARS. *Refrig. Eng.*, **63** (9), 1955.

4. TSOIMAN, G. I. *IFZh*, No. 7, 1963.
5. *Properties of commonly used refrigerants.* ARI, 1957.
6. MICHELS, A., T. WASSENAAR, G. J. WOLKERS, C. PRINS and L. KLUNDERT. *J. Chem. Eng. Data*, **11**, (4), 1966.
7. PEREL'SHTEIN, I. I. *IFZh*, No. 12, 1962.
8. PEREL'SHTEIN, I. I. *Metody eksperimental'nogo issledovaniya termodinamicheskikh svoistv kholodil'nykh agentov* (*Methods of experimental investigation of thermodynamic properties of refrigeration agents*). Gostorgizdat, Moscow, 1963.
9. PEREL'SHTEIN, I. I. *Kholodil'naya Tekhnika*, No. 9, 1966.

UDC 541.11

VISCOSITY OF BROMINATED FREONS

Z. I. Geller, R.K. Nikul'shin and *N. I. Pyatnitskaya*

Brominated freons such as F-113B2 (CFClBr-CF$_2$Br), F-114B2 (CF$_2$ClBr-CF$_2$Br), F-12B1 (CF$_2$ClBr), F-12B2 (CF$_2$Br), F-13B1 (CF$_3$Br) are among the least investigated substances and only recently have experimental data on their thermophysical properties appeared in the literature.

Table 1. Comparison of data on viscosity of brominated freons

T, °K	$\eta \cdot 10^3$ n . sec/m^2								
	F-13B1		F-12B1		F-12B2		F-114B2		F-113B2
	[3]	[2]	[1]	[2]	[3]	[2]	[3]	[2]	[3]
313	—	—	—	—	—	—	0.620	—	1.163
303	—	—	—	—	—	—	0.680	—	1.322
293	—	—	—	—	0.513	—	0.762	0.753	—
283	—	—	—	—	0.566	—	—	—	1.793
273	—	—	—	0.397	—	0.618	—	0.980	—
263	0.255	—	0.463	—	0.697	—	1.145	—	2.616
253	0.284	—	0.496	0.485	0.779	0.760	1.339	1.310	3.175
243	0.318	—	0.593	—	0.880	—	1.604	—	—
233	0.354	—	0.634	0.661	1.003	0.960	1.922	1.820	—
223	0.393	—	0.762	—	1.152	—	2.351	—	—
218	—	0.374	—	—	—	—	—	—	—
213	0.453	0.403	1.005	0.927	1.346	1.270	2.973	—	—
218	—	0.456	—	—	—	—	—	—	—
203	0.519	0.475	—	—	1.594	—	—	—	—
193	0.610	—	—	—	—	—	—	—	—

To supplement the insufficient data on viscosity of brominated freons [1, 2] and to extend the range of parameter variation, the present authors conducted an experimental investigation to determine the viscosity of brominated freons in the liquid phase at saturation in the temperature range of +50 to −80°C. The measurements were performed on two types of viscosimeters : (a) capillary type with capillary of $d=0.3$ mm and $l=130$ mm, and (b) falling cylinder type. Both of these viscosimeters are described in detail in reference [3].

Our experimental data and those of other authors are presented in Table 1. From the table the deviations appear to be 12.5% for F-13B1, 8.5% for F-12B1, 6% for F-12B2, and 5.6% for F-114B2.

The diagram below presents a graphical analysis of the existing data using the equation

$$\ln \eta = A + \frac{B}{T},\qquad(1)$$

where A and B are constants given in the diagram below.

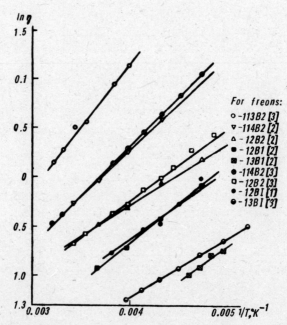

Relationship between logarithms of viscosity and the inverse of temperature.

The diagram indicates the data reported by all authors to be satisfactorily represented by linear relationships in the given coordinates; hence, it was considered impossible to favor the data of any individual author.

For data correlation and selection, the angles of inclination B, obtained at the experimental points by the least-square method, were converted by accepted methods [4] to values corresponding to the critical temperature, enabling determination of the probable numerical value of B within $\pm$ 1% and of A by using equation (1). These determinations were achieved by taking the coordinates of the points of intersection of the straight lines (see diagram) as the centers of rotation.

The values of constants A and B in equation (1) thus obtained are presented below :

	A	B
F-13B1	—3.86	649.2
F-12B1	—4.12	863.5
F-12B2	—3.06	706.3
F-114B2	—3.76	1021.9
F-113B2	—4.03	1310.0

Using these values of the constants A and B the viscosities were calculated and the averaged experimental data are presented in Table 2.

Table 2. Averaged experimental data on viscosity

T, °K	$\eta \cdot 10^3$, n . sec/m²				
	F-13B1	F-12B1	F-12B2	F-114B2	F-113B2
193	0.612	—	1.815	—	—
195	0.591	—	1.748	—	—
197	0.571	—	1.685	—	—
199	0.553	—	1.625	—	—
201	0.535	—	1.569	—	—
203	0.518	—	1.516	—	—
205	0.502	—	1.465	—	—
207	0.487	—	1.417	—	—
209	0.473	—	1.371	—	—
211	0.458	—	1.328	—	—
213	0.446	0.906	1.287	2.833	—
215	0.433	0.901	1.248	2.710	—
217	0.422	0.869	1.211	2.593	—
219	0.410	0.839	1.175	2.484	—
221	0.399	0.808	1.142	2.381	—
223	0.389	0.781	1.109	2.285	—
225	0.379	0.754	1.079	2.193	—
227	0.370	0.729	1.049	2.108	—
229	0.360	0.705	1.021	2.027	—
231	0.352	0.683	0.994	1.949	—
233	0.343	0.661	0.968	1.877	—
235	0.335	0.640	0.944	1.808	—
237	0.328	0.621	0.920	1.743	—
239	0.320	0.602	0.897	1.681	—

Table 2—*Continued*

T, °K	$\eta \cdot 10^3$, n . sec/m²				
	F-13B1	F-12B1	F-12B2	F-114B2	F-113B2
241	0.313	0.584	0.876	1.622	—
243	0.306	0.567	0.855	1.567	3.889
245	0.299	0.551	0.835	1.514	3.721
247	0.293	0.536	0.815	1.463	3.563
249	0.287	0.521	0.797	1.416	3.415
251	0.281	0.507	0.779	1.370	3.275
253	0.275	0.493	0.762	1.327	3.142
255	0.270	0.480	0.746	1.285	3.017
257	0.265	0.468	0.730	1.246	2.899
259	0.260	0.456	0.714	1.208	2.787
261	0.255	0.444	0.699	1.173	2.681
263	0.250	0.433	0.685	1.138	2.581
265	—	—	0.671	1.105	2.486
267	—	—	0.658	1.074	2.395
269	—	—	0.645	1.044	2.309
271	—	—	0.633	2.015	2.228
273	—	—	0.621	0.987	2.150
275	—	—	0.609	0.961	2.077
277	—	—	0.598	0.935	2.006
279	—	—	0.587	0.911	1.940
281	—	—	0.577	0.887	1.876
283	—	—	0.567	0.865	1.815
285	—	—	0.557	0.843	1.757
287	—	—	0.547	0.822	1.702
289	—	—	0.538	0.802	1.649
291	—	—	0.529	0.783	1.598
293	—	—	0.520	0.764	1.550
295	—	—	0.512	0.747	1.503
297	—	—	0.504	0.729	1.459
299	—	—	0.496	0.713	1.417
301	—	—	0.488	0.697	1.376
303	—	—	0.481	0.681	1.337
305	—	—	0.473	0.666	1.300
307	—	—	0.466	0.652	1.264
309	—	—	0.459	0.638	1.229
311	—	—	0.453	0.625	1.196
313	—	—	0.446	0.612	1.165

REFERENCES

1. KINSER, R. Viscosity of several fluorinated hydrocarbons in the liquid phase. M. S. Thesis, Purdue University, 1965.
2. LILIOS, N. Viscosity of several liquid refrigerants at atmospheric pressure. M. S. Thesis, Purdue University, 1957.
3. NIKUL'SHIN, R. K. *Kholodi'naya Tekhnika,* No. 11, 1966.
4. KARAPET'YANTS, M. Kh. *Metody gravnitel'novo rashcheta fiziko-khimicheskikh svoistv (Methods of comparative calculations of physicochemical properties).* Moscow, Nauka, 1965.

UDC 541.11

EXPERIMENTAL DETERMINATION OF THE COEFFICIENT OF THERMAL CONDUCTIVITY OF VAPORS OF N-ALKANES, SPIRITS AND ACIDS

A. A. Tarzimanov and *V. E. Mashirov*

Contemporary theories on thermal conductivity of complex organic compounds have thus far not provided sufficiently reliable results; hence, experimental investigations are required.

Considering the extensive and experimentally unamenable variety of organic compounds, selection of materials and methods for their investigation is complicated. Of greatest interest are those substances whose composition and structure undergo regular changes in series. These properties are observed in members of homologous series differing in composition only by the number of CH_2 groups.

Investigation of the coefficient of thermal conductivity of organic compounds belonging to certain homologous series has been conducted at the Kazan Chemical and Technological Institute. This investigation has assisted in establishing certain laws of behavior of thermal conductivity of substances in the liquid state [1].

Measurement of thermal conductivity λ of vapors of these compounds, particularly near atmospheric pressure, is another interesting objective in investigation, and the following three series have been selected :

(1) The normal limiting hydrocarbons or N-alkanes : nonpolar substances of the general formula C_nH_{n+2}.

(2) The normal limiting monatomic alcohols : polar substances of the general formula $C_nH_{2n+1}OH$.

(3) The normal limiting monobasic acids : highly polar substances of the general formula $C_nH_{2n+1}COOH$.

The objectives of our experiment were to cover as wide a range of molecular weight variation as possible and to further investigate those compounds likely to exhibit anomalous λ variation.

Determination of the thermal conductivity of N-alkanes has been attempted [2–13]. These investigations were primarily concerned with the lowest members of each series. N-alkanes containing more than eight carbon atoms in one molecule have not been investigated, hence experiments were undertaken by the present authors mainly on the higher alkanes : heptane C_7H_{16}, hendecane $C_{11}H_{24}$, tetradecane $C_{14}H_{30}$, hexadecane $C_{16}H_{34}$, and octadecane $C_{18}H_{38}$. Thermal conductivity measurements for substances with molecules containing more than 18 carbon atoms were unfeasible, since these substances decompose at temperatures above the boiling point and at atmospheric pressures.

Experimental data regarding the thermal conductivity of N-alcohols [6, 8, 10, 14, 15] are available upto $n < 5$ (anyl alcohol, pentanol), mainly for a limited temperature range (upto 130°C). Moreover, in the only work including all the alcohols from methyl to amyl [15], the experimental pressure did not exceed 120 mm Hg, judged from the given graphs. This should be considered very low because λ is strongly dependent on pressures near the boiling point.

Hence, our work involves measurement of thermal conductivity of the following N-alcohols : methyl alcohol CH_3OH, ethyl alcohol C_2H_5OH, propyl alcohol C_3H_7OH, butyl alcohol C_4H_9OH, heptyl alcohol $C_7H_{15}OH$, and decyl alcohol $C_{10}H_{21}OH$.

There are virtually no experimental data on the thermal conductivity of normal, limiting monobasic acids, and since these substances form compounds of the type $(C_nH_{2n+2}O_2)_2$, investigation of λ of this class of organic compounds is of special interest. We measured the thermal conductivity of the following acids :

acetic acid CH_3COOH, propynic acid C_2H_5COOH, butyric acid C_3H_7COOH, capronic acid $C_5H_{11}COOH$, caprylic acid $C_7H_{15}COOH$, undecanic acid $C_{10}H_{21}COOH$

Investigation of the thermal conductivity of alcohols and acids with a still higher molecular weight ($n > 11$) was impossible due to the thermal instability of these compounds at temperatures above the normal boiling point.

The measurements were performed on an apparatus using the "hot wire" method. The measuring tube and other components of the apparatus were constructed of molybdenum glass. Dimensions of the tube were as follows : measuring portion, $l = 133.00$ mm; central wire, $d = 0.100$ mm; capillary, $d_{inner} = 3.163$ mm and $d_{outer} = 4.40$ mm respectively; and eccentricity $= 0.07$ mm.

The internal resistance thermometer (hot wire) was centrally positioned with short cylinders. Tension in the central wire was created with a 3.9 g platinum weight. The measuring tube was placed inside a glass cylinder where a particular pressure of the vapor of the compound could be maintained upto 1 atm. The pressure was varied from 20 mm Hg to atmospheric and was measured by a mercury manometer. The temperature was maintained constant during measurement with three electric resistance heaters wound on a copper thermostat.

At all temperature levels investigated the internal resistance thermometer was calibrated with respect to the external thermometer, precalibrated with respect to a standard resistance thermometer. A potentiometer circuit was used for resistance measurement.

At each temperature, measurements were performed at one or two values of the heater current, while the temperature drop across the gas layer Δt_r was within the limits of 3-33°C. Under our experimental conditions the product of the Gr·Pr criteria was considerably below 1000, contraindicating convection.

While calculating the values of λ, corrections were undertaken to compensate for the heat radiation from the ends of the hot wire, for temperature drop in the walls of the capillary, for measurement of geometrical dimensions at higher temperatures, and for the influence of eccentricity. The total correction did not exceed 4–6%. Probable error in our experimental results was 1.5% and the scatter of the points near the average curves was within 1%.

Initially, the thermal conductivity of air at 20-420°C and of water at room temperature was measured. These measurements agreed with results of other investigators.

The reactants used were either "chemically pure" or "pure". Purities of acetic acid, methyl, and ethyl alcohols were especially noted. Acetic acid used was labeled "high purity—V-3", while the methyl and ethyl alcohols were subjected to special treatment in the chemical laboratory, where water and other impurities were removed, leaving 99.97% base material in the methyl and ethyl alcohols. Since these alcohols and acetic acid are hydrophilic, care was taken to remove water from the apparatus.

The tables presented below and subsequently in this paper give the results of our experiments covering a temperature range of 67-481°C at various pressures ($p \leqslant 1$ atm). Selection of the minimum temperature of each experiment was determined by the boiling point of the substance.

On the basis of parameter readings and the analysis of results, it may be postulated that at atmospheric pressure and at temperatures above 350-370°C, the high alkanes ($n > 10$), alcohols, and acids ($n > 7$) decompose appreciably. In our studies, such a disintegration was indicated by a number of signs : (1) by change in the residual pressure following each experiment, (2) by change in Δt_r with time despite constant power supply, and (3) by decrease in Δt_r with reduction in pressure.

The decrease in Δt_r with reduction in pressure in *n*-tetradecane disintegration at $t=381.5°C$ is shown in the table below (power supplied to the heating element was constant).

p, mm Hg	t_r, °C
741	14.44
352	14.22
202	13.88
64	9.59

At temperatures higher than that of decomposition of the substance, values of λ were measured repeatedly at relatively moderate temperatures, and the results appear to be considerably high. This phenomenon can also be used to estimate the thermal stability of organic compounds. We observed the acids to be the least stable of the compounds which we investigated.

While measuring the thermal conductivity of gases at low pressure ($p \leqslant 1$ atm) it is essential to consider the possibility of a sudden temperature change on the gas-solid boundary (wire). Theoretically, the magnitude of this sudden change depends upon the pressure, temperature, the physical properties of the gas, the geometrical dimensions of the instruments, and the "coefficient of accommodation". Moreover, the magnitude of change is lower for higher molecular weights and higher for higher temperatures. Study of this sudden temperature change is further complicated by the considerable variation in the magnitude of the coefficient of thermal conductivity of some organic compounds at $p \leqslant 1$ atm, especially at temperatures near the boiling point.

Fig. 1 presents experimental data on the dependence of thermal conductivity of N-heptane pressure along the isotherms, and shows that with an increase in temperature the slope of the isotherms decreases; dependence of λ on pressure becomes less prominent. At $t=220°C$ the thermal conductivity of heptane remains practically unaffected by a pressure change from 54 to 741 mm Hg. At a still higher temperature ($t=317°C$), an increase in λ again seems to appear with increasing pressure, but here the increase is probably due to the influence of the above-mentioned sudden temperature change. In view of this, the uppermost isotherm is shown by a dotted line and is considered provisional. Judging from the slope of the isotherm at 317°C, magnitude of the temperature change is negligible and at lower temperatures it can be expected to be still smaller. Consequently, it may be concluded that at $t \leqslant 220°C$ the influence of the sudden temperature change ($p > 100$ mm Hg) for

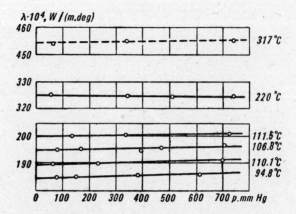

Fig. 1.   Dependence of λ of N-heptane on pressure along
the isotherms at different temperatures.

heptane is negligible.   This is especially valid for N-alkanes with higher
molecular weights.

The influence of the sudden temperature change above 317°C could
not be studied due to the thermal decomposition of the compounds at low
pressures.

A similar situation is observed in experiments with methyl alcohol
and propyl alcohol (see table near conclusion of present work).   Fig. 2
shows a rapid increase in λ with increasing pressure near the boiling
point (isotherms 67°C and 73°C).   At higher temperatures this effect is
reduced and at $t=121.7$°C there is almost no change in λ with p.   Hence

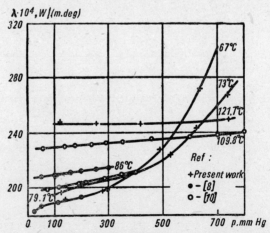

Fig. 2.   Dependence of λ of methyl alcohol on pressure along
the isotherms at different temperatures.

t may be assumed that at $t \leqslant 122°C$ and $p=100\text{-}740$ mm Hg, the influence of the sudden temperature changes must be negligible, and that the $\lambda\text{-}p$ relationship in acids is similarly unaffected by the sudden temperature change.

Let us discuss in somewhat greater detail the relationship between λ and p at near-atmospheric pressure. It is generally assumed that λ depends little on p at near-atmospheric or atmospheric pressures. For instance, the value of thermal conductivity of gases at 0.5 atm or lower is assumed to be identical to that at 1 atm. This assumption to some extent applies for nonpolar substances such as the N-alkanes (see Fig. 1). In polar substances, however, especially at temperatures near boiling point, a significant variation of λ is observed with an increase in pressure. For example, with increase from 139 to 639 mm Hg at $t=67°C$, the value of λ for methyl alcohol (boiling temperature$=64.5°C$) increases by 42% (Fig. 2). As the temperature increases (at increasing distances from the saturation curve) dependence of λ on p (at $p \leqslant 1$ atm) rapidly loses significance and at $\approx 120°C$ this effect is very low.

In the region near the saturation curve, neglect of the influence of p on λ would result in considerable error. A comparison of the tabulated data for methyl alcohol, based on Shushpanov's experiments at pressures of 100-120 mm Hg [15], with our data, obtained at $t=71.9°C$ and $p=741$ mm Hg, shows the data of work [16] lower by 28%.

Increased dependence of λ on p is observed in acetic acid. As is evident from Fig. 3, the thermal conductivity of acetic acid at $t < 150°C$ and $p=20\text{-}750$ mm Hg increases initially to about 2.5 times the original value and then decreases somewhat; thus, certain maximum values exist, and are almost identical for the isotherms 121°C, 131°C, and 151.5°C. At still higher temperatures, a considerable increase in λ is observed with

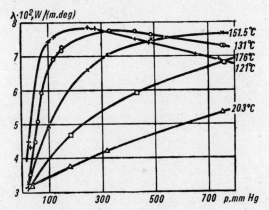

Fig. 3. Dependence of λ of acetic acid on pressure along the isotherms at different temperatures.

increasing pressures, though its magnitude is less; hence, it might be assumed that these isotherms have maximum values at pressures greater than 1 atm.

A similar pattern in λ-p variation at different temperatures has been observed in hydrogen fluoride [17], where, with pressure increase from 20 to 500 mm Hg, the magnitude of λ increases by about 30 times, passing through a maximum. Frank and Spalthoff attributed this irregular behavior to the presence of $(HF)_6$ complexes varied with temperature and pressure; however, due to the concentration gradient of the complexes in the gas, heat transfer occurred primarily due to the chemical reactions rather than conductivity.

Figs. 4-6 present experimental data for N-alkanes, alcohols, and acids at $p=1$ atm. For temperatures at which considerable decomposition initially occurs, the curves are shown by dotted lines. Figs. 4-6 indicate that with increasing molecular weight M, there is a decrease in the thermal conductivity for homologous series at all temperatures, in accordance with the molecular-kinetic theory of gases.

An analysis of the experimental values of λ presented in the table and in Fig. 4, as well as data on the lower N-alkanes [16], indicates that with increasing molecular weight of the compounds, the dependence of λ on t becomes more prominent. For example, with temperature increase

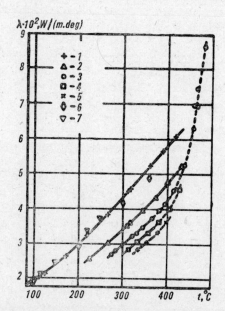

Fig. 4.   Variation of λ with temperature for N-alkanes at $p=1$ atm.
1—*Heptane;* 2—*Undecane;* 3—*Tetradecane;* 4—*Hexadecane;*
5—*Octadecane;* 6—*Heptane* [3]; 7—*Heptane* [6].

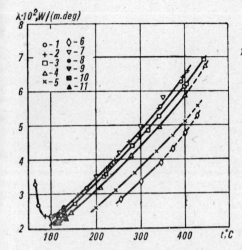

Fig. 5. Variation of λ with temperature for alcohols at $p=1$ atm.

1—CH_3OH; 2—C_2H_5OH; 3—C_3H_7OH;
4—C_4H_9OH; 5—$C_7H_{15}OH$; 6—$C_{10}H_{21}OH$;
7—C_2H_5OH [14]; 8—CH_3OH [15];
9—C_2H_5OH [15]; 10—C_3H_7OH [15];
11—C_4H_9OH [15].

Fig. 6. Variation of λ with temperature for acids at $p=750$ mm Hg.

1—CH_3COOH; 2—C_2H_5COOH;
3—C_3H_7COOH; 4—$C_5H_{11}COOH$;
5—$C_{10}H_{21}COOH$; 6—$C_7H_{15}COOH$.

from 220 to 380°C, the thermal conductivity of ethane increases 1.6 times, that of heptane 1.66 times, and that of undecane 1.71 times.

In experimentation with alcohols and especially with acids (Figs. 5 and 6), at near-boiling temperature an irregular variation of λ with temperature is observed. This is apparently due to the presence of complexes of the type $(C_nH_{2n+1}COOH)_m$ and $(C_nH_{2n+1}OH)_2$ with the monomers in the vapors of alcohols and acids.

A general theoretical expression [18] has been obtained for the thermal conductivity of chemically reactive gas mixtures. The thermal conductivity of HF has been calculated in accordance with the reaction $(HF)_6=6HF-Q$, where Q is the heat of the reaction. Butler and Brokaw [18] state that the thermal conductivity of a reactive gas mixture can be expressed in the form $\lambda_c=\lambda_f+\lambda_R$, where λ_f is the thermal conductivity of an equivalent "chemically frozen" gas mixture, while λ_R is the thermal conductivity due to the chemical reaction. Whereas λ_f increases with increasing temperature, λ_R is affected by a number of factors including the concentration gradient. The peak observed in the curve corresponding to the $\lambda=f(t)$ for acetic acid (Fig. 6) at $p=750$ mm Hg may be explained by a change in the concentration gradient of the dimers of the vapor. Preliminary calculations indicate that the concentration gradient increases with temperature increase upto 150°C, thereafter decreasing with rise in temperature. Such complex behavior of λ with change in temperature is observed upto 300°C. With increasing molecular weight of acids this effect is less prominent, but still significant even at $n=10$.

The irregular variation of λ for methyl and ethyl alcohols near 120°C (boiling point) is probably due also to the presence of complexes, though their concentration is less than in acids, and hence the λ variation is less prominent.

The experimental data obtained on λ of vapors of organic compounds enable certain conclusions regarding the change in thermal conductivity at constant molecular weight for different structures. Fig. 7 shows our data and those of other investigators [16] on the relationship between λM and M along the isotherms for vapors of N-alkanes, alcohols, and acids. Only one isotherm (at 350°C) relates to acids, since this is the only temperature where the association of molecules is absent and the behavior of thermal conductivity is not distorted by chemical reactions. Fig. 7 indicates that for all the three homologous series λM increases with increase in M. The difference in thermal conductivity of lower alcohols and acids from N-alkanes of the same molecular weight is probably due to their different polarities (viz., N-alkanes are nonpolar compounds while alcohols and especially acids are highly polar). With increasing values of M the influence of OH and COOH groups on λ decreases, while at

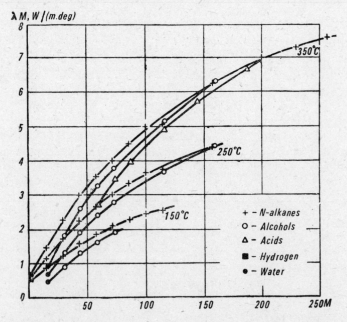

Fig. 7. Relationship between λM and the molecular weight along isotherms.

$M \geqslant 150$ the thermal conductivity of higher alcohols and acids becomes practically equal to that of the N-alkanes. It is interesting to note that at the beginning of the curve for N-alkanes there are points corresponding to λM of hydrogen, while for alcohols, there are points corresponding to λM of water. The hypothesis assuming a linear variation of λM with increasing molecular weight of the compound with a CH_2 group addition [15] has not been confirmed (see Fig. 7).

In Figs. 2, 4, and 5 we have presented our data on λ as well as data obtained by other investigators. A comparison of the experimental data on N-heptane shows the results by Gulubev and Naziev [3], using the method based on a regular schedule, to yield somewhat lower values at $t > 300°C$. The discrepancy between our data and those of work [3] is 4-6%. The results in work [6] are higher than our values by only 1-2% at all temperatures, suggesting satisfactory agreement within the limits of experimental accuracy. Fig. 2 also presents data due to Lambert [8] and Vines [10] along the isotherms in close agreement with our data. The isotherm for 66°C in work [8] coincides with our value at 67°C. Fig. 5 shows other experimental values of λ [14, 15]. At $t > 120°C$, when λ is practically independent of p, agreement is close and only at $t = 350°C$, Kerzhentsev's values are 3% higher than ours.

The results obtained by Shushpanov [15] deserve greater attention. He measured thermal conductivity of alcohols at $p \leqslant 120$ mm Hg and $t \leqslant 130°C$. In this region, as mentioned earlier, a strong influence of p on λ is observed which cannot be explained simply by the sudden temperature change. Fig. 8 presents an example, with the isotherm for 67°C for CH_3OH with coordinates $\triangle t_r$-$1/p$. The temperature drops of $\triangle t_r$ at 1 atm and $\triangle t$, obtained by extrapolation to $1/p = 0$ (dotted line), differ considerably. Using the value $\triangle t$ for calculating the thermal conductivity would result in considerably lower values of λ. This deviation increases as the saturation curve is approached.

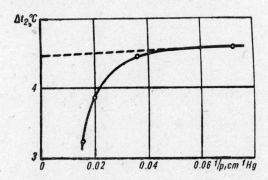

Fig. 8. Variation of the temperature drop $\triangle t$ in the gas layer with pressure at $t = 67°C$ and at constant power supply.

Table

Experimental values of thermal conductivity of vapors of organic compounds.

p mm Hg	Δt_r, °C	t, °C	$\lambda \cdot 10^4$ W/m . deg	p mm Hg	Δt_r, °C	t, °C	$\lambda \cdot 10^4$ W/m . deg
N-heptane				729	17.40	356.7	333.4
612	3.36	94.8	185.9	729	16.03	380.4	364.5*
382	3.37	94.8	185.5	729	14.60	402.2	404.8*
153	3.38	94.8	184.9	729	12.99	424.8	460.4*
80	3.39	94.8	184.3	N-tetradecane			
700	3.31	100.1	191.3	719	19.78	275.8	270.6
233	3.33	100.1	190.1	719	32.40	283.7	278.6
65	3.34	100.1	189.6	692	28.44	329.1	328.2
704	4.81	106.4	197.0	686	17.44	322.3	321.4
470	4.85	106.4	195.8	733	17.33	345.4	347.2
392	4.88	106.4	194.8	733	16.20	367.2	375.3
167	4.88	106.4	195.0	741	14.44	381.5	397.7*
79	4.89	106.4	194.7	733	14.84	393.0	413.4*
726	4.78	111.5	201.2	733	13.64	413.2	453.5*
337	4.80	111.5	200.5	733	11.92	433.6	521.9*
137	4.81	111.5	200.0	733	9.92	457.0	631.8*
741	25.18	123.9	211.8	733	14.77	462.2	745.9*
741	21.08	170.9	264.9	733	3.49	455.0	693.1*
741	17.97	218.0	323.6	733	12.72	481.2	867.0*
741	15.55	265.4	386.2	726	8.57	463.5	692.2*
741	13.62	312.4	452.5				
741	12.06	361.8	522.1	N-octadecane			
741	11.26	389.8	564.8	720	21.49	333.9	284.2
741	10.55	419.0	607.7	720	20.28	354.4	304.9
741	3.89	414.7	604.4	720	19.02	374.5	327.6*
741	17.58	219.5	324.7	720	17.46	393.6	359.9*
511	17.74	219.9	324.2	720	22.77	336.2	287.4
341	17.73	220.4	324.7	720	21.37	356.5	308.6
54	17.73	220.4	324.7	720	19.88	376.5	333.6*
743	13.38	317.0	455.4	720	18.47	394.2	361.3*
340	13.46	317.1	452.4				
64	13.55	317.2	449.3	Ethyl alcohol			
N-undecane				708	24.63	104.0	236.2
740	20.45	224.4	255.3	743	20.84	163.4	298.5
740	17.83	266.1	301.4	744	17.18	227.0	380.7
740	15.46	312.6	356.3	745	13.37	276.6	449.8
740	17.43	313.7	358.8	745	11.71	339.9	548.8
740	8.37	308.2	351.4	745	10.24	393.5	641.8
740	16.04	343.4	394.3	746	8.46	451.1	791.5*
740	14.84	371.4	430.9	745	21.29	124.6	255.0
740	13.55	399.9	475.6*	745	15.17	240.6	399.9
740	12.45	428.8	521.7*	745	11.71	340.4	548.4
N-hexadecane				746	9.97	405.4	659.6
729	19.92	311.3	283.4	746	5.20	88.7	235.3
729	18.64	333.3	307.6	746	22.73	101.4	235.6
				746	19.30	161.7	296.5

Table—*Continued*

p mm Hg	Δ t_r, °C	t, °C	λ·10⁴ W/m·deg	p mm Hg	Δ t_r, °C	t, °C	λ·10⁴ W/m·deg
747	16.02	221.7	376.5		N-heptyl alcohol		
	N-propyl alcohol			740	23.03	199.1	259.2
				740	20.01	243.0	308.6
430	23.68	116.0	229.7	740	17.61	288.2	361.3
745	20.93	151.9	271.9	740	15.45	335.0	421.0
310	21.18	153.1	269.1	740	14.08	373.0	469.2
158	21.24	153.5	267.9	740	13.01	402.3	511.7
743	17.20	215.1	350.1	740	12.10	428.9	554.2*
747	14.27	280.2	441.0		N-decyl alcohol		
747	12.30	339.8	525.9				
747	10.76	399.9	615.2	740	22.06	253.0	281.2
747	9.66	443.1	691.5*	740	18.94	300.5	336.8
731	22.20	120.8	239.9	740	16.54	344.0	393.2
732	16.12	222.1	364.5	740	15.24	372.4	431.1*
732	12.78	315.1	486.0	740	13.84	401.5	479.6*
732	10.33	402.6	623.0	740	12.66	429.0	528.3*
	Methyl alcohol				Acetic acid		
				749	7.64	134.0	737.7
741	3.35	71.9	267.5	749	9.13	182.6	649.9
531	4.00	72.6	223.4	750	14.68	237.4	421.0
302	4.41	73.0	202.3	750	15.82	285.9	401.0
645	3.68	73.0	243.6	750	14.48	237.0	424.5
163	4.54	73.0	197.0	750	9.48	185.0	624.1
639	3.25	66.4	272.1	750	7.61	134.4	737.2
494	3.87	66.8	228.0	750	4.85	132.0	729.6
277	4.45	67.4	197.8	317	4.59	132.0	769.6
139	4.59	67.4	192.2	154	4.93	132.0	715.8
743	21.28	121.5	250.3	78	5.96	132.4	591.2
414	21.67	121.7	246.0	49	7.79	133.5	452.1
256	21.81	121.7	247.0	750	12.01	209.9	500.2
122	21.74	121.7	247.8	753	15.75	287.7	399·2
741	22.11	100.5	234.9	752	14.74	337.6	435.7
742	18.01	178.6	314.0	752	13.39	387.6	486.0
743	15.36	232.3	384.8	752	10.51	436.3	619.7*
743	13.07	293.9	470.3	752	4.73	130.0	730.8
744	11.67	341.1	552.7	484	4.53	130.0	764.5
744	10.28	389.2	628.1	326	4.47	130.0	775.5
	N-butyl alcohol			154	4.78	130.0	723.9
				59	6.78	132.2	509.4
741	22.97	142.2	244.0	29	9.38	133.9	367.7
741	18.62	208.5	320.1	754	4.64	151.3	766.9
741	15.30	276.0	408.6	732	4.90	121.5	692.0
741	12.95	341.8	494.8	474	4.58	121.5	740.5
741	11.24	399.6	588.9	32	11.48	206.0	318.6
741	9.94	445.7	676.0	271	4.36	121.5	779.8

Table—*Continued*

p mm Hg	Δt_r, °C	t, °C	$\lambda.10^4$ W/m . deg	p mm Hg	Δt_r, °C	t, °C	$\lambda.10^4$ W/m . deg
122	4.49	121.5	756.2	740	15.30	285.7	406.8
29	7.81	123.6	434.0	740	13.71	343.0	465.6
753	4.62	150.3	766.2	740	12.59	388.4	515.9
478	4.72	150.5	749.4	740	11.01	435.4	598.3
318	5.01	150.8	705.5		Butyric acid		
98	7.13	152.5	495.0				
23	10.71	155.0	328.5	747	12.27	182.5	465.2
648	4.77	121.0	705.5	747	15.86	249.4	379.8
422	4.49	121.0	751.0	747	15.32	304.6	404.8
246	4.30	121.0	784.7	747	13.75	357.1	460.0
102	4.54	121.5	742.6	747	12.46	400.3	513.8
23	7.44	123.4	452.1	747	11.39	433.8	567.1*
423	4.40	131.0	776.8		Capronic acid		
265	4.44	131.1	766.9				
119	4.96	131.2	688.9	742	17.68	228.1	337.2
753	4.58	151.5	767.9	742	16.93	294.4	367.6
541	4.64	151.8	757.7	742	15.36	342.6	414.0
245	5.32	152.5	660.3	742	14.27	371.3	449.3*
753	5.28	176.4	685.1	742	13.31	400.7	487.8*
425	6.12	176.9	590.3	742	12.16	429.7	538.6*
183	7.72	178.0	467.3		Caprylic acid		
27	11.28	180.4	318.4				
754	6.90	203.0	534.9	740	19.08	264.6	315.4
316	8.72	204.4	423.5	740	17.29	315.5	359.9
176	9.91	205.4	372.2	740	15.30	364.2	415.7*
750	10.14	195.4	570.6	740	13.71	398.1	467.6*
750	13.73	233.3	432.8	740	11.96	435.7	541.9*
750	15.30	273.6	397.5		Undecanic acid		
750	14.70	322.2	423.5				
	Propynic acid			740	19.34	298.1	316.7
				740	17.84	345.0	351.9*
				740	16.54	371.8	383.6*
740	9.53	164.1	595.9	740	15.07	401.6	424.1*
740	13.68	220.6	437.6	740	13.57	426.6	474.6*

* Values marked (*) indicate that at those values of λ decomposition is observed.

Since the inclination of the dotted line in Fig 8 is quite gradual and the experiments [15] were conducted at $p=20$-120 mm Hg, the tabulated values due to Shushpanov for alcohols should be considered as values of λ obtained at $p\approx120$ mm Hg. With this condition, the thermal conductivity of methyl alcohol [15] agrees closely with the value obtained in the present work. The tabulated data of studies [8, 10] for λ of methyl alcohol are extrapolated to $p=0$ and hence are not shown in Fig. 5.

A comparison of our results with the data of other authors shows satisfactory agreement provided the influence of pressure and sudden temperature change are duly considered.

REFERENCES

1. MUKHAMEDZYANOV, G. KH., A. G. USMANOV and A. A. TAPZIMANOV. Izv. Vuzov, *Neft' i gaz*, No. 9, 1963, No. 1, 1964.
2. MOSER, E. Dissertation, 1913.
3. GOLUBEV, N. F. and YA. M. NAZIEV. *Izv. AN Azerb, SSR*, Ser. Fiz.-mat. nauk, No. 5, 1961; *Trudy energ. in-ta AN Azerb. SSR*, 15, 84, 1961.
4. GEIER, H. and K. SCHÄFER. *Wärmetechnik*, 10 (4), 70, 1961.
5. CHEUNG, H., L. BROMLEY and C. R. MILKE. *AICE J.*, 8, 221, 1962.
6. ZAITSEVA, L. S. *Trudy MAI*, No. 132, 1961; No. 51, 1955.
7. LENOIR, J. M., E. W. COMINGS, W. A. JUNK, and D. E. LENG. *CEP*, 49 (10), 539, 1953; 49 (12), 2042, 1957.
8. LAMBERT, J. D., E. N. STAINES and S. D. WOODS. *Proc. Roy. Soc.*, A200 (1061). 1950; A231 (1185), 1955.
9. KEYES, F. G. Trans. ASME, 76 (5), 1954.
10. VINES, A. G. and L. A. BENNETT. *J. Chem. Phys.*, 22 (3), 360, 1954; *Austr. J. Chem.*, 6 (1), 1953.
11. SMITH, W. J., L. D. DURBIN and R. KABAYASHI. *J. Chem. Eng. Data*, 5 (3), 316, 1960.
12. KRAMMER, F. A. and E. W. COMINGS. *J. Chem. Eng. Data*, 5 (4), 1960.
13. VILIM, O. Collect., *Czech. Chem. Comm.*, 25 (4), 993, 1960.
14. KERZHENTSEV, V. V. Author's abstract of Ph. D. dissertation, Moscow State University, 1951.
15. SHUSHPANOV, P. I. *ZhETF*, 9 (7), 1939; 10 (6), 1940.
16. VARGAFTIK, N. B. *Spravochnik po teplo-fizicheskim svoistvam gazov i zhidkostei (Handbook of thermophysical properties of gases and liquids)*. Fizmatgiz, Moscow, 1963.
17. FRANCK, E. U. and W. SPALTHOFF. *Naturwiss.*, 22, 580, 1953.
18. BUTLER, J. N. and R. S. BROKAW. *J. Chem. Phys.*, 26 (6), 1636, 1957.

UDC 541.11

EXPERIMENTAL INVESTIGATION OF THERMAL CONDUCTIVITY OF ORGANIC COMPOUNDS

G. Kh. Mukhamedzyanov

Numerous liquid organic compounds are used in industry as reagents or solvents, and thermophysical data are lacking for many of these. There is no reliable method for calculation of the coefficient of thermal conductivity, the experimental measurement of which presents difficulty.

It should be considered rational to obtain certain interpolation equations for the calculation of the coefficient of thermal conductivity for various classes of organic compounds on the basis of measured values of λ of a practicable number of representatives of each homologous series, rather than for individual liquids, even over a sufficiently wide temperature range.

The following five homologous series of organic compounds were selected for investigation by the present author :

Measurements were performed at atmospheric pressure in the temperature range of 0-200°C.

Series	Range of n variation	Number of compounds studied
Limiting hydrocarbons C_nH_{2n+2}	6-24	12
Normal alcohols $C_nH_{2n+1}OH$	1-18	8
Limiting monobasic acids $C_nH_{2n+1}COOH$	3-18	9
Complex esters of limiting monobasic acids $C_nH_{2n+1}COOC_nH_{2n+1}$	2-22	21
Simple esters $C_nH_{2n+1}OC_nH_{2n+1}$	8-16	7

Only "chemically pure", reagents were used in the experiments and the purity determined on the basis of refractive indices n^{20} and density $\rho_4{}^{20}$. It was assumed that the permissible small quantities of impurity, in the form of isomers or adjacent representatives of the same homologous series, could not significantly influence the magnitude of λ.

Special attention was paid to the purity of alcohols. All alcohols, except the methyl alcohol, were in a dehydrated state. Measurements were conducted with 99.5% alcohol ($\rho_4^{20} = 0.7934$; $n^{20} = 1.3296$).

The most perfect method of heated wire was used for these investigations. Care was taken to eliminate all posible errors resulting in a ±1.5% variation in the co-efficient of thermal conductivity. The control measurements of water, benzene and air, whose thermal conductivity has been studied with utmost precision, gave a deviation not exceeding ±1.0%.

The experimental results are presented in Figs. 1-3. Part of this data was published previously [1, 2]. It should be noted that data regarding complex esters (Fig. 3) are given only for methyl and butyl esters of the limiting monobasic acids.

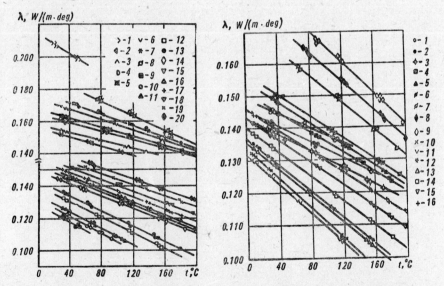

Fig. 1. Results of measurement of λ for limiting hydrocarbons and normal alcohols.

1—*methyl alcohol*; 2—*N-butyl alcohol*; 3—*N-hexyl alcohol*; 4—*N-nonyl alcohol*; 5—*N-decyl alcohol*; 6—*N-dodecyl alcohol*; 7—*N-tetradecyl alcohol*; 8—*N-octadecyl alcohol*; 9—*N-hexane*; 10—*N-heptane*; 11—*N-octane*; 12—*N-decane*; 13—*N-undecane*; 14—*N-tetradecane*; 15—*N-pentadecane*; 16—*N-hexadecane*; 17—*N-heptadecane*; 18—*N-nonadecane*; 19—*N-docosane*; 20—*N-tetracosane*.

Fig. 2. Results of measurement of λ for limiting monobasic acids and simple esters.

1—*propynic acid*; 2—*N-butyric acid*; 3—*N-valeric acid*; 4—*N-caprylic acid*; 5—*N-pelargonic acid*; 6—*N-caprynic acid*; 7—*N-myristic acid*; 8—*palmitic acid*; 9—*stearic acid*; 10—*di-butyl ester*; 11—*hexylethyl ester*; 12—*di-amyl ester*; 13—*octylethyl ester*; 14—*di-hexyl ester*; 15—*diheptyl ester*; 16—*di-octyl ester*.

Coefficients of thermal conductivity of individual compounds of the homologous series examined here have been studied by a number of investigators. Experimentation was generally limited to low-molecular-weight compounds and covered a small range of temperature. Moreover, measurements were conducted by different methods and hence resulted in varying degrees of accuracy. In order to compare the results of our measurements and those of other investigators, we used the values λ^*_{30} (Table 1) and the values λ^*_{30} obtained as a result of averaging the experimental data of other authors. In Table 1 we have indicated the degree of reliability of λ^*_{30} at $t = 30°C$ according to the data of work [3]. Table 1 shows only 1.2% maximum deviation for the majority of our data from the standard values of the coefficient of thermal conductivity λ^*_{30}. For methyl alcohol the deviations are somewhat larger. Therefore, at $t = 30°C$, in comparison with our data, the measurements by Vargaftik [7] gave higher values (+2.0%), while those by Riedel [8] were somewhat lower (−2.0%). This is pro-

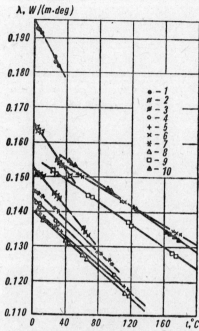

Fig. 3.   Results of measurement of λ for complex esters.

1—*methyl ester of formic acid*; 2—*methyl ester of acetic acid*; 3—*methyl ester of propynic acid*; 4—*methyl ester of valeric acid*; 5—*methyl ester of capronic acid*; 6—*methyl ester of stearic acid*; 7—*N-butyl ester of formic acid*; 8—*N-butyl ester of propynic acid*; 9—*N-butyl ester of palmitic acid*; 10—*N-butyl ester of stearic acid*.

bably related to the water content in the alcohol. Vargaftik's data were obtained with 99% purity alcohol, while Riedel's data were obtained with 99.7%. Our data were obtained with 99.5% purity.

Among the limiting hydrocarbons of normal structure, N-hexane, N-heptane, and N-octane have been investigated to a considerable extent. Study [1] gives a comparison of our data on N-heptane with those of other authors, indicating our data to closely agree with those of Filippov [3], Frontas'ev and Gusakov [9]. Data of Briggs [10], obtained by the coaxial cylinder method, evinced less agreement, whereas data of Golubev and Naziev [11], using the standard schedule method for N-heptane, N-octane, and other limiting hydrocarbons, agree closely with our own values.

Table 1. Comparison of the data on coefficient of thermal conductivity

Compound, source	λ^*_{30} W/m . deg	Accuracy of λ^*_{30} in [3]	λ^*_{30} W/m . deg	$\dfrac{\lambda_{30}{}^* - \lambda_{30}}{\lambda} . 100,$ %
Ethyl ester of acetic acid [3, 4, 5, 6]	0.1436	1.5	0.1432	+0.3
Propyl ester of formic acid [3, 5]	0.1454	1.7	0.1436	+1.2
Methyl alcohol [3, 4, 5, 6, 7, 8]	0.2000	0.5	0.2039	−2.0
Butyl alcohol [3, 7, 8]	0.1512	0.3	0.1523	−0.7

The curves of $\lambda = f(t)$ presented in Figs. 1-3 show that for all the classes of organic liquids investigated, the coefficient of thermal conductivity decreases with increasing temperature.

An examination of the curves $\alpha = f(n)$, presented in Fig. 4, reveals different patterns in variation of α for "associated" and "non-associated" substances. For all "non-associated" liquids (limiting hydrocarbons, simple and complex esters), α decreases with increasing n in the molecule. For "associated" liquids (alcohols, acids), an increase in α is observed with increasing n, except in lower representatives of the homologous series of alcohols, when a sharp decline in α is observed up to the normal butyl alcohol.

For all esters—complex $(C_n H_{2n+1}COOC_n H_{2n+1})$ as well as simple $(C_n H_{2n+1}OC_n H_{2n+1})$ —with the same number of carbon molecules, irrespective of hydrocarbon radical distribution, no appreciable variation in α was observed.

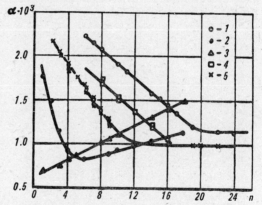

Fig. 4. Relationship between the temperature coefficient of thermal conductivity and the number of carbon atoms in the molecule of the substance n.
1—*limiting hydrocarbons;* 2—*normal alcohols;*
3—*limiting monobasic acids;* 4—*simple esters;*
5—*complex esters of carbonic acids.*

The values of the coefficient of thermal conductivity obtained for a wide variation of both n and t suggested the use of various equations giving the relationship $\lambda = f(n, t)$.

We consider a correct representation of the temperature relationship to be Vargaftik's equation [7]

$$\lambda = \frac{1}{\varepsilon} B \rho^{4/3} \tag{1}$$

and the expression [13]

$$\bar{U}_{exp} = f\left(\frac{s_1 - s}{R}\right). \tag{2}$$

Equation (1) enables determination of $\lambda = f(t)$ provided the relationship $\rho = f(t)$ is known.

We obtained favorable results from comparison of our measured values of the coefficient of thermal conductivity for 15 "non-associated" liquids ($\varepsilon = 1$) with those calculated by equation (1).

The maximum discrepancy was $\pm 3.8\%$ [14]. However, the use of equation (1) for "associated" liquids ($\varepsilon > 1$) is quite restrictive since data on ε accounting for the degree of "association" are not available.

The following equations were derived, based on analysis of our data and those of other investigators, and in accordance with equation (2) :

For λ of a "non-associated" liquid : $\lambda = \lambda_{s1}\left[1.75 - 0.75\frac{s}{s_1}\right]$ (3)

For λ of an "associated" liquid : $\lambda = \lambda_{s1}\left[1.375 - 0.375\frac{s}{s_1}\right],$ (4)

where λ and λ_{s1} are the coefficients of thermal conductivity for a state of the system corresponding to entropy s and, as far as possible, to closer values of entropy s_1.

For this generalization, the substances were selected to cover as wide a range of molecular weights as possible. For example, in hydrocarbons with a general formula n C_nH_{2n+2} the number of carbon atoms in the molecule varied from $n=6$ to $n=24$, while for alcohols it varied from $n=1$ to $n=18$.

Table 2 exemplifies comparison of the experimental data with those calculated from equations (3) and (4) for some representatives of the classes of compounds investigated, and clearly indicates the discrepancy between the calculated and experimental values to be within the limits of experimental accuracy. However, these relationships are not applicable at present for λ in higher members of the homologous series of limiting monobasic acids and complex and simple esters, due to the lack of data regarding the specific heats of these substances. Hence, the possibility of the "equivalent-state method" was considered as a basis for generalization of the experimental data.

Table 2. Comparison of the experimental values of the coefficient of thermal conductivity with those values calculated by equations (3) and (4)

Substance	t, °C	λ_{exp}	λ_{cal}	$\dfrac{\lambda_{cal}-\lambda_{exp}}{\lambda_{exp}} \cdot 100\%$
		W/m . deg		
n-decane	40	0.1305	0.1300	—0.4
n-$C_{10}H_{22}$	80	0.1209	0.1209	—
	160	0.1020	0.1028	0.8
n-tetradecane	80	0.1506	0.1506	—
n-$C_{24}H_{50}$	160	0.1373	0.1372	—0.1
	260	0.1206	0.1300	—0.5
n-octadecyl alcohol	80	0.1725	0.1728	0.1
n-$C_{18}H_{37}OH$	120	0.1649	0.1663	0.8
	200	0.1497	0.1517	1.4
n-butyric acid	0	0.1454	0.1450	—0.2
n-C_3H_7COOH	80	0.1356	0.1355	—
	160	0.1260	0.1270	0.8
Ethyl ether of acetic acid	0	0.1520	0.1518	—0.1
$CH_3COOC_2H_5$	40	0.1402	0.1408	0.4
	60	0.1346	0.1356	0.7

Fig. 5 presents the relationship between the coefficient of thermal conductivity at the relative temperature $\tau = T/T_{boil} = 0.8$ and n number of carbon atoms in the molecule. The relative temperature of 0.8 was selected to cover the entire range of the experimental results. Furthermore, for the "associated" liquids which we investigated, $\tau = 0.8$ was found to correspond, in respect to thermal conductivity, to a range of temperature sufficiently remote from the boiling point where the degree of "association" varies little with change in temperature.

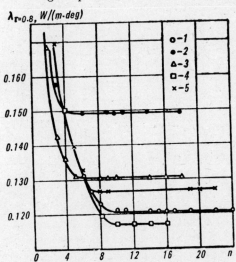

Fig. 5. Relationship between $\lambda_{\tau=0.8}$ and the number of carbon atoms in the molecule (n).

1—*limiting hydrocarbons;* 2—*normal alcohols;*
3—*limiting monobasic acids;* 4—*simple esters;*
5—*complex esters of carbonic acids.*

Fig. 5 shows that for all the lower members of the homologous series, $\lambda_{\tau=0.8}$ decreases rapidly with increasing n upto a certain critical value n and then remains constant. This critical value of n is ten for hydrocarbons, five for normal alcohols and monobasic acids, seven for the complex esters, and nine for the simple esters.

For "non-associated" liquids $\lambda_r = f(n)$ remained constant for the entire range of variation of τ. It was thus possible to obtain an equation of the form

$$\lambda = A + B(1 - \tau). \tag{5}$$

in terms of the coordinates $\dfrac{\lambda}{\lambda_{\tau=1}}$ and $\tau = \dfrac{T}{T_{boil}}$ for generalization of the experimental data and calculation of thermal conductivity of "non-associated" liquids.

The values for the constants A and B of the region for which equation (5) is applicable are as follows :

Homologous series		A	B
Limiting hydrocarbons,	$n \geqslant 10$	0.0984	0.109
Complex esters,	$n \geqslant 7$	0.1102	0.083
Simple esters,	$n \geqslant 9$	0.0984	0.092

With the hydrocarbon radicals of complex esters of the type $C_nH_{2n}COOC_nH_{2n+1}$ the carbon atoms may be distributed in different ways. We had established [2] that complex esters of various monobasic acids with an equal number of carbon atoms in the molecules have the same coefficients of thermal conductivity λ_τ; this is also true of simple esters. The equation (5) obtained above considerably simplifies calculation of λ for the classes of "non-associated" liquids. The only quantity to be determined is the boiling point temperature.

Table 3 compares the experimental values of λ with those calculated by equation (5) for N-decane and N-tetracosane.

Table 3. Comparison of the experimental values of the coefficient of thermal conductivity with values calculated by equation (5)

Compound	t, °C	$\lambda\exp$	$\lambda\mathrm{cal}$	$\dfrac{\lambda\mathrm{cal} - \lambda\exp}{\lambda_{\exp}} \cdot 100\%$
		$W/m \cdot deg$		
n-decane	40	0.1305	0.1310	+0.4
n-$C_{10}H_{22}$	80	0.1209	0.1214	+0.4
	120	0.1114	0.1115	+0.1
	160	0.1020	0.1019	—0.1
n-tetracosane	80	0.1506	0.1498	—0.5
	120	0.1440	0.1431	—0.6
n-$C_{24}H_{50}$	160	0.1373	0.1370	—0.2
	200	0.1306	0.1306	—

A comparison of the mean experimental values of the thermal expansion $\lambda_{30}*$ at 30°C obtained by different authors with those of λ_{30} calculated by equations (3-5) is given below :

	Ethyl alcohol [3-8, 15]	N-propyl alcohol [3, 5, 8]
$\lambda_{30}*$, W/m . deg	0.1663	0.1570
Degree of reliability of $\lambda_{30}*$, % [3]	0.3	0.5
λ_{30}, W/m . deg	0.1664	0.1567
$\dfrac{\lambda_{30}*-\lambda_{30}}{30}$. 100, %	−0.1	+0.2

This table shows the calculated values of λ to agree closely with the most reliable experimental values.

Tables 4-8 present adjusted values of λ based on our experimental results. For "non-associated" liquids the given values are calculated from equations (3-5). Equation (5) is not considered applicable for calculations in lower members of series investigated, since this would require correction for n and for "associated" liquids, with correction for the influence of "association" of molecules. With these corrections, equation (5) may be used for calculation of λ of organic compounds covering the entire range of liquid state.

Table 4. Coefficients of thermal conductivity of saturated

Hydrocarbon	$\lambda \cdot 10^4$ at t, °C								
	—80	—60	—40	—20	0	20	40	60	80
n-hexane C_6H_{14}	1482	1431	1381	1331	1285	1246	1184	1122	—
n-heptane C_7H_{16}	1525	1473	1419	1370	1323	1277	1221	1165	1109
n-octane C_8H_{18}	—	—	1451	1399	1346	1296	1248	1190	1138
n-nonane* C_9H_{20}	—	—	1465	1414	1364	1315	1264	1213	1162
n-decane $C_{10}H_{22}$	—	—	—	1446	1399	1351	1305	1257	1209
n-undecane $C_{11}H_{24}$	—	—	—	1475	1430	1384	1338	1293	1247
n-dodecane* $C_{12}H_{26}$	—	—	—	—	1463	1420	1377	1333	1288
n-tridecane* $C_{13}H_{28}$	—	—	—	—	1483	1442	1401	1359	1317
n-tetradecane $C_{14}H_{30}$	—	—	—	—	—	1455	1420	1384	1342
n-pentadecane $C_{15}H_{32}$	—	—	—	—	—	1475	1435	1395	1356
n-hexadecane $C_{16}H_{34}$	—	—	—	—	—	—	1454	1419	1380
n-heptadecane $C_{17}H_{36}$	—	—	—	—	—	—	1478	1437	1398
n-octadecane $C_{18}H_{38}$	—	—	—	—	—	—	1493	1456	1419
n-nonadecane $C_{19}H_{40}$	—	—	—	—	—	—	1507	1470	1433
n-icosane $C_{20}H_{42}$	—	—	—	—	—	—	1522	1486	1450
n-henicosane $C_{21}H_{44}$	—	—	—	—	—	—	—	1493	1458
n-docosane $C_{22}H_{46}$	—	—	—	—	—	—	—	1510	1476
n-tricosane $C_{23}H_{48}$	—	—	—	—	—	—	—	1526	1492
n-tetracosane $C_{24}H_{50}$	—	—	—	—	—	—	—	1540	1506

hydrocarbons n-C$_n$ H$_{2n+2}$, $\lambda \cdot 10^4$, W/m . deg

100	120	140	160	180	200	220	240	260	280	300	320	340
—	—	—	—	—	—	—	—	—	—	—	—	—
1053	—	—	—	—	—	—	—	—	—	—	—	—
1086	1034	—	—	—	—	—	—	—	—	—	—	—
1111	1061	1010	—	—	—	—	—	—	—	—	—	—
1162	1114	1066	1020	—	—	—	—	—	—	—	—	—
1200	1154	1107	1061	1014	—	—	—	—	—	—	—	—
1243	1199	1154	1109	1064	1019	—	—	—	—	—	—	—
1275	1232	1189	1146	1104	1061	1018	—	—	—	—	—	—
1300	1258	1216	1175	1134	1093	1051	1009	—	—	—	—	—
1317	1279	1240	1200	1161	1122	1083	1043	1004	—	—	—	—
1341	1302	1264	1225	1187	1148	1110	1072	1034	0996	—	—	—
1360	1323	1286	1249	1212	1175	1138	1101	1064	1026	0989	—	—
1382	1346	1309	1273	1237	1200	1164	1137	1101	1064	1028	—	—
1396	1359	1322	1286	1250	1214	1174	1142	1106	1070	1034	0998	—
1414	1378	1342	1306	1270	1234	1198	1162	1126	1090	1054	1028	0992
1422	1386	1351	1315	1279	1244	1209	1174	1139	1104	1069	1034	0999
1442	1408	1374	1340	1306	1272	1238	1204	1170	1136	1102	1068	1034
1458	1425	1391	1357	1324	1290	1256	1223	1189	1155	1122	1088	1054
1473	1440	1406	1373	1340	1306	1273	1240	1206	1173	1140	1106	1073

*Asterisk (*) denotes compounds whose calculated λ values have been given in Tables 4-6.

Table 5. Coefficients of thermal conductivity in

Alcohol		$\lambda \cdot 10^4$ at t, °C						
		—80	—60	—40	—20	0	20	40
Methyl	HCH_2OH	2329	2276	2223	2170	2117	2064	2011
Ethyl	CH_3CH_2OH	2000	1940	1878	1812	1748	1688	1638
n-propyl*	CH_3CH_2OH	1752	1718	1684	1650	1616	1584	1549
n-butyl	$CH_3(CH_2)_2CH_2OH$ . .	1688	1658	1628	1598	1568	1538	1508
n-amyl*	$CH_3(CH_2)_3CH_2OH$ . .	—	1658	1631	1604	1577	1550	1523
n-hexyl	$CH_3(CH_2)_4CH_2OH$ . .	—	—	1628	1603	1577	1551	1525
n-heptyl	$CH_3(CH_2)_5CH_2OH$ . .	—	—	—	1629	1603	1577	1551
n-octyl*	$CH_3(CH_2)_6CH_2OH$ . .	—	—	—	—	1629	1602	1575
n-nonyl	$CH_3(CH_2)_7CH_2OH$ . .	—	—	—	—	1652	1624	1596
n-decyl	$CH_3(CH_2)_8CH_2OH$ . .	—	—	—	—	—	1651	1620
n-undecyl*	$CH_3(CH_2)_9CH_2OH$ . .	—	—	—	—	—	1677	1646
n-dodecyl	$CH_3(CH_2)_{10}CH_2OH$ . .	—	—	—	—	—	—	1672
n-tridecyl*	$CH_3(CH_2)_{11}CH_2OH$ . .	—	—	—	—	—	—	1686
n-tetradecyl	$CH_3(CH_2)_{12}CH_2OH$ . .	—	—	—	—	—	—	1708
n-pentadecyl*	$CH_3(CH_2)_{13}CH_2OH$ . .	—	—	—	—	—	—	—
n-hexadecyl*	$CH_3(CH_2)_{14}CH_2OH$ . .	—	—	—	—	—	—	—
n-heptadecyl*	$CH_3(CH_2)_{15}CH_2OH$ . .	—	—	—	—	—	—	—
n-Octadecyl	$CH_3(CH_2)_{16}CH_2OH$ . .	—	—	—	—	—	—	—

normal alcohols n-$C_nH_{2n+1}OH$, λ . 10^4, W/(m . deg)

60	80	100	120	140	160	180	200	220	240	260	280	300
1958	—	—	—	—	—	—	—	—	—	—	—	—
1588	—	—	—	—	—	—	—	—	—	—	—	—
1514	1479	—	—	—	—	—	—	—	—	—	—	—
1478	1448	1418	—	—	—	—	—	—	—	—	—	—
1496	1469	1442	1415	—	—	—	—	—	—	—	—	—
1499	1473	1447	1421	1395	—	—	—	—	—	—	—	—
1525	1499	1473	1447	1421	1395	—	—	—	—	—	—	—
1548	1519	1492	1465	1438	1411	1384	—	—	—	—	—	—
1568	1540	1512	1484	1456	1428	1400	1372	—	—	—	—	—
1589	1558	1527	1496	1465	1434	1403	1391	1360	—	—	—	—
1615	1584	1553	1522	1491	1460	1429	1398	1367	1336	—	—	—
1640	1608	1576	1544	1512	1480	1448	1416	1384	1352	—	—	—
1653	1620	1587	1554	1521	1488	1455	1422	1389	1366	1333	—	—
1674	1640	1606	1572	1538	1504	1470	1436	1402	1368	1334	—	—
1692	1657	1622	1587	1552	1517	1482	1447	1412	1377	1342	1307	—
1712	1676	1640	1604	1568	1532	1496	1460	1424	1388	1352	1316	—
1736	1699	1662	1625	1588	1551	1514	1477	1440	1403	1366	1329	1292
1763	1725	1687	1649	1611	1573	1535	1497	1459	1421	1383	1345	1307

Table 6. Coefficients of thermal conductivity of limiting monobasic acids $C_nH_{2n+1}COOH$, $\lambda \cdot 10^4$, W/m·deg

Acid	$\lambda \cdot 10^4$ at t, °C																
	-20	0	20	40	60	80	100	120	140	160	180	200	220	240	260	280	300
Propynic CH_3CH_2COOH	1510	1488	1466	1444	1422	1400	1378	1356	1334	—	—	—	—	—	—	—	—
n-butyric $CH_3(CH_2)_2COOH$	—	1454	1430	1405	1380	1356	1332	1308	1284	1260	—	—	—	—	—	—	—
n-valeric $CH_3(CH_2)_3COOH$	1450	1425	1400	1375	1350	1325	1300	1275	1250	1225	1200	—	—	—	—	—	—
n-capronic $CH_3(CH_2)_4COOH$	—	1452	1425	1398	1371	1344	1317	1290	1263	1236	1209	1182	—	—	—	—	—
n-enantic $CH_3(CH_2)_5COOH$	—	1476	1447	1418	1389	1360	1331	1302	1273	1244	1215	1186	1157	—	—	—	—
n-caprylic $CH_3(CH_2)_6COOH$	—	—	1473	1443	1413	1383	1353	1323	1293	1263	1233	1203	1173	—	—	—	—
n-pelargonic $CH_3(CH_2)_7COOH$	—	—	1510	1478	1446	1414	1382	1350	1318	1286	1254	1222	1190	1158	—	—	—
n-caprynic $CH_3(CH_2)_8COOH$	—	—	—	1500	1467	1434	1402	1370	1337	1304	1272	1240	1207	1174	1141	—	—
n-decanoic $CH_3(CH_2)_9COOH$	—	—	—	1533	1498	1463	1428	1393	1358	1323	1288	1253	1218	1183	1148	1113	—

Table 6—*Continued*

λ . 10⁴ at t, °C

Acid	-20	0	20	40	60	80	100	120	140	160	180	200	220	240	260	280	300
n-lauric $CH_3(CH_2)_{10}COOH$	—	—	—	—	1530	1493	1456	1419	1382	1345	1308	1271	1234	1197	1160	1123	1086
n-tridecanoic $CH_3(CH_2)_{11}COOH$	—	—	—	—	1561	1522	1483	1444	1405	1366	1327	1288	1249	1210	1171	1132	1093
n-myristic $CH_3(CH_2)_{12}COOH$	—	—	—	—	1593	1553	1513	1473	1433	1393	1353	1313	1273	1233	1193	1153	1113
n-pentadecanoic $CH_3(CH_2)_{13}COOH$	—	—	—	—	1632	1590	1548	1506	1464	1422	1380	1338	1296	1254	1214	1172	1130
Palmitic $CH_3(CH_2)_{14}COOH$	—	—	—	—	—	1632	1588	1544	1500	1456	1412	1368	1322	1278	1234	1190	1146
Margaric $CH_3(CH_2)_{15}COOH$	—	—	—	—	—	1665	1619	1573	1527	1481	1435	1389	1343	1297	1251	1205	1159
Stearic $CH_3(CH_2)_{16}COOH$	—	—	—	—	—	1698	1650	1602	1554	1506	1458	1410	1362	1314	1266	1218	1170

Table 7. Coefficients of thermal conductivity of simple and complex esters $C_n H_{2n+1} OC_n H_{2n+1}$, $\lambda \cdot 10^4$, W/m. deg

Ester	$\lambda \cdot 10^4$ at t, °C																	
	−60	−40	−20	0	20	40	60	80	100	120	140	160	180	200	220	240	260	280
Dibutyl $C_4H_9OC_4H_9$	1468	1422	1376	1330	1284	1238	1192	1146	1100	1054	1008	—	—	—	—	—	—	—
Hexyl ethyl $C_6H_{13}OC_2H_5$	1450	1405	1359	1314	1268	1224	1180	1135	1090	1045	—	—	—	—	—	—	—	—
Diamyl $C_5H_{11}OC_5H_{11}$	1480	1440	1400	1360	1320	1280	1240	1200	1160	1120	1080	1040	1000	—	—	—	—	—
Octyl ethyl $C_8H_{17}OC_2H_5$	1472	1432	1392	1352	1312	1272	1232	1192	1152	1112	1072	1032	0992	—	—	—	—	—
Dihexyl $C_6H_{13}OC_6H_{13}$	—	1468	1431	1394	1357	1320	1284	1247	1211	1175	1138	1101	1064	1027	0990	—	—	—
Diheptyl $C_7H_{15}OC_7H_{15}$	—	—	1462	1428	1394	1360	1326	1292	1258	1224	1190	1156	1122	1088	1054	1020	0984	—
Dioctyl $C_8H_{17}OC_8H_{17}$	—	—	—	1458	1424	1392	1360	1328	1296	1264	1232	1199	1166	1134	1102	1070	1038	1006

Table 8. Coefficients of thermal conductivity of complex esters of carbonic acids $C_nH_{2n+1}COOC_nH_{2n+1}$, $\lambda \cdot 10^4$ W/m $\cdot$ deg

Ester	$\lambda \cdot 10^4$ at t, °C												
	0	20	40	60	80	100	120	140	160	180	200	220	240
Methyl ester of formic acid $HCOOCH_3$	1946	1862	—	—	—	—	—	—	—	—	—	—	—
Methyl ester of acetic acid CH_3COOCH_3	1649	1582	1514	—	—	—	—	—	—	—	—	—	—
Ethyl ester of formic acid $HCOOC_2H_5$	1670	1604	1538	—	—	—	—	—	—	—	—	—	—
Methyl ester of propynic acid $C_2H_5COOCH_3$	1528	1469	1410	1351	1292	—	—	—	—	—	—	—	—
n-propyl ester of formic acid $HCOOC_3H_7$	1520	1464	1408	1352	1296	—	—	—	—	—	—	—	—
Ethyl ester of acetic acid $CH_3COOC_2H_5$	1520	1462	1402	1346	—	—	—	—	—	—	—	—	—
n-butyl ester of formic acid $HCOOC_4H_9$	1464	1419	1374	1329	1283	1238	—	—	—	—	—	—	—
Methyl ester of valeric acid $C_4H_9COOCH_3$	1434	1388	1344	1300	1256	1212	1168	—	—	—	—	—	—
n-amyl ester of formic acid $HCOOC_5H_{11}$	1432	1390	1348	1306	1264	1222	1180	—	—	—	—	—	—
Ethyl ester of butyric acid $C_3H_7COOC_2H_5$	1422	1377	1332	1287	1242	1197	1152	—	—	—	—	—	—
Methyl ester of capronic acid $C_5H_{11}COOCH_3$	1406	1366	1326	1286	1245	1206	1164	1123	—	—	—	—	—
n-butyl ester of propynic acid $C_2H_5COOCH_3$	1404	1363	1322	1281	1240	1190	1158	1117	—	—	—	—	—
n-heptyl ester of formic acid $HCOOC_7H_{15}$	1418	1382	1316	1310	1274	1238	1202	1166	1130	—	—	—	—
Ethyl ester of capronic acid $C_5H_{11}COOC_2H_5$	1420	1382	1344	1306	1268	1230	1192	1154	1116	—	—	—	—
n-hexyl ester of acetic acid $CH_3COOC_6H_{13}$	1404	1368	1332	1296	1260	1224	1188	1152	1116	—	—	—	—
n-octyl ester of formic acid $HCOOC_8H_{17}$	1440	1406	1372	1338	1304	1270	1236	1202	1168	1134	—	—	—
n-hexyl ester of propynic acid $C_2H_5COOC_6H_{13}$	1406	1372	1339	1306	1273	1240	1207	1174	1141	1108	—	—	—
n-amyl ester of butyric acid $C_3H_7COOC_5H_{11}$	1440	1402	1364	1326	1288	1250	1212	1174	1136	1098	—	—	—
Methyl ester of stearic acid $C_{17}H_{35}COOCH_3$	—	—	1524	1497	1470	1443	1416	1388	1360	1333	1305	1277	1249
n-butyl ester of palmitic acid $C_{15}H_{31}COOC_4H_9$	—	1525	1494	1462	1430	1398	1367	1335	1306	1276	1237	1205	1175
n-butyl ester of stearic acid $C_{17}H_{35}COOC_4H_9$	—	—	1546	1514	1482	1450	1418	1386	1354	1322	1290	1258	1226

These investigations also facilitate clarification of the influence of the functional groups on the magnitude of λ. The shift of the hydrogen atom in the homologous series of limiting hydrocarbons of the type C_nH_{2n+2} to carboxyl group COOH, and especially to hydroxyl group OH, induces increase in thermal conductivity. However, a shift of the hydrogen atom in the homologous series of alcohols and limiting monobasic acids of the hydrocarbon radical C_nH_{2n+1} induces decrease in the thermal conductivity of liquids.

REFERENCES

1. MUKHAMEDZYANOV, G. KH., A. G. USMANOV and A. A. TARZIMANOV. Izv. Vuzov, *Neft' i Gaz*, No. 9, 1963; No. 1, 1964; No. 10, 1964.
2. MUKHAMEDZYANOV, G. KH. and A. G. USMANOV. Izv. Vuzov, *Neft' i Gaz*, No. 1, 1967; No. 4, 1967; *IFZh*, **13** (2), 1967.
3. FILIPPOV, L. P. *Vestnik MGU*, No. 12, 1954; *Fizika*, No. 3, 1960.
4. MASON, H. L. and D. S. WASHINGTON. *Trans. ASME*. No. 5, 817, 1954.
5. WEBER, H. F. and S. WIEDEMANN. *Ann. Phys. Chem.*, No. 5, 103, 1880.
6. DE HEEN. *Bull. Academie Royale de Belge*, **183**, 1889.
7. VARGAFTIK, N. B. *Izv. VTI*, No. 8, 6, 1949.
8. RIEDEL, L. *Forschung auf dem Gebiete des Ingenieurwesens*, **11** (6), 340, 1940.
9. FRONTAS'EV, V. P. and M. YA. GUSAKOV. *ZhTF*, **29** (10), 1959.
10. BRIGGS, D. K. H. *Ind. and Eng. Chem.*, **46**, 1947, 1956.
11. GOLUBEV, I. F. and YA. M. NAZIEV. *Trudy Energeticheskovo Instituta AN Azerb. SSR*, 15, 1961.
12. GUSEINOV, K. D. *Khim. Tekhn. Topliv i Masel*, No. 2, 1966; *Ukrainskii Fiz. Zh.*, No. 1, 1967.
13. MUKHAMEDZYANOV, G. KH. and A. G. USMANOV. Izv. Vuzov, *Neft' i Gaz*. No. 4, 1965.
14. KERZHENTSEV, V. V. Author's abstract of Ph.D. dissertation. MGU, 1951.
15. BAXTER, S., H. A. VOLDEN and S. DAVIES. *J. Appl. Chem.*, **3**, 1953.

IV. CARBON DIOXIDE

UDC 541.11

EXPERIMENTAL INVESTIGATION OF THE
DENSITY OF CARBON DIOXIDE

V. A. Kirillin, S. A. Ulybin and *E. P. Zherdev*

The density of carbon dioxide is one of the most widely studied properties. However, only four works in the literature thus far cover a wide range of parameters of state with accuracy sufficiently high for tabulation and standardization of thermodynamic functions of carbon dioxide in the gaseous phase. These four works are :

1. Van der Waals's investigations [1, 2] in the temperature range 0-150°C and pressure range 16-3000 atm. The highly accurate experimental data obtained were approximated by other investigators [3] to correspond to the following polynomial in terms of powers of the density :

$$P_v = A + (B+\beta)d + Cd^2 + \zeta d^3 + Dd^4 + Ed^6 + Fd^8 \qquad \text{(Units A)}$$

2. Experimental investigation by Canadian scientists [4] in the temperature range 0-600°C at pressures upto 50 atm.

3. The work of Vukalovich and Altunin [5] at the department of Theoretical Fundamentals of Heat Engineering of the Moscow Power Institute, in the temperature range 75-500°C at pressures upto 300 kg/cm².

4. The work of Vukalovich, Altunin, and Timoshenko at the same institute, covering a temperature range of 40-800°C at pressures upto 600 kg/cm² [6].

If the measurements of work [6] on the isotherms of 60 and 85°C were to be excluded, we would observe that in the experimental works mentioned above, the experimental points would be located at considerably large intervals over the temperature range, complicating interpolation at moderate temperatures; this is due to the low density values of CO_2. Thus, in the temperature range of 50-200°C the pitch of experimental points is 25°C, while above 200°C the readings are available at intervals of 50°C only. Since at temperatures above 150°C and pressures above 50 atm the only data available are those of works [5-7], experimental investigation of CO_2 density, using some procedure other than that employed in works [5-7], becomes necessary. Such investigations were undertaken at the department of Engineering Thermophysics of the Moscow Power Institute and the Institute of High Temperatures of the Academy of Sciences, USSR.

The construction and working principle of the experimental apparatus used to obtain new data on CO_2 density have been described in detail in reference [8].. Hence, in the present article, only those features in the apparatus design and experimental procedure necessary in the process of testing the apparatus have been described, and only those specifications of components and instruments essential for an appraisal of the reliability of the results have been given in the present work.

The apparatus consists of three basic functional units : the piezometer, the system of purification of the substance under investigation, and the system of determination of quantity of the substance (weighing). The purification system is fairly standard and has remained practically unchanged. Liquefied, dried CO_2, manufactured by the First Moscow Carbon Dioxide Plant, containing 99.5% of the main substance (according to the results of the analysis undertaken by the plant laboratory) was further purified by extraction of oil and other impurity gases and dried. For measuring a large number of parameters, an additional two-stage thermocompressor was included in the system, necessary to obtain higher pressures.

Fig. 1 shows the schematic arrangement of the apparatus (without the purification system).

The piezometer (5) located in the thermostat TS-24M was filled with the investigated substance upto the maximum pressure used in the experiments. An equilibrium state of the substance was then established in the piezometer and part of the gas was released either into cylinders (6) of the gas meter or into detachable metallic ampoules (3). A new equilibrium condition was then established at the same temperature but at a lower density (and, consequently, lower pressure). The mass of gases in the piezometer at any given equilibrium state was determined as the sum of the masses during the release processes and the mass of the remaining gas in the piezometer after the final release. Simultaneously, the corrections were introduced to compensate for the ballast volume of the piezometer and the gas meter (6).

The desired density was determined as the ratio of the mass of the gas to the volume of the piezometer at the experimental corresponding temperature and pressure.

A state of equilibrium was supposedly achieved if following 45 min the pressure within the piezometer did not vary by more than 0.02 bar and the temperature by more than 0.02°C.

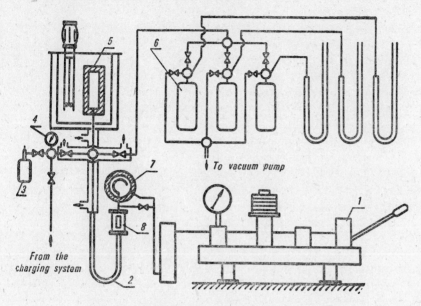

Fig. 1. Schematic arrangement of the apparatus.

The pressure in the piezometer, during filling and release of the gas and during all operations associated with considerable change in pressure, was controlled by a spring type differential manometer (7) suggested by Kirillin [8]. The change in volume of the spring was small even for large variations of pressure, and hence practically no mercury spilled into the gas meter from the U-shaped tube (2).

When an equilibrium state was achieved and the pressure remained nearly constant, the valve was opened and the differential manometer was short-circuited. The pressure from the piston manometer (1) was transmitted to the right-hand side bend of the mercury manometer through the dividing capacitor filled with distilled water. The level of mercury was controlled visually through a window (8) consisting of an organic glass cylinder pressed into a metallic ring with two vertical slits. Similar designs have been employed earlier [9]. The windows fabricated in our laboratory could endure pressures upto 600 bar during gas compression. During experimentation corresponding to the isotherms 40, 55, 60, 75 and 85°C for all the pressures used and corresponding to the isotherms 100, 110, 125 and 140°C at pressure over 60 bar, the manometer used was MP-600 of class 0.05 accuracy. For temperatures of 100, 110, 125 and 140°C at pressure below 60 bar, the manometer MP-60 (4) was used. The atmospheric pressure was measured by a cup-and-siphon mercury barometer.

Introduction of the necessary correction in the pressure to compensate for the difference in the mercury levels in the two arms of the mercury manometer was facilitated by the construction of the window (8) which had an internal diameter equal to the bore of the tube of the left arm. Prior to experimentation, both arms of the mercury manometer were exposed to the atmosphere and the zero position of the mercury level in the window (8) was noted. This corresponded to an equilibrium of the pressure in the piezometer and the system of the piston manometer. During the experiment the level of mercury in window (8) was measured several times. If the mean value of these readings did not coincide with the zero position, the level of mercury in the left arm also deviated from its zero position by the same amount, but in the reverse direction. In such case, the correction for the pressure was calculated by the following equation :

$$\Delta p_1 = 2\rho_{\mathrm{cal}}\ (H_{\mathrm{meas}} - H_0).$$

In our experimentation, this correction seldom exceeded 0.02 bar.

Corrections were also introduced to compensate for the difference in the height of the measuring column of the piston manometer and the level of mercury in window (8) ($\Delta p = +0.01$ bar) and for the hydrostatic pressure of the column of the substance due to the mercury level in the left arm of the differential mercury manometer positioned before the piezometer.

To monitor temperature field, the temperature in the thermostat TS-24M was measured by two platinum resistance thermocouples situated at two different points in the thermostat. For temperatures of 40, 55, 60, 75 and 85°C the liquid used in the thermostat was water and the two thermometers showed the same reading. At temperatures above 100°C the readings shown by the two thermometers differed by approximately 0.02-0.03°C. The secondary instruments used were the low-resistance potentiometer PMS-48 (for isotherms 40, 55, 60, 75, 85°C) and the semiautomatic self-adjusting potentiometer R308 (for isotherms 100, 110, 125, 140°C).

The temperature in the thermostat was maintained constant by means of a photothyratron regulator and the deviation of temperature from its mean value was limited to ±0.01°C.

As mentioned earlier, some of the experimental data was obtained while the gas was released into the cylinders of the gas meter. The construction of the gas meter was described in reference [8] and hence only the basic characteristics are given below.

The gas meter consists of three glass cylinders each with capacity of approximately 2500 cm³. The excess pressure in each of the cylinders was measured by a mercury manometer, while the barometric pressure was measured by a cup-and-siphon mercury manometer. The error in measurement did not exceed 0.5 mm Hg. The pressure of the gas in the gas meter was 2-2.5 bar, corresponding to a release of about 10 g gas into each cylinder. During the entire experimentation, the temperature inside the thermostat was quite stable and was maintained at 30°C. The quantity of the substance released into the gas meter was calculated from the equation [4] :

$$pv = A_T + B_T p + C_T p^2 + D_T p^4 \qquad \text{(Units A)}$$

A comparison of this equation with the data of authors using the same set of parameters shows this equation to represent the experimental values correct to an accuracy of at least 0.04%.

The ballast volume of gas meter cylinders was about 5 cm³, consisting of the volume of the connecting passages between the piezometer and the gas meter and between the cylinder and the mercury manometer. The correction accounting for the ballast volume was equal to 0.02-0.03 g (0.2-0.3%) of the weight of the gas released.

A major portion of the experimental data was obtained during releases into one or two detachable ampoules (3). Two sizes of ampoules were used in the present work. The smaller ones had a diameter of 85 mm and a volume of 550-600 cm³ with wall thickness of 0.4-0.5 mm and weight of 120-140 g. During gas compression, these ampoules withstood internal pressures upto 30 bar; however, the actual pressure during experimentation did not exceed 15 bar. At room temperature and pressure of 15 bar the weight of CO_2 in this type of ampoule was 17-18 g.

The larger ampoules had a diameter of 120 mm, a wall thickness of 1.1-1.2 mm, a volume of 1000-1200 cm³, and weighed 550 g. At pressures around 25 bar the mass of CO_2 reached 50-60 g.

The volume of the connecting passages between the valves of the ampoules and the valve of the piezometer was about 3.5 cm³. The correction accounting for the quantity of gas was implemented as the experiment progressed. Prior to releasing the gas, this volume was supplemented by the substance under investigation from the purification system upto a certain predetermined pressure (10-15 bar for smaller ampoules and 20-25 bar for larger ones). The gas was then released but in such a way that the gas pressure in the connecting passages did not vary following release. Consequently, within the accuracy of pressure measurements the quantity of the substance in these connecting passages did not change, thereby eliminating the requirement for correction. The pressure was measured by a manometer type MP-60.

When gas was collected in the smaller ampoules, weighing was performed on analytical balances and the error in determination of the mass of the gas did not exceed 2-3 mg, comprising 0.01-0.02% of the mass released. With the larger ampoules the T-1-1 balance of 10 mg accuracy was used. In such case the error in determination of the released mass constituted 20 mg (0.03-0.04%).

For calculating the remainder of the gas in the piezometer the following equation was used [4] :

$$pv = A_T + B_T p + C_T p^2 + D_T p^4 \qquad \text{(Units A)}$$

The values of the normal volumes required in these calculations were computed according to the formula in reference [4].

$$v_0 = 505.9 \text{ cm}^3/\text{g}$$

If the gas was finally released into the gas meter, the final excess pressure in the piezometer was measured by mercury manometer of the gas meter (1). In some of the experiments the final release of the gas was into the small ampoule, in which case the ampoule was cooled by liquid nitrogen in order to reduce the residual pressure in the piezometer. The final excess pressure in the piezometer of 10-20 mm Hg was measured by mercury manometer (2). Since the level of mercury in the left arm was determined by calculation, the error in measurement of pressure by this method was higher than that using a gas meter and constituted 2-3 mm Hg (0.3-0.4%) of the absolute pressure. At pressures close to atmospheric, the remainder of the gas constituted 450-600 mg and the error in determination did not exceed 2-3 mg.

It is not essential to use the gas meter and the detachable ampoules simultaneously. The apparatus was designed to operate with the gas meter, and a certain number of experiments at $t = 40°C$ were conducted exclusively with the gas meter. However, for experiments at temperatures of 55, 60, 75 and 85°C, and also in one experiment at 40°C, only the final release was made into the gas meter. Experiments at 100, 110, 125 and 140°C were conducted exclusively with detachable flasks and with CO_2 freezing in the final release. Use of detachable ampoules for weighing the gas improves the accuracy of determination of the quantity of the substance and also reduces the experiment time duration.

The ballast volume of the piezometer consists of the communication volume between the piezometer, the valves, and the mercury level in the left arm of the tube (2). In order to reduce requirement for correction for the ballast volume and for improving accuracy, the area of the ballast volume outside the thermostat was thermostatted at $t = 50°C$. Heating was accomplished by water from the auxiliary thermostat TS-15. Six chromel-alumel thermocouples were installed in the capillaries, valves, and the cross-piece for measurement and control of temperature. Thermostatting of the ballast volume at a temperature higher than critical maintained the ballast volume in single-phase state at all the pressures during the experiment. If this volume had not been maintained, it would have been quite difficult to determine the location of the boundary between the liquid and the vapor phases. Accordingly the ballast volume presumably consists of two major components, the first being the capillary with an internal diameter of 0.6 mm, length of 150 mm, volume of 0.042 cm^3, and temperature varying from the piezometer temperature to 50°C. The second component consists of the volumes under the locking needles of the valves and has a temperature of $t=50$°C. Other parameters of the second component are : $v_1=0.016$ cm^3; d_{int} of the capillary$=0.6$ mm; $l=110$ mm; $v_2=0.028$ cm^3; d_{int} of the capillary$=0.2$ mm; total length $l=565$ mm; $v_3=0.018$ cm^3; internal volume of the cross-piece $v_4=0.004$ cm^3; and clearances and gaps $v_5=0.038$ cm^3. The magnitude of the second component of the ballast volume was calculated as :

$$v=0.104+\frac{\pi\, d_2}{4}\, (H_{meas}-H_0),$$

where $d=2.1$ mm.

The second term of the above equation explains the variation of the ballast volume caused by the displacement of mercury in the left arm of the tube (2). It is clear that the alteration in the volume occupied by mercury in the left arm is equal in magnitude but opposite in sign to the change in the volume of mercury in the window (8).

The density of CO_2 at 50°C was determined from the data of works [1, 2, 4-6]. Data of other works were not used for introducing a correction for the ballast volume of the piezometer since the experiment could have been conducted for isotherm 50°C by the same procedure as that described above, and the density at pressures upto 600 bar could have been calculated from the results by the method of successive approximations. Since the correction accounting for the ballast volume is not large, only two approximations are required. While deriving the correction accounting for the ballast volume of the variable temperature zone, the density was taken as the arithmetic mean of the densities at the piezometer temperature and at 50°C.

The volume of the piezometer at room temperature was determined by repeated calibration with respect to water.

The coefficient of linear expansion for steel Kh18N10T was computed according to the results of normalization of the experimental data presented in paper [7].

The correction due to isothermal deformation was determined by Lame's equation :

$$\Delta v_p = v_0 \left[\frac{3(1-2\mu)\,(p-B)\alpha^2}{E(\alpha^2-1)} + \frac{2(1+\mu)(p-B)\alpha^2}{E(\alpha^2-1)} \right],$$

where $\alpha=$ the ratio of the external diameter of the piezometer d_2 to the internal diameter d_1. In our experiments, $d_2=125$ mm, $d_1=40$ mm, and $\alpha=3.125$.

Using the procedure described above the values of density of CO_2 were obtained for the isotherms 40.12, 55.31, 60.25, 75.26, 85.00, 100.04, 110.03, 125.01 and 140.01°C.

Reproducibility of the data obtained was checked in repeated experimentation for certain isotherms. The results are presented in the tables which follow.

Density of CO_2 obtained experimentally

$t=40.12°C$

Experiment I		Experiment II		Experiment III		Experiment IV	
p, bar	ρ, kg/m³	p, bar	ρ, kg/m³	p, bar	ρ, kg/m³	p, bar	ρ, kg/m³
19.75	36.607	15.98	29.062	17.99	33.087	30.37	59.778
34.50	69.527	27.51	53.274	33.21	66.469	49.77	112.28
45.83	100.02	39.09	81.337	44.90	97.362	75.48	234.97
55.77	132.70	49.27	110.63	54.82	129.26	84.08	334.73
63.95	166.18	58.61	143.51	63.17	162.75	88.39	437.42
69.77	196.35	65.50	173.59	69.22	193.34	93.64	559.26
						105.03	659.87
						139.82	762.92

$t=56.31°C$

p, bar	ρ, kg/m³
43.21	84.236
75.73	184.79
95.19	287.69
109.79	409.21
121.25	510.24
139.38	613.25
187.94	735.25
281.00	835.89
474.19	938.10

$t=60.25°C$

Experiment I		Experiment II	
p, bar	ρ, kg/m³	p, bar	ρ, kg/m³
37.45	69.174	26.91	47.404
75.39	174.13	68.52	150.58
98.17	278.59	93.88	254.35
116.10	402.69	113.14	379.56
130.98	509.70	127.01	483.33
152.28	611.07	146.52	588.56
207.77	734.81	194.28	713.25
280.49	814.02	282.87	815.90
463.86	919.06	465.85	919.87

$t=75.26°C$

Experiment I		Experiment II		Experiment III	
p, bar	ρ, kg/m³	p, bar	ρ, kg/m³	p, bar	ρ, kg/m³
28.65	47.744	32.62	55.166	42.89	75.381
57.69	107.75	71.11	141.34	74.64	150.97
				105.32	253.57
				120.65	320.41
				141.14	420.20
				164.23	520.87

$t=85.00°C$				$t=100.04°C$		$t=110.03°C$			
Experiment I		Experiment II				Experiment I		Experiment II	
				p, bar	ρ, kg/m³				
p, bar	ρ, kg/m³	p, bar	ρ, kg/m³			p, bar	ρ, kg/m³	p, bar	ρ, kg/m³
46.23	78.805	57.41	101.77	27.667	41.999	19.137	27.575	26.506	38.822
89.00	179.33	97.20	203.24	93.81	173.35	68.88	112.08	93.27	162.03
121.09	283.69	126.86	305.61	149.12	329.83	136.98	267.94	156.23	320.18
146.56	383.42	152.62	408.00	198.37	476.60	194.98	424.08	217.27	477.98
172.89	428.69	180.12	506.76	272.30	624.73	272.45	582.67	311.31	636.87
218.76	605.97	222.14	613.03	424.99	774.35	420.19	739.62	509.43	796.12
281.89	704.46	288.73	712.56	483.70	810.01	477.89	777.98		
392.75	802.21	411.13	814.07						

$t=125.01°C$		$t=140.01°C$			
		Experiment I		Experiment II	
p, bar	ρ, kg/m³	p, bar	ρ, kg/m³	p, bar	ρ, kg/m³
30.071	42.364	17.084	22.523	26.511	35.468
93.08	149.52	85.80	127.19	77.19	112.71
163.95	303.07	169.09	285.31	160.61	268.12
233.44	456.62	250.90	443.10	239.31	422.57
332.63	609.88	366.02	600.84	346.30	579.10
524.26	764.86	579.88	758.63	534.15	733.10

For the isotherms 40.12, 75.26 and 125.01°C comparison was undertaken between the values of density of CO_2 obtained by the present authors and in other works [1, 2] (see Fig. 2).

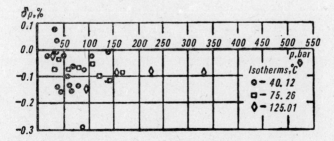

Fig. 2. Deviation of values of densities obtained in the present work from values obtained in works [1. 2].

As is obvious from Fig. 2, the average deviation of the values obtained by the present authors from values of works [1, 2] is ±0.1%. At all points except one, the deviations are less than 0.2% and at only one point, $p=84.08$ bar, the deviation is 0.29%.

REFERENCES

1. MICHELS, A. and C. MICHELS. *Proc. Roy. Soc.*, **A153**, 201, 1935.
2. MICHELS, A., C. MICHELS and WOUTERS. *Proc. Roy. Soc.*, **A153**, 214, 1935.
3. MICHELS, A. and C. MICHELS. *Proc. Roy. Soc.*, **A160**, 348, 1937.
4. McCORMACK, K. E. and W. G. SCHNEIDER. *J. Chem. Phys.*, **18** (9). 1269, 1950.
5. VUKALOVICH, M. P. and V. V. ALTUNIN. *Teploenergetika,* No. 11, 1959.
6. VUKALOVICH, M. P., V. V. ALTUNIN, and N. I. TIMOSHENKO. *Teploenergetika,* No. 5, 1962; Nos. 1, 2, 1963.
7. VUKALOVICH, M. P. and V. V. ALTUNIN. *Teplofizicheskie svoistva dvuokisi ugleroda (Thermophysical properties of carbon dioxide).* Atomizdat, Moscow, 1965.
8. KIRILLIN, V. A. and A. E. SHEINDLIN. *Issledovanie termodinamicheskikh svoistv veshchestv (Investigation of the thermodynamic properties of substances).* GEI, 1963.
9. RIVKIN, S. L. *Teploenergetika,* No. 1, 1962.

UDC 541.11

THERMODYNAMIC PROPERTIES OF LIQUID CARBON DIOXIDE

E. A. Golovskii and *V. A. Tsimarnyi*

When formulating the equation of state for liquid CO_2, the data of reference [1] are generally used because of their high degree of accuracy. The present authors have undertaken experimental investigation of the thermal properties of liquid carbon dioxide, and on the basis of the experimental results obtained [2], we have formulated an equation in the form suggested in work [3] :

$$p = A(T)\rho + B(T)\rho^3 + C(T)\rho^5, \tag{1}$$

where

$$A(T) = 19039.9 - 1022\Theta - 107708\Theta^{-1} + 251694\Theta^{-2} - 193436\Theta^{-3} + 1684\Theta^{-4};$$
$$B(T) = 18903 - 1584\Theta - 62128\Theta^{-1} + 45942\Theta^{-2};$$
$$C(T) = 3069 - 5.7T;$$

$$\Theta = \frac{100}{T}.$$

This equation is valid for densities of $CO_2 = \dfrac{\rho}{\rho_{cr}} > 1.8$.

The formulation procedure and applicability of this equation have been verified in many substances, in particular in experiments with liquid nitrogen [4]. The deviation of the calculated values of density from the reference values for CO_2 does not exceed 0.1% for most of the points and attains 0.15% at only six points. Comparison of our values of thermodynamic quantities i, s and c_p, obtained by calculation using the above

Calculated values of c_p, i, s and ρ for rounded values of temperature and pressure

p, bar	ρ, g/cm³	i, kJ/kg	s kJ/k . deg	c_p	ρ, g/cm³	i, kJ/kg	s kJ/k . deg	c_p
		$T=220°$K				$T=225°$K		
10	1.1680	395.9	2.697	1.79	1.1489	405.0	2.738	1.83
15	1.1691	396.0	2.696	1.78	1.1501	405.1	2.736	1.82
20	1.1702	396.2	2.694	1.78	1.1514	405.2	2.735	1.82
25	1.1713	396.3	2.693	1.77	1.1526	405.3	2.733	1.81
30	1.1723	396.4	2.692	1.77	1.1538	405.4	2.732	1.81
35	1.1734	396.6	2.690	1.76	1.1549	405.6	2.730	1.80
40	1.1745	396.7	2.689	1.76	1.1561	405.7	2.729	1.80
45	1.1756	396.8	2.688	1.76	1.1573	405.8	2.728	1.80
50	1.1766	397.0	2.686	1.75	1.1584	405.9	2.726	1.79
60	1.1787	397.2	2.684	1.75	1.1607	406.2	2.724	1.78
70	1.1807	397.5	2.681	1.75	1.1630	406.4	2.721	1.77
80	1.1828	397.8	2.679	1.74	1.1652	406.7	2.718	1.77
90	1.1848	398.1	2.676	1.74	1.1673	407.0	2.716	1.77
100	1.1867	398.4	2.671	1.73	1.1694	407.2	2.713	1.76
125	1.1915	399.2	2.668	1.73	1.1746	408.0	2.707	1.74
150	1.1961	400.0	2.662	1.71	1.1796	408.7	2.701	1.73
175	1.2006	400.9	2.656	1.70	1.1845	409.5	2.695	1.72
200	1.2050	401.7	2.651	1.69	1.1891	410.3	2.689	1.71
225	1.2092	402.6	2.646	1.68	1.1937	411.2	2.684	1.70
250	1.2133	403.5	2.640	1.68	1.1980	412.1	2.678	1.69
275	1.2173	404.5	2.635	1.67	1.2023	413.0	2.673	1.68
300	1.2212	405.4	2.630	1.66	1.2065	413.9	2.668	1.67
325	1.2250	406.4	2.625	1.66	1.2105	414.8	2.663	1.67
350	1.2287	407.4	2.621	1.65	1.2144	415.8	2.658	1.66
375	1.2323	408.4	2.616	1.65	1.2183	416.8	2.653	1.65
400	1.2359	409.4	2.611	1.64	1.2220	417.7	2.648	1.65
425	1.2394	410.5	2.607	1.63	1.2257	418.7	2.644	1.64
450	1.2428	411.5	2.602	1.63	1.2293	419.7	2.639	1.64
475	1.2461	412.6	2.598	1.63	1.2328	420.8	2.635	1.63
500	1.2494	413.6	2.594	1.62	1.2362	421.8	2.630	1.63
525	1.2526	414.7	2.590	1.62	1.2396	422.9	2.626	1.63
550	1.2557	415.8	2.586	1.61	1.2429	424.0	2.622	1.62
575	1.2588	416.9	2.582	1.61	1.2461	425.1	2.618	1.61
600	1.2618	418.0	2.578	1.60	1.2493	426.2	2.614	1.60
		$T=230°$K				$T=235°$K		
10	1.1294	414.3	2.779	1.85	—	—	—	—
15	1.1307	414.4	2.777	1.85	1.1106	423.9	2.799	1.88
20	1.1320	414.4	2.776	1.84	1.1121	423.9	2.797	1.87
25	1.1334	414.5	2.774	1.84	1.1135	424.0	2.795	1.87
30	1.1347	414.6	2.772	1.84	1.1151	424.0	2.794	1.86
35	1.1360	414.7	2.771	1.83	1.1165	424.1	2.792	1.85
40	1.1373	414.8	2.770	1.82	1.1179	424.2	2.791	1.85

Table—*Continued*

p, bar	ρ, g/cm³	i, kJ/kg	s kJ/k.deg	c_p	ρ, g/cm³	i, kJ/kg	s kJ/k.deg	c_p
45	1.1386	414.9	2.768	1.82	1.1193	424.3	2.789	1.84
50	1.1397	415.0	2.767	1.82	1.1207	424.4	2.788	1.84
60	1.1423	415.3	2.764	1.81	1.1235	424.5	2.784	1.83
70	1.1448	415.5	2.761	1.80	1.1262	424.7	2.781	1.82
80	1.1472	415.7	2.758	1.80	1.1282	424.9	2.778	1.81
90	1.1495	415.9	2.755	1.79	1.1314	425.1	2.776	1.80
100	1.1519	416.2	2.753	1.78	1.1339	425.3	2.773	1.79
125	1.1575	416.8	2.746	1.77	1.1400	425.9	2.769	1.78
150	1.1629	417.5	2.740	1.75	1.1459	426.5	2.759	1.76
175	1.1681	418.3	2.734	1.74	1.1515	427.2	2.753	1.75
200	1.1731	419.0	2.728	1.73	1.1569	427.9	2.746	1.73
225	1.1779	419.8	2.722	1.71	1.1621	428.6	2.740	1.72
250	1.1826	420.7	2.716	1.70	1.1671	429.4	2.734	1.71
275	1.1872	421.5	2.711	1.69	1.1719	430.2	2.729	1.70
300	1.1916	422.4	2.705	1.68	1.1766	431.0	2.723	1.69
325	1.1959	423.3	2.700	1.68	1.1812	431.8	2.718	1.68
350	1.2001	424.2	2.695	1.67	1.1856	432.7	2.713	1.67
375	1.2041	425.1	2.690	1.66	1.1899	433.6	2.708	1.66
400	1.2081	426.1	2.685	1.65	1.1940	434.5	2.703	1.65
425	1.2119	427.1	2.681	1.65	1.1982	435.5	2.698	1.64
450	1.2157	428.1	2.676	1.64	1.2021	436.4	2.693	1.64
475	1.2194	429.1	2.671	1.63	1.2060	437.4	2.688	1.63
500	1.2230	430.1	2.667	1.62	1.2098	438.4	2.684	1.63
525	1.2266	431.1	2.663	1.62	1.2135	439.4	2.679	1.62
550	1.2300	432.2	2.658	1.61	1.2172	440.4	2.675	1.61
575	1.2334	433.2	2.654	1.61	1.2207	441.5	2.670	1.60
600	1.2367	434.3	2.650	1.60	1.2242	442.5	2.666	1.60

		$T=240°$K					$T=245°$K		

15	1.0897	433.3	2.859	1.93	—	—	—	—
20	1.0914	433.3	2.857	1.92	1.0697	443.1	2.898	1.96
25	1.0930	433.4	2.856	1.91	1.0716	443.1	2.896	1.96
30	1.0946	433.4	2.854	1.90	1.0734	443.1	2.894	1.96
35	1.0963	433.4	2.852	1.90	1.0752	443.1	2.892	1.94
40	1.0978	433.5	2.850	1.89	1.0769	443.2	2.890	1.93
45	1.0994	433.5	2.849	1.89	1.0787	443.2	2.888	1.93
50	1.1010	433.6	2.847	1.88	1.0804	443.2	2.887	1.92
60	1.1040	433.7	2.844	1.87	1.0838	443.2	2.883	1.91
70	1.1070	433.8	2.840	1.86	1.0871	443.3	2.880	1.89
80	1.1098	434.0	2.837	1.85	1.0903	443.4	2.876	1.87
90	1.1127	434.1	2.834	1.84	1.0934	443.5	2.873	1.86
100	1.1154	434.3	2.831	1.83	1.0964	443.6	2.870	1.85
125	1.1221	434.8	2.824	1.80	1.1037	444.0	2.862	1.83
150	1.1284	435.3	2.817	1.78	1.1106	444.4	2.854	1.81
175	1.1345	435.9	2.810	1.76	1.1172	444.9	2.847	1.79

Table—*Continued*

p, bar	ρ, g/cm³	i, kJ/kg	s kJ/k·deg	c_p kJ/k·deg	ρ, g/cm³	i, kJ/kg	s kJ/k·deg	c_p kJ/k·deg
200	1.1403	436.5	2.803	1.75	1.1234	445.4	2.840	1.77
225	1.1459	437.2	2.797	1.74	1.1294	446.0	2.834	1.75
250	1.1512	437.9	2.791	1.72	1.1352	446.7	2.827	1.73
275	1.1564	438.6	2.785	1.71	1.1407	447.3	2.821	1.72
300	1.1614	439.4	2.779	1.70	1.1460	448.0	2.815	1.71
325	1.1662	440.2	2.774	1.69	1.1511	448.8	2.810	1.70
350	1.1709	441.0	2.769	1.68	1.1561	449.6	2.804	1.69
375	1.1755	441.9	2.763	1.67	1.1609	450.4	2.798	1.68
400	1.1790	442.8	2.758	1.66	1.1656	451.2	2.793	1.67
425	1.1842	443.7	2.753	1.65	1.1701	452.1	2.787	1.66
450	1.1884	444.6	2.748	1.64	1.1746	453.0	2.782	1.65
475	1.1925	445.5	2.743	1.64	1.1788	453.9	2.777	1.64
500	1.1965	446.5	2.738	1.63	1.1830	454.8	2.773	1.63
525	1.2004	447.5	2.734	1.63	1.1871	455.7	2.768	1.63
550	1.2042	448.5	2.729	1.62	1.1911	456.7	2.763	1.62
575	1.2079	449.5	2.725	1.61	1.1950	457.7	2.759	1.62
600	1.2115	450.5	2.720	1.61	1.1988	458.7	2.754	1.61

$T=250°$K $\qquad\qquad\qquad\qquad$ $T=255°$K

p, bar	ρ, g/cm³	i, kJ/kg	s kJ/k·deg	c_p kJ/k·deg	ρ, g/cm³	i, kJ/kg	s kJ/k·deg	c_p kJ/k·deg
20	1.0468	453.1	2.938	2.04	—	—	—	—
25	1.0489	453.1	2.936	2.02	1.0249	463.3	2.977	2.09
30	1.0510	453.0	2.934	2.01	1.0273	463.2	2.974	2.08
35	1.0530	453.0	2.932	2.00	1.0297	463.1	2.972	2.07
40	1.0551	453.0	2.930	1.99	1.0320	463.0	2.970	2.05
45	1.0570	452.9	2.928	1.98	1.0342	462.9	2.968	2.04
50	1.0590	452.9	2.926	1.97	1.0364	462.9	2.966	2.03
60	1.0628	452.9	2.922	1.95	1.0407	462.8	2.961	2.01
70	1.0665	452.9	2.918	1.93	1.0448	462.7	2.957	2.00
80	1.0700	452.9	2.914	1.93	1.0488	462.6	2.953	1.98
90	1.0734	453.0	2.911	1.91	1.0527	462.6	2.949	1.95
100	1.0768	453.0	2.907	1.89	1.0564	462.6	2.945	1.93
125	1.0848	453.2	2.899	1.87	1.0652	462.6	2.936	1.90
150	1.0923	453.5	2.891	1.84	1.0735	462.8	2.928	1.87
175	1.0994	453.9	2.883	1.81	1.0812	463.0	2.920	1.84
200	1.1062	454.4	2.876	1.80	1.0885	463.4	2.912	1.82
225	1.1126	454.9	2.870	1.78	1.0955	463.8	2.905	1.80
250	1.1188	455.4	2.862	1.76	1.1021	464.2	2.898	1.78
275	1.1247	456.0	2.856	1.74	1.1084	464.8	2.891	1.76
300	1.1304	456.7	2.850	1.73	1.1145	465.4	2.884	1.75
325	1.1358	457.4	2.844	1.72	1.1203	466.0	2.878	1.74
350	1.1411	458.1	2.838	1.71	1.1259	466.6	2.872	1.73
375	1.1462	458.9	2.832	1.70	1.1313	467.3	2.866	1.72
400	1.1511	459.7	2.826	1.69	1.1365	468.1	2.860	1.70
425	1.1559	460.5	2.821	1.68	1.1416	468.8	2.855	1.69
450	1.1606	461.3	2.816	1.67	1.1465	469.6	2.849	1.68

Table—*Continued*

p, bar	ρ, g/cm³	i, kJ/kg	s kJ/k.deg	c_p	ρ, g/cm³	i, kJ/kg	s kJ/k.deg	c_p
475	1.1651	462.2	2.811	1.66	1.1512	470.4	2.844	1.67
500	1.1695	463.1	2.806	1.65	1.1558	471.3	2.839	1.66
525	1.1738	464.0	2.801	1.64	1.1604	472.2	2.834	1.65
550	1.1779	464.9	2.796	1.63	1.1647	473.1	2.829	1.64
575	1.1820	465.8	2.791	1.63	1.1689	474.0	2.824	1.64
600	1.1860	466.8	2.789	1.62	1.1731	474.9	2.819	1.63

		$T=260°K$				$T=265°K$		
25	0.9992	473.9	3.018	2.18	—	—	—	—
30	1.0020	473.7	3.015	2.17	0.9746	484.7	3.057	2.28
35	1.0048	473.6	3.013	2.15	0.9778	484.4	3.054	2.24
40	1.0074	473.4	3.010	2.13	0.9811	484.2	3.051	2.22
45	1.0101	473.2	3.008	2.11	0.9841	483.9	3.048	2.20
50	1.0126	473.1	3.005	2.09	0.9871	483.7	3.046	2.17
60	1.0175	472.9	3.001	2.06	0.9928	483.3	3.040	2.14
70	1.0222	472.7	2.996	2.04	0.9982	483.0	3.035	2.11
80	1.0267	472.5	2.992	2.02	1.0034	482.7	3.030	2.08
90	1.0311	472.4	2.988	1.99	1.0082	482.4	3.026	2.05
100	1.0352	472.3	2.983	1.97	1.0130	482.2	3.021	2.03
125	1.0450	472.1	2.974	1.94	1.0240	481.9	3.011	1.98
150	1.0541	472.1	2.965	1.89	1.0340	481.7	3.001	1.94
175	1.0625	472.3	2.956	1.87	1.0433	481.6	2.992	1.89
200	1.0705	472.5	2.948	1.84	1.0519	481.7	2.983	1.87
225	1.0780	472.8	2.940	1.82	1.0601	481.9	2.975	1.85
250	1.0851	473.2	2.932	1.79	1.0678	482.1	2.967	1.82
275	1.0919	473.6	2.925	1.77	1.0760	482.5	2.959	1.80
300	1.0983	474.1	2.918	1.76	1.0820	482.9	2.952	1.78
325	1.1045	474.6	2.912	1.74	1.0886	483.4	2.945	1.76
350	1.1105	475.2	2.905	1.73	1.0949	483.9	2.938	1.75
375	1.1162	475.9	2.899	1.72	1.1010	484.5	2.932	1.74
400	1.1217	476.5	2.893	1.70	1.1068	485.1	2.926	1.72
425	1.1271	477.3	2.887	1.69	1.1124	485.7	2.920	1.71
450	1.1322	478.0	2.882	1.68	1.1179	486.4	2.914	1.70
475	1.1372	478.8	2.876	1.67	1.1231	487.1	2.908	1.69
500	1.1421	479.6	2.871	1.66	1.1282	487.9	2.902	1.68
525	1.1468	480.4	2.866	1.66	1.1332	488.7	2.897	1.67
550	1.1514	481.2	2.861	1.65	1.1380	489.5	2.892	1.66
575	1.1559	482.1	2.856	1.64	1.1427	490.3	2.887	1.65
600	1.1602	483.0	2.851	1.63	1.1472	491.2	2.882	1.64

		$T=270°K$				$T=275°K$		
35	0.9483	495.9	3.097	2.40	—	—	—	—
40	0.9522	495.5	3.094	2.37	0.9197	507.3	3.138	2.56
45	0.9559	495.1	3.090	2.33	0.9244	506.8	3.134	2.50
50	0.9595	494.8	3.087	2.30	0.9289	506.2	3.130	2.46
60	0.9663	494.2	3.080	2.25	0.9373	505.3	3.123	2.38

Table—*Continued*

p, bar	ρ, g/cm³	i, kJ/kg	s kJ/k . deg	c_p kJ/k . deg	ρ, g/cm³	i, kJ/kg	s kJ/k . deg	c_p kJ/k . deg
70	0.9726	493.7	3.075	2.20	0.9450	504.5	3.116	2.32
80	0.9786	493.2	3.070	2.16	0.9521	503.9	3.110	2.26
90	0.9843	492.8	3.064	2.12	0.9587	503.3	3.104	2.22
100	0.9896	492.5	3.059	2.10	0.9649	502.8	3.098	2.17
125	1.0020	491.8	3.048	2.04	0.9790	501.8	3.085	2.10
150	1.0132	491.4	3.037	1.99	0.9916	501.1	3.074	2.04
175	1.0234	491.2	3.027	1.95	1.0089	500.7	3.069	1.98
200	1.0329	491.1	3.018	1.92	1.0133	500.4	3.053	1.95
225	1.0418	491.1	3.009	1.88	1.0230	500.3	3.043	1.91
250	1.0500	491.3	3.001	1.86	1.0319	500.3	3.035	1.89
275	1.0579	491.5	2.993	1.83	1.0404	500.4	3.026	1.86
300	1.0653	491.8	2.985	1.80	1.0483	500.6	3.018	1.83
325	1.0723	492.2	2.978	1.79	1.0559	500.9	3.011	1.82
350	1.0791	492.6	2.971	1.78	1.0630	501.2	3.003	1.79
375	1.0855	493.1	2.964	1.76	1.0699	501.6	2.996	1.78
400	1.0917	493.7	2.958	1.74	1.0764	502.1	2.991	1.77
425	1.0977	494.3	2.951	1.73	1.0827	502.6	2.983	1.75
450	1.1034	494.9	2.945	1.72	1.0888	503.2	2.977	1.74
475	1.1089	495.6	2.940	1.71	1.0946	503.8	2.971	1.73
500	1.1143	496.3	2.934	1.70	1.1003	504.5	2.965	1.72
525	1.1195	497.0	2.928	1.69	1.1057	505.2	2.959	1.71
550	1.1245	497.8	2.923	1.68	1.1110	506.2	2.954	1.70
575	1.1294	498.7	2.918	1.67	1.1161	506.7	2.948	1.69
600	1.1342	499.4	2.912	1.66	1.1211	507.4	2.943	1.68

	$T=280°$K					$T=285°$K		
45	0.8879	519.5	3.181	2.77	—	—	—	—
50	0.8940	518.7	3.176	2.68	—	—	—	—
60	0.9049	517.3	3.167	2.56	0.8671	530.5	3.211	2.87
70	0.9145	516.2	3.159	2.45	0.8800	528.7	3.201	2.68
80	0.9232	515.2	3.151	2.37	0.8912	527.2	3.192	2.56
90	0.9311	514.3	3.145	2.31	0.9010	526.0	3.184	2.46
100	0.9385	513.6	3.138	2.28	0.9099	525.0	3.176	2.39
125	0.9548	512.2	3.123	2.15	0.9292	523.0	3.160	2.24
150	0.9690	511.1	3.110	2.09	0.9454	521.5	3.145	2.16
175	0.9816	510.4	3.099	2.03	0.9596	520.5	3.133	2.08
200	0.9932	510.0	3.088	1.98	0.9724	519.8	3.121	2.02
225	1.0037	509.6	3.078	1.94	0.9839	519.2	3.110	1.98
250	1.0134	509.5	3.069	1.90	0.9945	518.9	3.100	1.94
275	1.0225	509.5	3.060	1.87	1.0044	518.7	3.091	1.91
300	1.0311	509.5	3.051	1.85	1.0136	518.7	3.081	1.89
325	1.0392	509.7	3.049	1.83	1.0222	518.8	3.073	1.86
350	1.0468	510.0	3.036	1.81	1.0304	518.9	3.066	1.84
375	1.0541	510.3	3.028	1.80	1.0381	519.2	3.058	1.82
400	1.0610	510.7	3.021	1.77	1.0455	519.5	3.051	1.80
425	1.0676	511.2	3.015	1.76	1.0525	519.9	3.044	1.79

Table—*Continued*

p, bar	ρ, g/cm³	i, kJ/kg	s kJ/k . deg	c_p kJ/k . deg	ρ, g/cm³	i, kJ/kg	s kJ/k . deg	c_p kJ/k . deg
450	1.0741	511.7	3.008	1.75	1.0593	520.3	3.037	1.78
475	1.0802	512.2	3.002	1.74	1.0657	520.8	3.030	1.77
500	1.0862	512.8	2.996	1.73	1.0720	521.3	3.024	1.75
525	1.0919	513.5	2.990	1.71	1.0780	521.9	3.018	1.74
550	1.0974	514.2	2.984	1.70	1.0838	522.6	3.012	1.73
575	1.1028	514.9	2.979	1.69	1.0894	523.2	3.006	1.72
600	1.1080	515.6	2.973	1.69	1.0948	523.9	3.001	1.71

$T = 290°$K $\qquad\qquad$ $T = 295°$K

p, bar	ρ, g/cm³	i, kJ/kg	s	c_p	ρ, g/cm³	i, kJ/kg	s	c_p
90	0.8673	541.3	3.226	2.66	—	—	—	—
100	0.8785	537.2	3.217	2.52	—	—	—	—
125	0.9017	534.4	3.197	2.33	0.8721	546.3	3.239	2.43
150	0.9207	532.5	3.181	2.21	0.8943	543.7	3.220	2.28
175	0.9367	531.1	3.167	2.12	0.9127	541.8	3.204	2.17
200	0.9505	530.0	3.154	2.06	0.9286	540.4	3.191	2.09
225	0.9636	529.2	3.143	2.01	0.9426	539.4	3.178	2.03
250	0.9731	528.7	3.132	1.97	0.9553	538.6	3.167	1.98
275	0.9858	528.4	3.122	1.94	0.9668	538.1	3.156	1.94
300	0.9957	528.2	3.113	1.90	0.9776	537.7	3.146	1.92
325	1.0050	528.1	3.104	1.88	0.9875	537.6	3.137	1.88
350	1.0137	528.2	3.095	1.86	0.9968	537.5	3.128	1.86
375	1.0219	528.3	3.088	1.84	1.0056	537.5	3.120	1.84
400	1.0298	528.6	3.080	1.81	1.0139	537.6	3.112	1.82
425	1.0372	528.9	3.073	1.79	1.0218	537.9	3.104	1.80
450	1.0443	529.2	3.066	1.78	1.0293	538.2	3.097	1.78
475	1.0511	529.7	3.059	1.77	1.0365	538.6	3.090	1.77
500	1.0577	530.2	3.052	1.76	1.0434	540.0	3.083	1.76
525	1.0640	530.7	3.046	1.75	1.0500	539.5	3.077	1.75
550	1.0701	531.3	3.040	1.73	1.0564	540.0	3.071	1.74
575	1.0760	531.9	3.034	1.72	1.0626	540.6	3.065	1.73
600	1.0817	532.6	3.028	1.72	1.0685	541.2	3.054	1.72

$T = 300°$K $\qquad\qquad$ $T = 305°$K

p, bar	ρ, g/cm³	i, kJ/kg	s	c_p	ρ, g/cm³	i, kJ/kg	s	c_p
150	0.8663	555.4	3.259	2.36	—	—	—	—
175	0.8876	552.9	3.241	2.23	0.8581	564.2	3.280	2.31
200	0.9054	551.1	3.226	2.14	0.8786	561.9	3.262	2.19
225	0.9211	549.8	3.212	2.07	0.8960	560.2	3.247	2.11
250	0.9350	548.8	3.200	2.02	0.9114	558.9	3.234	2.06
275	0.9476	548.0	3.189	1.97	0.9251	557.9	3.221	2.00
300	0.9591	547.5	3.178	1.94	0.9376	557.2	3.210	1.96
325	0.9698	547.2	3.168	1.90	0.9490	556.7	3.200	1.93
350	0.9798	547.0	3.159	1.88	0.9597	556.4	3.190	1.90
375	0.9891	546.9	3.150	1.85	0.9696	556.2	3.181	1.88
400	0.9979	546.9	3.142	1.83	0.9790	556.1	3.172	1.85
425	0.0063	547.1	3.134	1.82	0.9878	556.2	3.164	1.83

Table—*Continued*

p, bar	ρ, g/cm³	i, kJ/kg	s kJ/k.deg	c_p	ρ, g/cm³	i, kJ/kg	s kJ/k.deg	c_p
450	0.0142	547.3	3.127	1.80	0.9962	556.3	3.156	1.81
475	1.0218	547.6	3.120	1.78	1.0042	556.5	3.148	1.80
500	1.0291	548.0	3.113	1.77	1.0118	556.8	3.141	1.78
525	1.0360	548.4	3.106	1.76	1.0190	557.2	3.134	1.77
550	1.0427	548.9	3.100	1.75	1.0260	557.6	3.127	1.77
575	1.0491	549.4	3.093	1.74	1.0327	558.1	3.121	1.76
600	1.0553	550.0	3.087	1.74	1.0392	558.6	3.114	1.75
		$T=310°K$					$T=315°K$	
200	0.8566	573.0	3.298	2.23	—	—	—	—
225	0.8759	570.8	3.282	2.14	—	—	—	—
250	0.8928	569.2	3.268	2.07	0.8710	579.7	3.302	2.10
275	0.9078	568.0	3.255	2.01	0.8874	578.2	3.288	2.05
300	0.9213	567.1	3.243	1.97	0.9020	577.0	3.276	1.99
325	0.9337	566.4	3.232	1.93	0.9153	576.2	3.264	1.96
350	0.9451	566.0	3.222	1.90	0.9275	575.5	3.253	1.93
375	0.9557	565.6	3.212	1.87	0.9388	575.1	3.243	1.90
400	0.9656	565.5	3.203	1.85	0.9493	574.8	3.234	1.87
425	0.9750	565.4	3.195	1.83	0.9592	574.6	3.225	1.85
450	0.9838	565.5	3.187	1.81	0.9686	574.6	3.217	1.84
475	0.9922	565.6	3.179	1.80	0.9774	574.6	3.209	1.82
500	1.0003	565.8	3.172	1.78	0.9858	574.8	3.201	1.81
525	1.0079	566.1	3.165	1.77	0.9939	575.0	3.194	1.80
550	1.0152	566.5	3.158	1.76	1.0016	575.4	3.187	1.78
575	1.0223	566.9	3.152	1.75	1.0089	575.7	3.180	1.76
600	1.0291	567.4	3.145	1.74	1.0160	576.2	3.174	1.75

p, bar	ρ, g/cm³	i, kJ/kg	s kJ/k.deg	c_p kJ/k.deg
		$T=320°K$		
300	0.8824	587.0	3.307	2.00
325	0.8967	585.9	3.295	1.96
350	0.9097	585.1	3.284	1.92
375	0.9218	584.5	3.273	1.90
400	0.9330	584.1	3.264	1.87
425	0.9434	583.9	3.255	1.85
450	0.9533	583.7	3.246	1.83
475	0.9626	583.7	3.238	1.81
500	0.9714	583.8	3.230	1.80
525	0.9798	584.0	3.222	1.79
550	0.9879	584.2	3.215	1.78
575	0.9956	584.6	3.208	1.77
600	1.0030	585.0	3.202	1.75

equation of state, with the tabulated values in works [5, 6], shows close agreement between our results and those of work [5], but discrepancy between our data and those of work [6]. This may be due to the use of unreliable data on measurement of p-v-T relationships in work [1]. The calculated values of the adiabatic differential Drossel' effect at low temperatures agree satisfactorily with the experimental data due to Rozbuk, Merrel, and Miller, cited in reference [7]. The discrepancy does not exceed 0.013 deg/atm.

The calculated values of the thermodynamic quantities under investigation are presented in the preceding tables.

REFERENCES

1. AMAGAT, E. H. *Ann. de Chemie et de Phys.*, 6, **29**, 68, 109, 1893.
2. GOLOVSKY, E. A. and V. A. TSIMARNY. *Teploenergetika,* No. 1, 1969.
3. VASSERMAN, A. A. and V. A. RABINOVICH. In : *Teplofizicheskie kharakteristiki veshchestv* (*Thermophysical properties of substances*). *Series Fiz. Konst. i svoistva Vesh.* No. 1, 1968.
4. VASSERMAN, A. A. and V. A. RABINOVICH. *IFZh*, **12** (3), 1967.
5. KESSEL'MAN, P. M., P. A. KOTLYAREVSKY and M. M. AFANAS'YEV. *IFZh*, **9** (4), 1965.
6. NEWITT, D. M., M. U. PAI, N. R. KULOOR and T. HUGGIL. *Thermodynamic functions of gases,* 1, London, 1956.
7. VUKALOVICH. M. P. and V. V. ALTUNIN. *Teplofizicheskie svoistva dvuokisi ugleroda* (*Thermophysical properties of carbon dioxide*). Atomizdat, Moscow, 1965.

UDC 541.27

THERMAL CONDUCTIVITY OF CARBON DIOXIDE IN THE NEAR-CRITICAL REGION

P. M. Kessel'man and *V. R. Kamenetskii*

Thermal conductivity of carbon dioxide at high pressures has been studied by a number of investigators. A detailed survey and analysis of the experimental works on this topic have been presented in monograph [1]. However, there are few works devoted to the tabulation of the coefficient of thermal conductivity of CO_2 at high pressures. Most interesting from the practical viewpoint are the tables by Tsederberg and Morozova [2, 3] at $t= -75\text{-}1200°C$ and $p=1\text{-}200$ kg/cm².

Vukalovich and Altunin [1] have prepared more detailed tables of thermal conductivity of CO_2 at $t=0\text{-}1000°C$, $p=1\text{-}600$ bar, following careful analysis of the available experimental data. Calculations utilized an equation of the type $\Delta\lambda=f(\rho)$, where $\Delta\lambda=\lambda_{p,T}-\lambda_T$ is the excess thermal conductivity; $\lambda_{p,T}$ is the coefficient of thermal conductivity at pressure p and temperature T; λ_T is the coefficient of thermal conductivity at temperature T but at atmospheric pressure, and $f(\rho)$ is an exponential polynomial in terms of density ρ.

$$f(\rho)= \sum_{i=1}^{n} a_i\, \rho^{i}.$$

Hence, during tabulation [1] the values of the excess thermal conductivity were calculated using a single-parameter equation without accounting for the temperature dependence of the coefficients of the polynomial $f(\rho)$. It is well-known that such a method can ensure high accuracy only at temperatures sufficiently remote from the critical point, as was also noted by the authors of work [1]. Naturally, the region of liquid phase and the near-critical region of CO_2 could not have been analyzed accurately and in detail in work [1]. Experimental data by other investigators on the near-critical region are less accurate and do not evince consistently satisfactory common agreement. For example, Guildner's works [4-6] and Michels's work [7] observe maxima for the thermal conductivity in coordinates λ and p approaching critical density and critical temperature. However, Tsederberg [2] considers Guildner's data to require experimental verification since the occurrence of the maxima of thermal conductivity is probably caused by the convective heat transfer in the apparatus. Amirkhanov and Adamov [8] observed a similar effect in their experiments but, similar to Tsederberg, attributed this to convection.

Vukalovich and Altunin [1], following careful analysis of the data and methods of works [4-8], concluded that the existence of peaks of thermal conductivity in λ and ρ coordinates at near-critical point cannot be considered as experimentally established.*

Hence, at present there are no reliable and detailed data on the thermal conductivity of CO_2 in the near-critical region, which data are essential for design of the prospective CO_2-based power stations.

Considering these factors, the present authors have attempted tabulation of the coefficient of thermal conductivity of CO_2 in the near-critical region, utilizing an equation representing the thermal conductivity of a real gas and a function of two variables, density and temperature.

In reference [9] an equation and equation-formulation method are given for calculation of viscosity of compressed gases. This method is based on reliable experimental data on viscosity, and the equation has the following form :

$$\eta_{p,T}/\eta_T = p_0\,(\omega) + p_1\,(\omega)\,\frac{1}{\tau} + p_2\,(\omega)\,\frac{1}{\tau_2} + \cdots, \tag{1}$$

where

$$p_0\,(\omega) = 1 + \sum_{i=1}^{n} a_i\,\omega^i;\; p_1\,(\omega) = \sum_{i=1}^{n} b_i\,\omega^i;\; p_2\,(\omega) = \sum_{i=1}^{n} c_i\,\omega^i,\; \cdots$$

---

* After the present article was written, some papers have been published concerning the relationship betw. en thermal conductivity and temperature and density in the near-critical region (e.g., Brokaw, R. S., *Statistical mechanical theories of transport properties*, NASA TMX-52478, 1968). In the present article, λ has been calculated assuming that its magnitude does not evince any peculiar behavior in the near-critical region. Nevertheless, the procedure proposed is sufficiently universal and can also explain the "maxima" of λ, if the existence of these maxima is finally established.

$\omega = \rho/\rho_{cr}$ is transferred density; $\tau = T/T_{cr}$ is transferred temperature; ρ_{cr} is critical density; T_{cr} is critical temperature; and a_1, b_1 and c_1 are individual constants.

Reference [9] also gives the coefficients occurring in equation (1) for CO_2, and shows equation (1) to represent, with sufficient accuracy, data on viscosity of CO_2 [10] in the gaseous and liquid phases on the saturation curve. At temperatures greater than or equal to 250°C, equation (1) can reproduce the calculated data of work [1] with an average accuracy within 0.6%.

Using a procedure analogous to that of study [9], we have derived an equation for calculation of thermal conductivity of CO_2 which also has a structure similar to equation (1) :

$$\lambda_{p,T}/\lambda_T = \varphi_0(\omega) + \varphi_1(\omega) \cdot \frac{1}{\tau} + \varphi_2(\omega) \frac{1}{\tau^2}, \qquad (2)$$

In this equation, the polynomials $\varphi_0(\omega)$, $\varphi_1(\omega)$, and $\varphi_2(\omega)$ are analogous to $p_0(\omega)$, $p_1(\omega)$, and $p_2(\omega)$ in equation (1). The values of coefficients occurring in equation (2) are given below. Values of $T_{cr} = 304.20°K$ and $\rho_{cr} = 0.4682$ g/cm³ have been assumed.

Equation (2) represents the experimental data of Amirkhanov and Adamov [8] on thermal conductivity of CO_2 on the saturation curve with an average accuracy of 2.5% and 4.0% for saturated vapor and liquid respectively. Calculated values obtained by Vukalovich and Altunin [1] on thermal conductivity of CO_2 over the entire range of parameters can be reproduced with an average accuracy of 1.0%.

Using equation (2), we have calculated the values of the coefficient of thermal conductivity of CO_2 in the temperature range 273-313°K and pressures of 50-80 bar (see tabulated data below). Values of the coefficients of thermal conductivity under atmospheric pressure λ_T and the values of density have been taken directly from work [1].

		a_1	b_1	c_1
1	..	0.08635	0.54652	0.50941
2	..	0.11259	0.71231	0.66408
3	..	—0.07952	—0.50346	—0.46920
4	..	0.02726	0.17245	0.16078

Considering that our data agree within 2-3% with the experimental and theoretical data obtained by other authors, it may be assumed that our recommended tabulated values of λ for CO_2 (preceding table) in the near-critical region are reasonably accurate.

Thermal conductivity of CO_2 in the near-critical region
$\lambda \cdot 10^{-4}$, $W/m \cdot deg$

p, bar	$\lambda \cdot 10^{-4}$ at T, °K								
	273	274	275	276	277	278	279	280	281
50	1125	1113	1101	1088	1075	1062	1048	1035	1021
51	1127	1115	1103	1090	1077	1064	1051	1037	1023
52	1129	1117	1105	1092	1079	1066	1053	1039	1025
53	1131	1119	1107	1094	1082	1068	1055	1041	1027
54	1133	1121	1109	1096	1084	1071	1058	1044	1030
55	1135	1123	1111	1099	1086	1073	1060	1047	1033
56	1137	1125	1113	1101	1089	1076	1063	1050	1036
57	1139	1127	1115	1103	1091	1078	1065	1052	1038
58	1141	1129	1117	1105	1093	1080	1067	1054	1041
59	1143	1131	1119	1108	1096	1083	1070	1057	1044
60	1144	1133	1122	1110	1098	1085	1073	1060	1046
61	1145	1135	1124	1112	1100	1088	1075	1062	1048
62	1147	1136	1125	1114	1102	1090	1077	1064	1051
63	1149	1138	1127	1116	1104	1092	1079	1066	1053
64	1150	1140	1129	1118	1106	1094	1082	1069	1056
65	1152	1142	1131	1120	1108	1096	1084	1072	1059
66	1154	1144	1133	1122	1111	1099	1087	1074	1062
67	1156	1146	1135	1124	1113	1101	1089	1076	1064
68	1157	1147	1137	1126	1115	1103	1092	1079	1067
69	1158	1149	1139	1128	1117	1106	1094	1082	1070
70	1160	1150	1140	1130	1119	1108	1096	1084	1073
71	1161	1152	1142	1132	1121	1110	1098	1087	1075
72	1162	1154	1144	1134	1123	1112	1100	1089	1077
73	1164	1156	1146	1136	1125	1114	1102	1091	1079
74	1165	1158	1148	1138	1127	1116	1104	1093	1081
75	1167	1159	1150	1140	1129	1118	1107	1095	1083
76	1169	1161	1152	1142	1131	1120	1109	1098	1085
77	1171	1163	1153	1144	1134	1123	1112	1100	1088
78	1173	1164	1155	1146	1136	1125	1114	1103	1091
79	1175	1166	1157	1148	1138	1127	1116	1105	1093
80	1177	1168	1159	1150	1140	1129	1118	1107	1095

Table—*Continued*

p, bar	$\lambda \cdot 10^{-4}$ at T, °K								
	282	283	284	285	286	287	288	289	290
50	1006	990.7	975.0	958.9	942.6	926.0	247.4	246.3	245.2
51	1008	993.2	977.8	962.0	945.9	929.0	912.0	250.7	249.4
52	1010	995.7	980.1	964.6	948.3	932.1	915.5	897.5	254.3
53	1013	998.0	983.0	967.0	952.0	935.0	919.0	902.0	259.7
54	1016	1001	986.4	971.1	956.6	939.2	923.4	904.5	885.9
55	1019	1005	990.0	975.1	959.6	943.5	926.9	909.4	891.5
56	1022	1008	993.0	977.8	963.5	947.0	930.3	914.4	895.5
57	1024	1010	996.0	981.0	965.9	950.1	933.9	916.9	899.5
58	1027	1013	998.8	984.0	969.0	953.6	937.4	920.9	903.3
59	1030	1016	1002	986.9	972.0	956.5	940.8	924.6	907.4
60	1032	1018	1004	989.9	975.0	960.0	944.6	928.5	911.9
61	1035	1021	1008	993.2	978.3	963.7	948.2	932.5	915.9
62	1038	1024	1010	995.8	981.5	967.0	951.8	935.9	919.2
63	1040	1027	1013	998.9	984.8	970.0	955.1	939.6	923.2
64	1043	1030	1016	1002	987.8	973.2	958.6	943.3	927.2
65	1046	1033	1019	1005	991.3	976.8	961.9	946.4	930.5
66	1049	1036	1022	1008	994.4	979.9	965.2	950.0	934.3
67	1051	1038	1025	1011	997.2	983.0	968.2	953.0	937.1
68	1054	1041	1028	1014	1000	985.9	971.1	954.0	940.3
69	1057	1044	1030	1017	1003	988.8	974.5	959.5	944.4
70	1059	1044	1033	1019	1006	991.7	977.2	962.8	947.8
71	1062	1049	1035	1022	1008	994.4	980.2	965.8	951.0
72	1064	1051	1038	1024	1011	997.0	983.3	969.5	954.8
73	1066	1053	1040	1024	1013	1000	986.0	972.0	957.2
74	1068	1055	1042	1029	1016	1003	989.1	975.0	960.4
75	1070	1057	1045	1032	1019	1006	992.5	978.7	964.5
76	1073	1060	1048	1035	1022	1009	996.0	982.3	968.2
77	1076	1064	1051	1038	1025	1012	999.0	985.4	971.8
78	1079	1066	1054	1041	1028	1015	1002	988.3	974.8
79	1081	1069	1057	1044	1031	1018	1005	991.7	978.1
80	1084	1072	1059	1047	1034	1021	1008	994.9	981.5

Table—*Continued*

p, bar	$\lambda \cdot 10^{-4}$ at T, °K								
	291	292	293	294	295	296	297	298	299
50	244.3	243.5	242.6	242.1	241.6	241.1	240.8	240.5	240.1
51	248.3	247.3	246.4	245.6	244.9	244.4	243.9	243.5	243.0
52	252.8	251.6	250.4	249.5	248.6	247.9	247.3	246.7	246.2
53	257.8	256.3	254.8	253.6	252.5	251.6	250.7	250.0	249.4
54	263.2	261.4	259.6	258.1	256.8	255.6	254.6	253.5	252.8
55	872.3	266.5	264.6	262.8	261.2	259.8	258.4	257.3	256.3
56	877.2	857.7	270.6	268.2	266.2	264.4	262.7	261.4	260.2
57	881.6	862.8	277.3	274.5	271.9	269.8	267.7	266.1	264.6
58	885.3	866.5	846.2	281.1	277.6	274.9	272.4	270.5	268.8
59	889.7	870.9	851.7	831.0	284.5	281.3	278.3	275.9	273.8
60	894.2	875.9	856.3	835.3	813.0	288.3	284.7	282.2	279.2
61	898.2	880.3	861.1	841.0	819.9	296.9	292.4	289.0	285.4
62	902.4	884.8	866.0	846.1	825.0	802.2	300.8	295.6	291.6
63	906.2	889.0	870.8	851.3	830.4	807.8	783.7	304.5	299.3
64	910.5	893.2	874.9	856.1	836.0	814.3	791.1	315.6	308.2
65	914.1	896.9	878.9	860.0	840.1	819.5	797.5	773.5	319.0
66	917.8	900.5	882.9	864.2	845.1	824.8	802.5	778.0	750.0
67	920.8	904.0	886.8	868.9	850.5	830.8	809	785.9	758.7
68	924.5	907.9	891.0	873.2	855.0	835.3	814.5	791.9	766.2
69	928.5	912.2	895.5	877.9	859.9	841.0	820.3	797.7	773.0
70	932.1	916.1	899.5	882.5	864.8	846.1	826.1	804.9	781.3
71	935.8	920.0	903.9	887.0	869.3	851.5	832.5	806.9	789.0
72	939.6	924.1	908.0	891.5	874.1	856.4	837.8	817.8	795.7
73	942.4	927.1	911.3	895.2	878.5	861.7	843.7	824.2	802.7
74	945.8	930.9	915.4	899.5	883.2	866.4	849.1	830.1	809.5
75	950.0	935.2	920.4	904.3	888.2	871.3	854.0	835.8	816.1
76	953.9	939.1	924.3	909.0	893.3	876.9	859.3	842.0	823.5
77	957.5	943.0	928.1	913.2	897.8	881.9	864.8	848.1	828.1
78	960.9	946.6	932.3	917.5	902.4	886.5	870.2	853.0	835.0
79	964.3	950.2	936.1	921.5	906.5	890.9	874.8	857.8	839.6
80	967.9	954.0	939.8	925.3	910.5	895.1	879.2	862.5	844.9

Table—*Continued*

p, bar	$\lambda.10^{-4}$ at T, °K								
	300	301	302	303	304	305	306	307	308
50	240.0	239.8	239.7	239.6	239.5	239.5	239.5	239.6	239.7
51	242.7	242.5	242.2	242.0	242.0	242.0	242.0	242.0	242.0
52	245.8	245.4	245.1	244.9	244.6	244.5	244.5	244.5	244.5
53	248.9	248.5	248.0	247.7	247.4	247.2	247.0	246.9	246.8
54	252.1	251.5	251.0	250.5	250.1	249.9	249.6	249.4	249.3
55	255.4	254.6	254.0	253.4	252.9	252.5	252.2	252.0	251.7
56	259.3	258.4	257.5	257.0	256.3	255.8	255.4	255.0	254.7
57	263.3	262.2	261.2	260.4	259.6	259.0	258.4	257.9	257.4
58	267.3	266.0	264.9	263.9	263.1	262.3	261.6	261.0	260.4
59	272.0	270.4	269.0	267.7	266.7	265.7	264.9	264.0	263.5
60	276.9	275.0	273.3	271.7	270.4	269.3	268.3	267.5	266.7
61	282.6	280.2	277.9	276.2	274.6	273.4	272.2	271.0	270.2
62	288.2	285.4	282.9	280.7	279.0	277.5	276.1	274.8	273.8
63	295.2	291.8	288.9	286.3	284.0	282.2	280.3	278.7	277.5
64	302.6	298.4	294.9	291.8	289.3	286.9	284.8	283.1	281.5
65	311.8	306.3	301.7	297.4	294.7	291.9	289.5	287.5	285.6
66	322.7	315.2	309.3	304.7	300.8	297.7	294.8	292.4	290.3
67	337.3	325.5	317.9	312.2	307.5	303.6	300.3	297.6	295.0
68	737.8	340.1	329.2	320.8	314.7	310.1	306.3	303.0	300.2
69	744.5	710.0	342.7	332.5	323.8	317.9	313.1	309.1	305.8
70	755.0	724.0	363.2	346.4	334.4	327.1	321.3	316.4	312.3
71	764.0	735.1	698.5	363.6	348.0	337.4	329.3	323.4	318.5
72	771.2	743.2	710.2	662.0	364.2	340.2	339.4	332.0	325.1
73	779.1	752.6	723.0	681.8	385.0	363.7	350.9	341.7	334.7
74	786.2	760.1	732.2	697.2	622.0	388.3	366.1	352.6	343.4
75	795.2	772.8	747.2	715.0	669.5	435.8	385.7	366.6	354.4
76	803.6	781.9	757.5	728.8	690.2	626.5	417.5	382.0	367.0
77	808.6	788.2	764.8	737.3	703.6	657.0	513.0	411.5	383.5
78	815.3	795.0	772.3	746.4	714.9	674.8	603.0	452.5	404.0
79	820.2	800.3	779.2	754.8	727.3	691.5	634.6	534.0	433.5
80	826.0	806.1	785.2	762.3	735.5	704.3	660.3	603.0	482.5

Table—*Continued*

p, bar	$\lambda.10^{-4}$ at T, °K				
	309	310	311	312	313
50	239.9	240.0	240.1	240.2	240.3
51	242.0	242.1	242.2	242.3	242.4
52	244.5	244.5	244.5	244.5	244.6
53	246.8	246.8	246.7	246.7	246.7
54	249.2	249.1	249.1	249.2	249.2
55	251.6	251.5	251.5	251.4	251.4
56	254.5	254.2	254.0	253.8	253.6
57	257.0	256.8	256.5	256.3	256.1
58	260.0	259.6	259.3	259.0	258.6
59	263.0	262.5	262.1	261.7	261.5
60	266.0	265.5	264.9	264.5	264.0
61	269.4	268.7	268.0	267.4	266.8
62	272.9	272.0	271.4	270.6	269.9
63	276.3	275.3	274.5	273.7	273.1
64	280.1	279.0	277.8	276.9	276.0
65	284.2	282.8	281.7	280.8	279.9
66	288.6	286.4	285.6	284.4	283.4
67	293.0	291.0	289.4	288.0	286.7
68	297.7	295.6	293.7	292.0	290.5
69	302.9	300.5	298.4	296.3	294.6
70	308.6	305.5	302.7	300.4	298.4
71	314.5	310.9	308.0	305.4	303.3
72	321.1	317.2	313.7	310.6	308.1
73	328.4	323.5	319.7	316.4	313.7
74	336.4	330.7	326.0	322.3	319.1
75	345.6	338.8	333.3	328.8	325.0
76	356.3	347.8	340.8	335.2	330.2
77	368.0	357.5	349.5	342.8	337.4
78	383.4	370.0	359.7	351.4	345.0
79	401.5	382.6	369.8	359.6	350.9
80	423.0	398.1	382.3	368.7	357.3

REFERENCES

1. VUKALOVICH, M. P. and V. V. ALTUNIN. *Teplofizicheskie svoistva dvuokisi ugleroda (Thermophysical properties of carbon dioxide).* Atomizdat, Moscow, 1965.

2. TSEDERBERG, N. V. *Teploprovodnost' szhatykh gazov i zhidkostei (Thermal conductivity of compressed gases and liquids)* 1963.

3. TSEDERBERG, N. V. and N. A. MOROZOVA. *Teploenergetika*, No. 1, 75, 1960.

4. GUILDNER, L. A. Transport properties in gases. *Proc. Second Biennial Gas Dynamics Symposium*, Evanston, North-western Univ. Press, p. 55, 1958.

5. GUILDNER, L. A. *Proc. Nat. Acad. Sci. U.S.A.*, No. 11, 1149, 1958.

6. GUILDNER, L. A. *Res. Nat. Bur. Standards A*, **66**, 333, 1962.

7. MICHELS, A., J. V. SENGERS and P. S. VAN DER GULIK. *Physica*, **28**, 1216, 1962.

8. AMIRKHANOV, KH. I. and V. R. KAMENETSKY. *Teploenergetika*, No. 7, 77, 1963.

9. KESSEL'MAN, P. M. and V. R. KAMENETSKY. *Teploenergetika*, No. 9, 73, 1967.

10. GOLUBEV, I. F. *Vyazkost' gazov i gazovykh smesei (Viscosity of gases and gas mixtures).* Fizmatgiz, Moscow, 1959.

UDC 541.27

THERMODYNAMIC PROPERTIES OF
DISSOCIATED CARBON DIOXIDE

P. M. Kessel'man and *P. A. Kotlyarevskii*

The aim of the present work is to determine the properties of dissociated carbon dioxide in respect to the real-gas effects of the components at temperatures upto 4000°K and pressures upto 600 bar.

Analysis of the data in work [1], which presents the properties of dissociated CO_2 (ideal-gas components), enabled the present authors to devote full attention to study of the following reactions

$$CO_2 \rightleftharpoons CO + \tfrac{1}{2}O_2, \tag{1}$$
$$O_2 \rightleftharpoons 2O, \tag{2}$$

since these reactions mainly determine the composition of the mixture at temperatures upto 4000°K. The ionized components and the atomic carbon which may exist in molal fractions of the order of $1 . 10^{-10}$ at $T \leqslant 4000°K$ may be neglected, as these have practically no influence on the properties of the mixture. Thus, it may be accurately stated that the mixture consists of CO_2, CO, O_2 and O.

The thermodynamic properties of the molecular components of these materials were determined by methods described in works [2, 3]. The equations of state of carbon monoxide [5, 10] and molecular oxygen [11-17] were formulated using the values of the second and third virial coefficients obtained on the basis of numerous p-v-T data. These equations of state have the following form :

$$p\, v = RT \left(1 + \frac{B\,(T)}{v} + \frac{C\,(T)}{v^2} \right), \tag{3}$$

where

$$B = b_0 + b_1\Theta + b_2\Theta^2 + \ldots, \text{cm}^3/\text{mole} \tag{4}$$

$$C = c_0 + c_1\Theta + c_2\Theta^2 + \ldots, \text{cm}^6/\text{mole}^2 \tag{5}$$

and $\Theta = \dfrac{1000}{T°K}$

The equations of state of "pure" carbon dioxide have been published in a previous work [4].

The values of coefficients occurring in the above equations for the temperature interval of 300-4000°K are presented in Table 1.

Table 1.   Values of coefficients in the equations of state for CO_2 O_2 and O

Coefficient	Values of the coefficients for components			Coefficient	Values of the coefficients for components	
	CO	O_2	O		CO	O_2
b_0	29.7446	24.3554	16.8697	c_0	469.174	301.846
b_1	22.5678	21.0417	—0.584038	c_1	1843.61	1485.77
b_2	—39.5364	—42.1618	—0.890279	c_2	—2075.62	—1941.19
b_3	23.1851	27.6441	0.469843	c_3	1341.51	1428.53
b_4	—7.75688	—10.2136	—0.111492	c_4	—489.337	—583.095
b_5	1.36043	1.95211	0.0129799	c_5	94.0901	123.613
b_6	—0.0978379	—0.151023	—0.0059228	c_6	—7.35297	—10.5212

It has been generally established that the range of pressures described by two virial coefficients considerably increases with increasing temperatures. Investigations have shown that for the materials mentioned above the pressure range covers 1-600 bar at $T \approx 1000°K$. Consequently, at temperatures $T \approx 1000$-4000°K the equations can be used for considerably higher pressures.

The close agreement between the theoretical and experimental values of high-temperature viscosity can serve as a reliable criterion of authenticity of the values of B and C obtained above. This is valid because a single potential parameter describes not only the thermal quantities, but also the transfer function. It has been established that the average magnitude of the deviation of the theoretical values of the coefficient of viscosity η_T of CO_2 from the experimental values [18-20], upto T=1600°K constitutes only 1% (the maximum deviation is 2.4%). The calculated values of the thermal conductivity also agree with the experimental values within limits of experimental accuracy. It is significant that experimental data on viscosity of O_2 and CO are also available for a much wider temperature range, in comparison to that of the p-v-T data. For the p-v-T data are available only upto 470°K with viscosity data upto 1500°K, and for CO the corresponding figures are 670°K and 1500°K.

An equation of state for atomic oxygen with one virial coefficient B [3] was obtained based on analysis of the electron configuration of atoms O in reference to all 18 curves of potential energy. The coefficients of this equation, corresponding to the equations (3-5), are also presented in Table 1.

Data on the different properties of the components of the reactive system enabled the present authors to investigate the influence of the real-gas effect on the constants of equilibrium K_{p1} and K_{p2} (of reactions 1 and 2) and, consequently, on the equilibrium composition and the properties of dissociated carbon dioxide. Assuming that the mixture obeys Amagat's law, we shall discuss the accuracy of this law later on. We calculated the equilibrium composition X_i of the real mixture with reference to the function K defined in terms of the coefficient of volatility, $\tau_i = \dfrac{f_i}{p}$. It has been established that the differences between the absolute values of X_i, as determined with the ideal-gas constants $K^0{}_p$ and those related to the real-gas effects K_p, do not exceed $\Delta X_i = 0.003$ at temperature $T = 4000°K$ and pressure $p = 600$ bar.*

Calculations have shown that the deviations in the equilibrium composition of a chemically reactive system affect the magnitudes of enthalpy due to the comparatively high values of heats of reaction, while the specific volumes are affected to a lesser extent.

It has also been established that the maximum errors in ΔX_i result in enthalpy change not exceeding 15 kJ/kg (at minimum, corresponding to $T = 4000°K$ and $p = 600$ bar). This observation permitted us to calculate the equilibrium composition on the basis of the well-known values of the equilibrium constants $K_p{}^0$ [21]. Within the limits of the required accuracy, the influence of the interaction of the dissimilar molecules j and k within the investigated ranges of parameters may be estimated on the basis of solely the second virial coefficients of the components.

Accordingly, the equation of state of the mixture is represented in the form :

$$v_{cm} = \sum_i v_i X_i + \sum_{\substack{j,\,k \\ j \neq k}} X_j X_h \triangle v_{j,k}, \tag{6}$$

where $\qquad \triangle v_{j,k} = 2 B_{j,k} - (B_j + B_k) + \dfrac{(B_j - B_k)^2}{RT} p;$

and v_i is real volumes of the components.

* At these values of the parameters, ΔX_i constitutes the highest value.

For the determination of the second virial coefficient $B_{j,k}$, which accounts for the dual interaction of the dissimilar molecules j and k of the mixture, it is necessary to determine the potential of interaction $U_{j,k}$. It is established [2, 3] that a function with variable potential parameters $\sigma(T)$ and $\varepsilon(T)$, universal for a large group of materials, enables reliable description of the desired potential $U_{j,k}$ which is determined by its potential parameters $\sigma_{j,k}$ and $\varepsilon_{j,k}$. The latter value can be determined from the following equation :

$$\sigma_{j,k} = \frac{1}{2} (\sigma_j + \sigma_k) \; ; \; \varepsilon_{j,k} = \sqrt{\varepsilon_j \, \varepsilon_k}.$$

The accuracy of this equation for the given function is discussed in reference [3].

On the basis of data on the known potential parameters, the virial coefficients of the components of the mixture, and on the calculated composition of the mixture, it has been established that the contribution of the term $\Sigma X_j X_k \triangle v_{j,k}$ for molecular components at $T > 1800°K$ and at pressures upto 600 bar may be neglected. The magnitude of this contribution is only 0.1% and $\sim 0.2\%$ with respect to the effect of the atomic-molecular interaction on v_{mix}. This factor has served as the basis for calculation of the properties of dissociated carbon dioxide by treating it as a mixture of variable composition in accordance with Amagat's law [21]

It is interesting to compare the results of calculation of properties of the real-gas mixture (viz., the specific volume v_{mix} and the enthalpy i_{mix}) with the corresponding values determined by the ideal-gas equations.

$T, °K$	Correction due to real-gas effect in v_{mix}, % at pressures :		$T, °K$	Correction due to real-gas effect in i_{mix}, kJ/kg at pressures :	
	100 bar	600 bar		100 bar	600 bar
2000	2.0	12.0	2000	2.5	23.3
3000	1.4	8.7	3000	7.2	40.8
4000	1.0	6.0	4000	0.8	52.8

This comparison clearly emphasizes importance of the real-gas effect of the components in determination of the properties of dissociated CO_2 in the particular pressure range despite the relatively high temperatures.

Tables 2-6 present selected values of the various properties of dissociated carbon dioxide.

Table 2. Equilibrium composition of dissociated carbon dioxide

T, °K

p, bar	2000				3000				4000			
	X_O	X_{O_2}	X_{CO}	X_{CO_2}	X_O	X_{O_2}	X_{CO}	X_{CO_2}	X_{O_2}	X_O	X_{CO}	X_{CO_2}
1	$5774 \cdot 10^{-8}$	$7454 \cdot 10^{-6}$	$1497 \cdot 10^{-5}$	$9775 \cdot 10^{-4}$	$4505 \cdot 10^{-5}$	$1585 \cdot 10^{-4}$	$3620 \cdot 10^{-4}$	$4344 \cdot 10^{-4}$	$6721 \cdot 10^{-5}$	$3857 \cdot 10^{-4}$	$5201 \cdot 10^{-4}$	$2700 \cdot 10^{-5}$
5	$1982 \cdot 10^{-8}$	$4392 \cdot 10^{-6}$	$8803 \cdot 10^{-6}$	$9868 \cdot 10^{-4}$	$1756 \cdot 10^{-5}$	$1204 \cdot 10^{-4}$	$2583 \cdot 10^{-4}$	$6038 \cdot 10^{-4}$	$1388 \cdot 10^{-4}$	$2479 \cdot 10^{-4}$	$5256 \cdot 10^{-4}$	$8770 \cdot 10^{-5}$
10	$1250 \cdot 10^{-8}$	$3493 \cdot 10^{-6}$	$6999 \cdot 10^{-6}$	$9895 \cdot 10^{-4}$	$1150 \cdot 10^{-5}$	$1032 \cdot 10^{-4}$	$2179 \cdot 10^{-4}$	$6673 \cdot 10^{-4}$	$1628 \cdot 10^{-4}$	$1898 \cdot 10^{-4}$	$5155 \cdot 10^{-4}$	$1318 \cdot 10^{-4}$
40	$4967 \cdot 10^{-9}$	$2207 \cdot 10^{-6}$	$4419 \cdot 10^{-6}$	$9934 \cdot 10^{-4}$	$4824 \cdot 10^{-6}$	$7271 \cdot 10^{-5}$	$1502 \cdot 10^{-4}$	$7722 \cdot 10^{-4}$	$1824 \cdot 10^{-4}$	$1005 \cdot 10^{-4}$	$4653 \cdot 10^{-4}$	$2518 \cdot 10^{-4}$
60	$3792 \cdot 10^{-9}$	$1929 \cdot 10^{-6}$	$3863 \cdot 10^{-6}$	$9942 \cdot 10^{-4}$	$3727 \cdot 10^{-6}$	$6508 \cdot 10^{-5}$	$1339 \cdot 10^{-4}$	$7973 \cdot 10^{-4}$	$1811 \cdot 10^{-4}$	$8174 \cdot 10^{-5}$	$4440 \cdot 10^{-4}$	$2932 \cdot 10^{-4}$
80	$3131 \cdot 10^{-9}$	$1754 \cdot 10^{-6}$	$3510 \cdot 10^{-6}$	$9947 \cdot 10^{-4}$	$3100 \cdot 10^{-6}$	$6004 \cdot 10^{-5}$	$1231 \cdot 10^{-4}$	$8137 \cdot 10^{-4}$	$1786 \cdot 10^{-4}$	$7029 \cdot 10^{-5}$	$4275 \cdot 10^{-4}$	$3236 \cdot 10^{-4}$
100	$2698 \cdot 10^{-9}$	$1628 \cdot 10^{-6}$	$3260 \cdot 10^{-6}$	$9951 \cdot 10^{-4}$	$2686 \cdot 10^{-6}$	$5635 \cdot 10^{-5}$	$1154 \cdot 10^{-4}$	$8256 \cdot 10^{-4}$	$1758 \cdot 10^{-4}$	$6238 \cdot 10^{-5}$	$4140 \cdot 10^{-4}$	$3477 \cdot 10^{-4}$
150	$2060 \cdot 10^{-9}$	$1424 \cdot 10^{-6}$	$2848 \cdot 10^{-6}$	$9957 \cdot 10^{-4}$	$2068 \cdot 10^{-6}$	$5012 \cdot 10^{-5}$	$1023 \cdot 10^{-4}$	$8455 \cdot 10^{-4}$	$1693 \cdot 10^{-4}$	$4998 \cdot 10^{-5}$	$3885 \cdot 10^{-4}$	$3922 \cdot 10^{-4}$
200	$1700 \cdot 10^{-9}$	$1293 \cdot 10^{-6}$	$2589 \cdot 10^{-6}$	$9961 \cdot 10^{-4}$	$1717 \cdot 10^{-6}$	$4606 \cdot 10^{-5}$	$9384 \cdot 10^{-5}$	$8584 \cdot 10^{-4}$	$1637 \cdot 10^{-4}$	$4256 \cdot 10^{-5}$	$3699 \cdot 10^{-4}$	$4239 \cdot 10^{-4}$
250	$1466 \cdot 10^{-9}$	$1202 \cdot 10^{-6}$	$2403 \cdot 10^{-6}$	$9964 \cdot 10^{-4}$	$1486 \cdot 10^{-6}$	$4311 \cdot 10^{-5}$	$8770 \cdot 10^{-5}$	$8677 \cdot 10^{-4}$	$1589 \cdot 10^{-4}$	$3750 \cdot 10^{-5}$	$3552 \cdot 10^{-4}$	$4484 \cdot 10^{-4}$
300	$1298 \cdot 10^{-9}$	$1130 \cdot 10^{-6}$	$2263 \cdot 10^{-6}$	$9966 \cdot 10^{-4}$	$1320 \cdot 10^{-6}$	$4082 \cdot 10^{-5}$	$8295 \cdot 10^{-5}$	$8749 \cdot 10^{-4}$	$1547 \cdot 10^{-4}$	$3378 \cdot 10^{-5}$	$3432 \cdot 10^{-4}$	$4683 \cdot 10^{-4}$
350	$1172 \cdot 10^{-9}$	$1074 \cdot 10^{-6}$	$2148 \cdot 10^{-6}$	$9968 \cdot 10^{-4}$	$1194 \cdot 10^{-6}$	$3897 \cdot 10^{-5}$	$7913 \cdot 10^{-5}$	$8807 \cdot 10^{-4}$	$1510 \cdot 10^{-4}$	$3091 \cdot 10^{-5}$	$3330 \cdot 10^{-4}$	$4850 \cdot 10^{-4}$
400	$1071 \cdot 10^{-9}$	$1027 \cdot 10^{-6}$	$2056 \cdot 10^{-6}$	$9969 \cdot 10^{-4}$	$1094 \cdot 10^{-6}$	$3742 \cdot 10^{-5}$	$7594 \cdot 10^{-5}$	$8855 \cdot 10^{-4}$	$1478 \cdot 10^{-4}$	$2860 \cdot 10^{-5}$	$3242 \cdot 10^{-4}$	$4994 \cdot 10^{-4}$
450	$9907 \cdot 10^{-10}$	$9879 \cdot 10^{-7}$	$1977 \cdot 10^{-6}$	$9970 \cdot 10^{-4}$	$1014 \cdot 10^{-6}$	$3611 \cdot 10^{-5}$	$7323 \cdot 10^{-5}$	$8896 \cdot 10^{-4}$	$1449 \cdot 10^{-4}$	$2670 \cdot 10^{-5}$	$3165 \cdot 10^{-4}$	$5119 \cdot 10^{-4}$
500	$9236 \cdot 10^{-10}$	$9540 \cdot 10^{-7}$	$1908 \cdot 10^{-6}$	$9971 \cdot 10^{-4}$	$9163 \cdot 10^{-7}$	$3496 \cdot 10^{-5}$	$7088 \cdot 10^{-5}$	$8932 \cdot 10^{-4}$	$1422 \cdot 10^{-4}$	$2510 \cdot 10^{-5}$	$3096 \cdot 10^{-4}$	$5230 \cdot 10^{-4}$
600	$8179 \cdot 10^{-10}$	$8977 \cdot 10^{-7}$	$1796 \cdot 10^{-6}$	$9973 \cdot 10^{-4}$	$8400 \cdot 10^{-7}$	$3307 \cdot 10^{-5}$	$6697 \cdot 10^{-5}$	$8991 \cdot 10^{-4}$	$1376 \cdot 10^{-4}$	$2253 \cdot 10^{-5}$	$2978 \cdot 10^{-4}$	$5420 \cdot 10^{-4}$

Table 3. Molecular weight of mixture

p, bar	Molecular weight at T, °K										
	2000	2200	2400	2600	2800	3000	3200	3400	3600	3800	4000
1	43.682	43.123	42.036	40.275	37.876	35.088	32.251	29.617	27.328	25.478	24.130
5	43.818	43.483	42.823	41.701	40.061	37.967	35.604	33.193	30.906	28.839	27.042
10	43.857	43.593	43.060	42.147	40.781	38.984	36.875	34.635	32.435	30.385	28.539
40	43.914	43.746	43.405	42.808	41.886	40.614	39.025	37.213	35.301	33.405	31.606
60	43.927	43.779	43.480	42.954	42.137	40.996	39.551	37.873	36.068	34.245	32.486
80	43.934	43.800	43.528	43.048	42.298	41.244	39.897	38.314	36.589	34.823	33.100
100	43.940	43.816	43.562	43.115	42.414	41.424	40.150	38.640	36.978	35.260	33.568
150	43.949	43.840	43.618	43.225	42.606	41.724	40.576	39.196	37.652	36.027	34.399
200	43.954	43.856	43.654	43.295	42.729	41.917	40.854	39.563	38.103	36.547	34.971
250	43.958	43.867	43.679	43.345	42.817	42.057	41.057	39.832	38.438	36.937	35.404
300	43.961	43.874	43.698	43.384	42.884	42.165	41.212	40.042	38.700	37.246	35.749
350	43.964	43.882	43.714	43.414	42.939	42.251	41.338	40.213	38.914	37.500	36.035
400	43.966	43.887	43.727	43.440	42.984	42.323	41.444	40.356	39.095	37.715	36.279
450	43.968	43.892	43.737	43.461	43.022	42.384	41.534	40.478	39.250	37.901	36.490
500	43.969	43.896	43.747	43.480	43.055	42.437	41.612	40.585	39.386	38.064	36.676
600	43.972	43.903	43.762	43.511	43.109	42.525	41.742	40.762	39.613	38.339	36.991

Table 4. Specific volume of mixture, cm³/g

p, bar	v at T, °K										
	2000	2200	2400	2600	2800	3000	3200	3400	3600	3800	4000
1	3808	4242	4748	5368	6147	7110	8251	9546	10954	12402	13784
5	759.7	842.0	932.8	1038	1163	1315	1496	1704	1938	2192	2461
10	379.9	420.4	464.2	513.7	571.7	640.7	722.4	817.1	923.8	1041	1166
40	95.42	105.3	115.7	127.1	139.8	154.4	171.3	190.8	212.9	237.4	264.1
60	63.84	70.41	77.29	84.70	92.93	102.3	113.0	125.3	139.2	154.7	171.6
80	48.06	52.98	58.16	63.60	69.64	76.46	84.25	93.14	103.2	114.4	126.6
100	38.60	42.53	46.61	50.96	55.73	61.08	67.15	74.06	81.87	90.56	100.0
150	25.98	28.60	31.30	34.16	37.27	40.71	44.59	48.98	53.92	59.40	65.41
200	19.67	21.64	23.66	25.79	28.08	30.61	33.44	36.62	40.19	44.15	48.50
250	15.89	17.46	19.08	20.77	22.59	24.58	26.79	29.28	32.06	35.14	38.52
300	13.37	14.68	16.03	17.43	18.93	20.57	22.39	24.42	26.68	29.19	31.95
350	11.57	12.70	13.85	15.05	16.33	17.72	19.26	20.97	22.87	24.99	27.30
400	10.22	11.21	12.21	13.26	14.38	15.58	16.91	18.39	20.04	21.85	23.84
450	9.169	10.05	10.94	11.87	12.86	13.93	15.10	16.40	17.84	19.43	21.18
500	8.329	9.122	9.928	10.76	11.65	12.60	13.65	14.80	16.09	17.50	19.05
600	7.070	7.732	8.405	9.101	9.834	10.62	11.48	12.43	13.48	14.63	15.90

Table 5. Enthalpy of mixture, kJ/kg

p, bar	i at T, °K										
	2000	2200	2400	2600	2800	3000	3200	3400	3600	3800	4000
1	2387.8	2827.8	3436.1	4285.0	5420.0	6830.3	8447.3	10180.6	11936.3	13591.3	14999.2
5	2348.4	2720.7	3194.6	3818.6	4634.6	5661.3	6882.3	8250.3	9707.3	11200.8	12677.0
10	2337.1	2689.6	3123.8	3679.4	4393.6	5288.4	6360.4	7579.4	8898.8	10273.1	11663.1
40	2321.9	2646.4	3023.4	3479.5	4041.3	4729.9	5554.2	6507.1	7566.0	8699.7	9877.5
60	2319.2	2637.7	3002.5	3436.8	3964.8	4606.0	5370.8	6276.1	7244.9	8311.0	9426.3
80	2317.8	2632.6	2989.7	3410.3	3916.6	4527.4	5253.4	6093.7	7034.9	8054.3	9125.9
100	2317.1	2629.2	2980.8	3391.6	3882.5	4471.4	5169.2	5976.4	6882.1	7866.1	8904.2
150	2316.5	2624.6	2967.3	3342.1	3827.5	4380.1	5030.7	5781.8	6626.2	7547.9	8526.3
200	2316.9	2622.4	2959.7	3334.4	3793.8	4323.2	4943.4	5657.8	6461.2	7340.7	8277.8
250	2317.7	2621.6	2955.0	3332.6	3770.6	4283.4	4881.6	5569.2	6342.6	7190.4	8096.3
300	2318.7	2621.5	2952.0	3324.3	3773.6	4253.6	4834.9	5501.8	6217.5	7074.3	7955.2
350	2319.9	2621.8	2950.1	3318.2	3740.4	4230.4	4798.1	5448.2	6178.7	6980.9	7841.0
400	2321.2	2622.4	2948.9	3313.6	3730.1	4211.7	4768.1	5404.2	6118.6	6903.4	7745.9
450	2322.6	2623.3	2948.3	3310.0	3721.8	4196.3	4743.2	5367.3	6067.9	6837.8	7665.0
500	2324.0	2624.3	2948.1	3307.4	3715.1	4183.4	4722.0	5335.9	6024.4	6781.2	7594.9
600	2326.9	2626.6	2948.5	3303.8	3704.8	4163.1	4688.1	5284.8	5953.2	6688.0	7479.0

Table 6. Entropy of mixture, kJ/kg

s at T, °K

p, bar	2000	2200	2400	2600	2800	3000	3200	3400	3600	3800	4000
1	7.0839	7.2927	7.5560	7.8937	8.3118	8.7956	9.3148	9.8380	10.3383	10.7848	11.1456
5	6.7583	6.9352	7.1406	7.3892	7.6899	8.0421	8.4340	8.8466	9.2612	9.6634	10.0409
10	6.6210	6.7886	6.9769	7.1983	7.4616	7.7687	8.1128	8.4803	8.8556	9.2255	9.5807
40	6.3498	6.5041	6.6678	6.8197	7.0570	7.2934	7.5581	7.8454	8.1465	8.4515	8.7521
60	6.2709	6.4225	6.5808	6.7541	6.9490	7.1692	7.4148	7.6818	7.9629	8.2480	8.5343
80	6.2150	6.3649	6.5199	6.6877	6.8746	7.0844	7.3176	7.5710	7.8386	8.1128	8.3862
100	6.1717	6.3203	6.4729	6.6369	6.8181	7.0204	7.2445	7.4880	7.7455	8.0101	8.2750
150	6.0929	6.2395	6.3884	6.5459	6.7178	6.9077	7.1167	7.3432	7.5833	7.8312	8.0808
200	6.0369	6.1824	6.3288	6.4842	6.6483	6.8302	7.0295	7.2450	7.4734	7.7099	7.9490
250	5.9933	6.1380	6.2828	6.4335	6.5953	6.7715	6.9637	7.1711	7.3910	7.6190	7.8500
300	5.9576	6.1017	6.2453	6.3939	6.5524	6.7243	6.9111	7.1122	7.3254	7.5466	7.7713
350	5.9274	6.0710	6.2136	6.3606	6.5165	6.6849	6.8673	7.0634	7.2711	7.4867	7.7061
400	5.9010	6.0444	6.1862	6.3318	6.4856	6.6511	6.8299	7.0218	7.2248	7.4358	7.6507
450	5.8778	6.0209	6.1620	6.3064	6.4585	6.6216	6.7973	6.9855	7.1847	7.3916	7.6026
500	5.8569	5.9998	6.1404	6.2838	6.4344	6.5954	6.7684	6.9535	7.1492	7.3527	7.5602
600	5.8206	5.9632	6.1030	6.2448	6.3929	6.5504	6.7190	6.8990	7.0890	7.2864	7.4881

References

1. PLESHANOV, A. S. and S. G. LAITSEV. In : *Fizicheskaya gazodinamika, teploobmen i termodinamika gazov vysokikh temperatur (Physical gas dynamics, heat transfer, and thermodynamics of high-temperature gases).* Izd. AN SSSR, 1962.

2. KESSEL'MAN, P. M. *Teplofizika vysokikh temperatur (Thermophysics of high temperatures),* Vol. **2**, No. 6, 1964.

3. KESSEL'MAN, P. M. Author's abstract of doctoral dissertation, M. V. Lomonosov Technological Institute, Odessa, 1966.

4. KESSEL'MAN, P. M., P. A. KOTLYAREVSKY and M. M. AFANASYEV. *IFZh,* **9** (4), 1965.

5. SCOTT, G. A. *Proc. Roy. Soc.,* **A125**, 330, 1929.

6. GOID, M. S. *Comtes Rend., Paris,* **189**, 5, 1929.

7. TOWNEND, P. T. A. and L. A. BHATT. *Proc. Roy. Soc.,* **A134**, 502, 1931.

8. BARTLETT, E. P., H. C. HETHERIGTON, H. M. KVALNES and J. H. THEMEARNE. *J. Am. Chem. Soc.,* **52**, 1374, 1930.

9. DEMING, W. E. and L. E. SHUPE. *Phys. Rev.,* **38**, 2245, 1931.

10. MICHELS, A., J. M. LUPTON, T. WASSENAAR and W. DE GRAAFF. *Physica,* **18** (2), 1952.

11. KAMERLINGH-ONNES, H. and H. P. HYNDMAN. *Commun. Phys. Lab. Univ. Leiden,* 786, 1902.

12. KUYPERS, H. A. and H. KAMERLINGH-ONNES. *Commun. Phys. Lab. Univ. Leiden,* 165a, 1923.

13. VAN URK, A. T. and G. P. NIJHOFF. *Commun. Phys. Lab. Univ. Leiden,* No. 169c, 1924.

14. KAMERLINGH-ONNES, H. and H. A. KUYPERS. *Commun. Phys. Lab. Univ. Leiden,* No. 169a, 1924.

15. HOLBORN, L. and J. OTTO. *Z. fur Physik,* **10**, 367, 1922; **23**, 77, 1924.

16. AMAGAT, E. H. *Ann. Chem. Phys.,* **29**, 68, 1893.

17. MICHELS, A., H. W. SCHAMP and W. DE GRAAFF. *Physica,* **10**, 1209, 1954.

18. JOHNSTON, H. and K. E. McCLOSKEY. *J. Phys. Chem.,* **44**, 1038, 1940.

19. VASILESCO, V. *Ann. de Phys.,* Series 11, **20**, 137, 1945.

20. BONILLA, C. F., R. O. BROOKS and P. L. WALKER. *Proc. Gen. Disc. Heat Transfer,* II, 167, Inst. Mech. Eng., London, 1951.

21. GURVICH, L. V. and G. A. KHACHUARUZOV. *Termodinamicheskie svoistva individual'nikh veshchestv (Thermodynamic properties of individual substances).* Izd. AN SSSR, 1962.

V. METALS AND THEIR COMPONENTS

UDC 541.11

COEFFICIENT OF THERMAL EXPANSION OF MERCURY IN THE TEMPERATURE RANGE 0-350°C

L. R. Fokin and *A. T. Yakovlev*

An analysis of the published experimental data on the thermal expansion of mercury in the temperature range of 0-350°C under normal pressure shows greatest accuracy in the data of Beattie and colleagues [1]; this opinion is shared by Cook [2], in his survey of the literature on the coefficient of thermal expansion of mercury α_{Hg}. Beattie expressed his results in the form of the following equation for the average coefficient of thermal expansion, which has been widely applied [3, 4, 5] :

$$\alpha_B = \frac{v - v_0}{v_0\ t} = (18144.01 + 70.16 \cdot 10^{-2}\ t + 28.625 \cdot 10^{-4} t^2 + \tag{1}$$

$$+ 2.617 \cdot 10^{-6} t^3)\ \cdot\ 10^{-8}\ 1/\text{deg},$$

where the error in α_B in the original work has been taken as

$$\triangle \alpha_{B_0} \cdot 10^8 = 0.62\ 1/\text{deg}.$$

The accuracy with which α for mercury is determined is crucial in the estimation of errors in thermal and thermometric measurements. Hence, while preparing handbook data on mercury, the present authors have analyzed the experimental data of work [1], and have concluded that equation (1) does not represent the optimal approximation (in regard to mean-square approximations) of the experimental data. Near the boundaries of the region covered by the experiments, the maximum error

$\Delta \alpha_{Hg} > 3 \Delta \alpha_{Bo}$ and the discrepancy between equation (1) and the optimal approximation α_{Hg} frequently contributes to the total error.

In work [1], the mass ΔM_{w_t} of mercury displaced from the quartz bulb when the bulb was heated from t_1 to t_2 has been determined by weighing. Using the symbols

$$\Delta M_{w_t} = M_{w_{t_2}} - M_{w_{t_1}} = M_{Hg_0}\left[\frac{1+\alpha_b(t_1)t_1}{1+\alpha_{Hg}(t_1)t_1} - \frac{1+\alpha_b(t_2)t_2}{1+\alpha_{Hg}(t_2)t_2}\right], (2)$$

where $M_{w_{t_1}}$, $M_{w_{t_2}}$ and ΔM_{w_t} are respectively the masses of mercury in the balance pan at t_1 and t_2 and the mass of displaced mercury on heating from t_1 to t_2, converted to a volume of $v_0 = 1000$ ml; M_{Hg_0} is the mass of mercury of standard density ($\rho_0 = 13.59546$ g/ml) in a bulb having v_0; $\alpha_{Hg}(t)$ and $\alpha_b(t)$ are the average volumetric coefficients of mercury and the bulb at temperature t.

Experiments were simultaneously performed with two bulbs, "red" and "green", placed in the same thermostat. The coefficient of quartz α_b was measured in a special experiment with the green bulb and has been reported in work [1]. For each of the bulbs, 39 different values of Δ_{w_t} were obtained in the temperature range of 25-350°C. From these readings the magnitudes of $m = M_{w_t} - M_{w_0}$ were obtained using the least-square method. From the values of m so obtained, α_{Hg} was computed and later approximated according to equation (1).

In order to avoid duplicated approximation of the experimental data, we attempted to formulate an approximation of the function (2) to the experimental values of ΔM_{w_t} obtained in work [1] for determining the coefficient of expansion of mercury using the least-square method. The expression used for $\alpha_{Hg}(t)$ in work [1] and equation (2) was expressed in the form of a polynomial :

$$\alpha_{Hg}(t) = \sum_{i=1}^{n} a_i \left(\frac{t}{100}\right)^{i-1}.$$

The determination of the constants a_i from the condition of minimum of the functional

$$F = \sum_{j=1}^{N}\left(\Delta M_{w_{tj_{exp}}} - \Delta M_{w_{tj_{cal}}}\right)^2, \quad (3)$$

where N = number of experimental points, in this case a nonlinear problem with respect to a_i was performed using the method of linearization with standard programs. The experimental data on ΔM_{w_t} were processed both separately, for each of the bulbs ($N=39$) and conjointly ($N=78$) using $n=4$-7 number of terms in the polynomial.

Table 1 gives the formally calculated standard deviations

$$\sigma_0 = \sqrt{\frac{F_{\min}}{N-n}} \, .$$

For comparison, the second row of the table gives the values of σ_0 obtained with equation (1), calculated, as in the original work, by the formula

$$\sigma_0 = \sqrt{\frac{F_{\min}}{N}} \, .$$

Table 1.   Standard deviations of the experimental values
from the calculated values

n	σ_0 for bulb, g		
	red	green	both
	($N=39$)		($N=78$)
4	0.02084	0.02609	0.03432
4 [1]	0.03316	0.03884	0.03612
5	0.01497	0.01718	0.02920
6	0.00946	0.01343	0.02825
7	0.00961	0.01295	0.02837

From Table 1 it can be seen that even when a high-order polynomial is used ($n=6$-7), the value of $\sigma_0(\Delta M_{wt}) \approx 10$mg for each of the bulbs, which is one order higher than the weighing accuracy. This is probably due to the inaccurate determination of the mercury level in the capillary (± 1 mm) during experimental weighing of the measuring flask. Data on the two bulbs together yield a standard deviation 1.5-2 times greater than data on the bulbs individually, thus confirming the accepted theory [1] that there exists a systematic error in the analyzed data. Table 1 indicates that by increasing the order of the polynomial the interpretation of experimental data is improved even for the combined result. However, with $n > 6$ the functional of deviations changes insignificantly and hence imposes the restriction of $n=7$.

The relationship presented below optimally represents the experimental data of work [1] :

$$\alpha_{Hg} \cdot 10^8 = 18144.51 + 68.508 \cdot 10^{-2}t + 32.791 \cdot 10^{-4}t^2 - 5.6747 \cdot 10^{-6}t^3 +$$
$$+ 7.0884 \cdot 10^{-8}t^4 - 2.47554 \cdot 10^{-10}t^5 + 0.29745 \cdot 10^{-12}t^6 \text{ 1/deg.} \qquad (4)$$

For convenience of analysis of the results and estimation of error in the coefficient of expansion of mercury α_{Hg}, we have additionally determined, by the least-square method, the most probable values of the expected displacements $m = M_{w_t} - M_{w_0}$ if the bulb were to be heated from 0 to $t°C$ at ten different intervals. The values of m, coinciding with those of work [1], are presented in Table 2. In column 8 of Table 2 the values of m as calculated by equations (2) and (4) are given. It should be noted that the deviations $\sigma_0(\triangle M_{w_t})$ from the experimental values $(\triangle M_{w_t})_{exp}$ from the calculated values $(\triangle M_{w_t})_{cal} = m(t_2) - m(t_1)$ also nearly coincide with those values given in Table 1 for $n = 7$.

Using the values of the anticipated displacements m, the mean coefficient of expansion at the nodal points can be determined:

$$\alpha_{Hg_m} = \frac{m}{t(M_{Hg_0} - m)} + \frac{M_{Hg_0} \, \alpha_b}{M_{Hg_0} - m} , \qquad (5)$$

and if the error $\triangle m$ is known, then as a first approximation:

$$\triangle \alpha_{Hg} = -\frac{\triangle m}{t} \cdot \frac{1 + \alpha_{Hg} t}{M_{Hg_0} - m} . \qquad (6)$$

In work [1], the error in the coefficient of expansion of mercury has been assumed equal to the standard deviation of the values of α_{Hg} as calculated by equation (5) and derived from equation (1) without respect to the deviations of the experimental values $(\triangle M_{w_t})_{exp}$ from the most probable averaged values $(\triangle M_{w_t})_m$, i.e., $\triangle \alpha_B = 0.62 \cdot 10^{-8}$ deg^{-1}.

Table 2 and the authors of work [1] indicate that between the displacements m of the red bulb and the green bulb there exist systematic discrepancies (of an unknown nature) of as much as 180 mg at 350°C, considerably exceeding the standard deviations σ_m for each of the bulbs.

It can be noted that the standard error in the values of m_{red} of the expected displacement is:

$$\sigma_{m_{red}} = \sigma_0 \sqrt{(\overline{Z^{-1}})_{kk}} \, [6], \quad \text{where} \quad \sigma_0 = \sqrt{\frac{F_{min}}{N - n}}$$

(see the last two lines of Table 2), and $(Z^{-1})_{kk}$ is the kth diagonal element of the inverse matrix of the system of normal equations.

In the combined processing ($N = 78$) the formally calculated values of σ_m (Table 2, column 7) at high temperatures are considerably less than the systematic discrepancies between m_{red} and m_{green} and therefore do not characterize the errors in the magnitude of m.

Table 2. Calculated errors $\Delta\alpha_{Hg}$

1	2	3	4	5	6	7	8	9	10	11	12	13	14
t, °C	m_{red}	$\sigma_{m\ red}\cdot10^2$	m_{green}	$\sigma_{m\ green}\cdot10^3$	m_{both}	$\sigma_{m\ both}\cdot10^3$	m_{cal}	$(\nabla m)_{lim}\cdot10^3$	$\nabla\alpha\cdot10^8$	$(\alpha-\alpha_g)\cdot10^8$	$\nabla\alpha_B\cdot10^6$ deg⁻¹	$\Delta\rho_B\cdot10^5$ g/cm³	$\nabla\rho_{lim}\cdot10^5$ [5]
25	61.0267	4.9	61.0354	6.5	61.0310	9.8	61.0310	23.9	7.1	0.02	7.12	1	1
50	121.6026	5.3	121.5989	7.1	121.6008	10.9	121.6014	23.2	3.47	0.10	3.57	2	4
75	181.7668	5.1	181.7745	6.8	181.7707	10.5	181.7696	24.2	2.42	0.20	2.62	3	6
100	241.5892	5.2	241.5996	7.0	241.5944	10.7	241.5953	26.2	2.34	0.36	2.70	4	10
150	360.4517	6.6	360.4692	8.7	360.4605	13.4	360.4619	34.8	1.79	0.12	1.91	4	10
152.315	365.9369	5.1	365.9562	6.8	365.9465	10.5	365.9461	30.8	1.57	0.10	1.67	4	10
200	478.6647	7.3	478.6831	9.7	478.6739	14.9	478.6743	38.3	1.52	0.78	2.30	7	20
250	596.6377	7.8	596.6659	10.4	596.6518	16.0	596.6514	45.3	1.45	0.76	2.21	8	20
300	714.7792	7.3	714.8321	9.7	714.8057	14.9	714.8056	55.5	1.52	1.40	2.92	12	20
350	833.7217	7.8	833.9018	10.4	833.8118	16.0	833.8116	121.2	2.90	0.54	3.44	16	—
$F_{min}\cdot10^2$, g		0.2885		0.5133		5.7070							
$G_o\cdot10^3$, g		9.97		13.3		29.0							

The limiting error in the expected displacements, due to the errors in the experimental data, can be determined sufficiently accurately in respect to the systematic discrepancies in the following manner :

$$(\Delta m)_{\text{lim}} = \frac{1}{2}\left(m_{\text{grn}} - m_{\text{red}}\right) + \frac{3}{2}\left(\sigma_{m_{\text{grn}}} + \sigma_{m_{\text{red}}}\right). \tag{7}$$

The values of $(\Delta m)_{\text{lim}}$ and the corresponding values of $\Delta\alpha$, as calculated from equation (6), are given under columns 9 and 10 in Table 2.

The error in determining the coefficient of expansion α_{Hg} is the largest at the boundaries of the experimental region : at 25°C, due to the small displacements and at 350°C, due to considerable systematic error.

While estimating the error in the coefficient of expansion of mercury α_{B} calculated by equation (1), the error due to approximation of α_{Hg_m} in the form of a polynomial of third degree should be added to the error $\Delta\alpha$, as calculated above, due to the error in the experimental data for ΔM_{w_t}. The diagram below shows the deviations of the various alternatives given by our calculations of α_{Hg} from the corresponding α_{B} [1]. At 200°C and 300°C the difference $(\alpha - \alpha_{\text{B}})$ (Table 2, column 11), where α is calculated according to equation (4), is greater than the standard error α_{B_0} given in the original work.

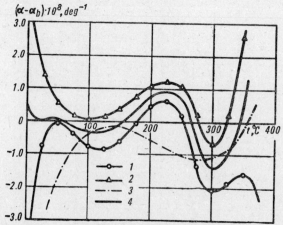

Deviations $(\alpha - \alpha_{\text{B}})$ of the Different Alternative Approximation
[According to Equations (2, 3)].
1—*red bulb, n=7*; 2—*green bulb, n=7*; 3—*both bulbs, n=4*; 4—*both bulbs, n=7*.

The total error α_{B} in the coefficient of expansion of mercury calculated according to equation (1), as a first approximation, can be taken as :

$$\Delta\alpha_{\text{B}} = \Delta\alpha + \mid \alpha - \alpha_{\text{B}} \mid \tag{8}$$

This value has been given under column 12 of Table 2. It is seen that, at the boundaries of the interval $\Delta\alpha_B > 3_{\alpha_{B0}}$, where $3\alpha_{B_0}$ is the limiting error calculated from the standard deviation in the work by Beattie and colleagues [1], whose investigation was concerned with the mean coefficient of the expansion of mercury α_{Hg} in the range $t=25\text{-}350°\text{C}$. However, although there was no special analysis of the extrapolation of the data obtained upto $0°\text{C}$, equation (1) was considered applicable throughout the range of $0\text{-}350°\text{C}$ with a uniform error.

Since the error is large near the boundaries, there will be considerable error on extrapolation. The error $\Delta\alpha$ at $0°\text{C}$ can be assumed approximately equal to the error in the first coefficient a_1 of equation (4) (since $\alpha=a_1$ at $0°\text{C}$), which has been determined equal to $3\times7.6 \cdot 10^{-8}$ deg^{-1}.

These estimated values of the total error in the coefficient of thermal expansion of mercury calculated from equation (1) facilitate determination of the error in the density of liquid mercury in the range of 0-350 °C. In fact,

$$\Delta\rho_B = \Delta\rho_0 + \rho_0\Delta\alpha_B t. \tag{9}$$

It follows from works [3, 4] that $\Delta\rho_0 \leqslant 1 \cdot 10^{-5}$ g/cm^3. However, the contribution of the error due to the dissolved gases in mercury to the total error $\Delta\rho_0$ remains unknown. The values of $\Delta\rho_B$ are given under column 13 of Table 2. The last column of Table 2 gives the limiting errors $\Delta\rho$, taken from the tables of density of mercury [5], calculated using the data of works [1, 3, 4]. Errors $\Delta\rho$ estimated in work [5] are approximately twice our errors.

We should mention that although equation (4) corresponds to more probable values of α_{Hg}, equation (1), which is already widely known, may still be recommended for calculation of the coefficient of thermal expansion of mercury upto $350°\text{C}$, in respect to the above-mentioned errors.

The analysis of both random and systematic errors in the results of work [1] shows that the coefficient of expansion of mercury in the particular temperature range could be measured far more accurately than in work [1], and that such an investigation would have a great scientific and theoretical significance.

REFERENCES

1. BEATTIE, J. A., B. E. BLAISDELL, J. KAYE, H. T. GERRY and C. A. JOHNSON. *Proc. Am. Acad. Arts Sci.*, **74**, 371, 1941.
2. COOK, A. H. *Brit. J. Appl. Phys.*, **7**, 285, 1956.

3. COOK, A. H. and M. W. STONE.   *Phil. Trans. Roy. Soc.*, **A250**, 277, 1957.
4. COOK, A. H.   *Phil. Trans. Roy. Soc.*, **A254**, 125, 1961.
5. BIGG, P. H.   *Brit. J. Appl. Phys.*, **15**, 1111, 1964.
6. LINNIK, U. V.   *Metod naimen'shikh kvadratov i osnovy matematiko-statis-cheskoi teorii obrabotki nablyudenii* (*Least-mean square method and the fundamentals of mathematical statistical theory of processing observations*). Fizmatgiz, Moscow, 1958.

UDC 541.11

MEASUREMENT OF THERMAL CONDUCTIVITY AND LAWRENCE NUMBER OF CONDUCTING MATERIALS IN THE SOLID AND LIQUID STATES OVER A WIDE TEMPERATURE RANGE

R. P. Yurchak and *B. P. Smirnov*

Thermal conductivity of materials at high temperatures, including those materials involving a change of the state of aggregation, are measured by a method belonging to a group of difficult but highly interesting investigations. One difficulty in such measurement is due to the influence of heat radiation. Where a liquid phase is formed, there is the influence of natural convection in addition to radiation, and in such cases measurement is directed to study of the thermophysical properties such as heat-transfer rate, flow of electric current, and nature of the liquid state. Needless to mention, such measurements are invaluable in those branches of industry concerned with the thermophysical properties of various substances.

The present work describes a method for investigation of the thermal conductivity and the Lawrence number of a large group of conducting materials in a wide temperature range involving a change of the aggregate state of the material. This method can be considered as a development of the method employed in works [1, 2].

The method is based on the measurement of the small increment in the electrical resistance of the narrow segment of a specimen, the crosspiece (see Fig. 1), caused by heating due to the passage of a direct current throughout. The geometry of the specimen under investigation is such that

$$d \gg a \gg l. \tag{1}$$

As has been shown [1, 2], when the above dimensions (equation 1) are observed, the heat of radiation is negligible for small temperature increments of the cross-piece with respect to the average temperature of the specimen.

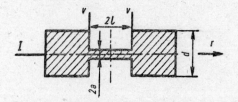

Fig. 1.   Configuration of the specimen.

v—voltage, 2l—length of the cross-piece, 2a—diameter of the cross-piece, d—diameter of the specimen, r—resistance, I—current intensity

The increment in electrical resistance is related to the thermal conductivity by the following relationship :

$$\delta R = \frac{dR}{dT} \left[P \frac{\sigma}{2\lambda} V + \frac{\sigma}{3\lambda} V^2 \right], \tag{2}$$

where dR/dT = temperature coefficient of electrical resistance of the cross-piece for a uniformly heated specimen; V = half of the voltage measured between the probes; P = Thompson's coefficient; σ = electrical conductivity of the specimen; λ = thermal conductivity of the specimen.

It is important to note that in equation (2) only the ratio σ/λ appears; hence, the geometric properties of the specimen do not significantly influence the measurement. Equation (2) also reveals the experimentally measured quantities to be predominantly electrical (with exception of the average temperature of the specimen, the temperature of reference for the measured quantity); these quantities can be determined with a high degree of accuracy, one advantage of this method over other known methods.

Difficulties in application of this method are the preparation of the specimen (see Fig. 1) and preservation of the specimen components, especially the cross-piece, from mechanical damage, thermal stress, contamination and other hazards.

The most convenient method of specimen preparation is to melt the material in a specially designed crucible (see Fig. 2), ensuring considerable mechanical durability and preventing contamination of the narrow portion of the specimen, and, especially important, enabling measurement in both the solid and liquid phases. In current experimental practice, the influence of radiation on the measurement of thermal conductivity has been replaced by the influence of heat conduction by the wall of the crucible in the vicinity of the cross-piece (holes in the wall of the crucible), filled by the material under study. Calculations show this influence to be represented by the following expression :

$$\frac{Q_{con}}{P_\lambda} \leqslant \frac{\lambda_1}{\lambda} \cdot \frac{l}{a} ,\qquad (3)$$

where Q_{con} = heat conducted by the wall; P_λ = total power discharged in the cross-piece; λ_1 and λ = values of thermal conductivity for the wall material and the specimen respectively.

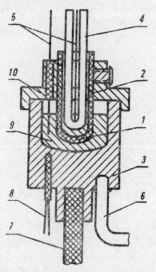

Fig. 2. Design of the measuring cell.
1—working opening ; 2—cap ; 3—crucible ; 4, 6—lead wire ; 5—potential conductors ; 7—holder (ceramic) ; 8—thermocouple ; 9—test substance; 10—cover.

As seen from expression (3), in order to reduce the heat conduction it is necessary to select the wall material of low thermal conductivity and, as far as possible, to reduce the ratio l/a. For metals this ratio should be $\leqslant 0.3$ (with $a \approx 0.1\text{-}0.2$ mm), and for semiconductors the ratio should be $\leqslant 0.1$ (with $a \approx 0.3$ mm). The resistance of the cross-piece under these conditions is of the order of 1×10^{-3} ohm. Direct estimations according to equation (3) show that the correction due to heat conduction is $\sim 1\text{-}4\%$ in respect to the cross-piece dimensions. With measurements for the two different wall thicknesses, this correction can be eliminated by extrapolation for zero wall thickness.

In contrast to radiation, heat conduction by the wall undergoes little change over a wide temperature range. Moreover, for a majority of insulating materials, thermal conductivity decreases with increase in temperature, and hence the correction required due to heat conduction will be less at higher temperatures.

The opening (1) in the wall of the cap (2), which is constructed of nonconducting material (quartz, ceramic or glass) is filled with the material and serves as a connection in the measuring cell (Fig. 2). The hole of diameter $a \approx 0.15$ mm and $l/a \leqslant 0.2$ can be constructed with an optical laser or a drill of tungsten, cobalt, carbon or titanium alloy. The crucible (3) is constructed of graphite and serves as one of the electrodes, the tungsten (or titanium) wires (4) serving as the other electrode and as a dual conductor. Hence the electrical contact between the internal and external crucibles is established through the material. The use of a crucible of a conducting material and also the special shape of the electrode considerably improve the sensitivity and stability of operation of the measuring circuit, as the specimen with the lead wires is included in one of the arms of the measuring bridge (see Fig. 3) during measurement. The thin wires (5) serve as potential probes during measurement of the electrical resistance of the voltage drop which heats the cross-piece.

The thermocouple inserted into the body of the crucible measures the average temperature of the specimen. The components designed to come into contact with the investigated material are fabricated of materials selected on the basis of their chemical reactivity. The crucibles filled with the material and the cap in the assembled form are placed inside a vacuum chamber. Filling of the passage by the liquid metal during the melting process is controlled by the ohmic contact between the lead wires. The resistance of the cross-piece at room temperature is within $0.5-1 . 10^{-3}$ ohm, depending upon the material under investigation. The vacuum furnace used is of a design improved beyond the furnace described in reference [4]. In the new apparatus, the design of the heater has been changed, the vacuum unit VA-0.5 has been replaced by a similar one of the type VA-0.1, and the water-cooled quartz body has been replaced by copper.

The line diagram of the measuring circuit, assembled in the form of a four-armed asymmetrical bridge, is shown in Fig. 3. In one of the arms of the bridge the specimen R_1 is connected in series with the standard coil having resistance $R_4 = 10^{-3}$ ohm; R_2, R_3' and R_3'' are variable resistances of the type MSR-50 with minimum decade $b . 10^{-2}$ ohm. These resistances are much larger than R_1 and R_4, so that most of the current passes through the specimen without heating of the resistances. The resistance $R_3' \gg R_3''$ serves to give a smooth null-balancing of the bridge.

The circuit is fed from an acid accumulator (6V) with a high capacitance and continuous recharging during operation of the voltage stabilizer of the type VSA-5A. The load resistance is comprised of several rheostats connected in parallel, each with 15 ohm and 10 *a* capacity. In the measuring diagonal is connected a multirange photoelectric instrument F 116/I, which is highly sensitive to voltage. Since the resistance of the cross-piece is low, the connecting wire should also have as low a resistance R_n as possible, since the sensitivity of the circuit is inversely proportional to the magnitude of R_n. The supply voltage of the bridge is commuted with the help of switch K_1, enabling isolation of the electromotive force proportional to the current.

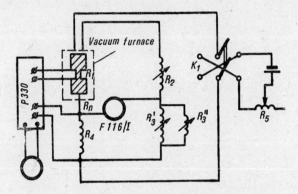

Fig. 3. Line diagram of measuring circuit.

The operational principle of the apparatus is as follows. At a certain average specimen temperature T_1 the balancing of the bridge is achieved by varying the resistances R_2 and R_3. Balancing of the circuit is achieved only when it is possible to break the circuit of the feeding diagonal with the switch K_1. The current flowing through the specimen would be increased through rheostats R_5. If the current density I_1 induces heating of the cross-piece, the circuit is unbalanced. From the values of ΔV_1 applied across the diagonal of the bridge it is possible to determine ΔR_1, the increment in the resistance of the narrow portion of the specimen :

$$\Delta R_1 = \frac{\Delta V_1}{I_1}\left[\left(1 + \frac{R_2}{R_3}\right) + \frac{R_2}{R_g}\right], \qquad (4)$$

where R_g is the resistance of the galvanometer.

If the parameters in the circuit are selected so that $R_g \gg R_2$, equation (4) is simplified.

$$\Delta R_1 = \frac{\Delta V_1}{I}\left(1 + \frac{R_2}{R_3}\right). \qquad (5)$$

ΔR_1 can be determined by another method, achieving a secondary balancing of the bridge. From the balancing condition of the bridge is obtained :

$$\Delta R_1 = \frac{R_2 R_4}{R_3^2} \Delta R_3 = \frac{R_1 + R_n}{R_3} \Delta R_3, \tag{6}$$

where ΔR_3 is that change in the resistance R_3 due to which the balance of the bridge is restored. Then with a type R330 potentiometer, the current I_1 passing through the specimen and the voltage drop are measured. At that temperature the resistance of the specimen is measured prior to heating of its narrow portion. All measurements are repeated several times and mean values are obtained. Similar measurements are performed at a different temperature T_2. Using the values of ΔR_1, dR_1/dT and V determined from equation (2), the Lawrence number can be determined

$$L_T = \frac{\lambda}{\sigma T} = \frac{1}{12} \left(\frac{dR}{dT} \right) \frac{V_1^2}{\Delta R_1}, \tag{7}$$

where ΔR_1 is half the sum of the increments in the resistance of the narrow portion, observed with the passage of direct current and reversed current through the specimen. Using the difference in the measurements of resistance and the value of λ/σ obtained above, Thompson's coefficient can be determined.

$$P = \frac{\lambda}{\sigma} \frac{1}{V[\Delta R_1(+I) - \Delta R_1(-I)]} \left(\frac{dR}{dT} \right)^{-1}, \tag{8}$$

where $\Delta R_1 (+I)$ and $\Delta R_1 (-I)$ represent, respectively, the changes in the resistance R_1 for direct current and reversed current flows. In order to determine the thermal conductivity by equation (7), the value of the electrical conductivity must be determined at any one temperature, such as at room temperature in solid state and at melting point in liquid state.

The error in the measurement of Lawrence number is due to the cumulative errors in the measurement of individual quantities occurring in equation (7). The major error occurs in the measurement of ΔR and is around 1.5%, according to the readings of the photoelectric instrument F 116/I. The doubled error in the measurement of voltage on the potentiometer R330 is 0.03%. The maximum error in the determination of the temperature coefficient of resistance due to differentiation is about 1.5%. The systematic error due to introduction of the correction for the heat conducted away by the wall is 0.1-0.2% provided the thermal conductivity of the wall is known with an accuracy of 10-20%. The error in measurement of temperature is about 0.02%. In the determination of thermal conductivity, additional systematic error can arise from the error in measurement of the electrical conductivity, usually not exceeding 0.5-1.0%. Thus the maximum error in the determination of L can be 3.2% and the maximum error in the thermal conductivity, 4.2%.

The operation of the apparatus was studied under various experimental conditions. In particular, the resistance of the cross-piece was varied, either by grinding the punctured diaphragm, by varying its diameter, or by changing other parameters of the bridge circuit. Measurements were made for various voltage drops over the specimen (different intensity of heating). Some of the results for liquid mercury and tin are presented in Table 1. It can be seen that the values of $\triangle R_1/V^2R_1$ obtained for the different voltages (one value being nearly twice the other) show a close agreement between mercury and tin, indicating the absence of convection in the liquid metal during measurement. The possibility of monitoring or preventing convection is one important advantage of the present method. The deviations in $\triangle R_1/V_1^2R_1$ of the order of 10% for different diaphragm thicknesses (for the same R_1), with the identical material being investigated, can be attributed to the heat conduction by the wall. Table 1 also presents values of $\triangle R_1/V_1^2R_1$ extrapolated for a zero thickness of the diaphragm.

Table 1. Results of trial testing of the method

Metal at experimental temperature	$R_1 \cdot 10^3$ ohm	$V_1^2 \cdot 10^4$ volts^{-2}	$\triangle R_1/V_1^2R_1$, volts^{-2}	$\lambda \cdot 10^3$ W/cm . deg
Hg	5.12	144.0	8.65	—
		216.9	8.68	—
20°C			9.05*	85.2
	13.41	134.5	8.05	84.0[3]
		207.8	8.2	—
Sn	4.13	1220.0	3.0	—
		2052.0	3.05	—
241°C			3.14*	308.0
	13.22	1085.0	2.71	305.0[4]
		1710.0	2.75	—

*Values marked with asterisk (*) are the extrapolated values for zero wall thickness.

From Table 1 it follows that the values of $\triangle R_1/V_1^2R_1$ obtained for smaller wall thicknesses differ considerably from the extrapolated values. A reduction in the wall thickness by half may minimize to insignificance the influence of the wall on the results of the measurements. The results of the trial assays agree closely with the available data in works [5, 6].

The thermal conductivities of indium and gallium were measured with very thin walls because the resistance of the cross-piece was of the order of 0.5 . 10^{-3}-1 . 10^{-3} ohm. Rounded data of the results of measurement of thermal conductivity and Lawrence number for gallium and indium in the solid and liquid states are presented in Table 2. Results obtained for the super-cooled state of gallium are also given. The mean values are obtained for both gallium and indium under the following experimental conditions : during repeated melting, solidification, under widely different heating currents for the cross-piece, and so on. Thus, the maximum deviation of the various results did not exceed 3%, which agrees with the estimation of experimental error mentioned earlier. As seen from Table 2, in case of gallium there is no appreciable fluctuation in the thermal conductivity due to the transformation from the solid to liquid states : $\lambda_{solid}/\lambda_{liquid}=1.03$, and there is no significant difference in the thermal conductivity of the liquid or the super-cooled gallium. In solid state conditions, our results show favorable agreement with those of Pashaev [7], the difference being only 2%, and differ from the data of work [8] by 5%. The thermal conductivity of liquid gallium increases linearly with temperature with the coefficient $\beta_{liq}= 2.9$. 10^{-4} deg^{-1}, which does not agree with Pashaev's results [7], where the behavior of the thermal conductivity is observed to be unusual and irregular in the vicinity $t=393$ and $543°K$, and where a rapid (nonlinear) increase of thermal conductivity with increasing temperature has been observed. Only near the melting temperature do our data agree with those of work [7]. Close agreement is observed with the data of Briggs [9] who had measured λ for liquid gallium with respect to mercury for a small temperature range; the deviation here did not exceed the magnitude of experimental error.

In determining the thermal conductivity the mean value of the resistance of liquid gallium near the melting point has been based on data from references [10, 11]. The temperature coefficient of resistance of liquid and super-cooled gallium in the temperature range 283-650°K determined in the process of measurements equals 77×10^{-5} deg^{-1}, which agrees well with the results of work [16].

The thermal conductivity of indium (Table 2) in the solid state consistently decreases with increasing temperature and the coefficient $\beta_{solid}=1.04$. 10^{-3} deg^{-1}. With change of state from solid to liquid the thermal conductivity increases suddenly $\lambda_{solid}/\lambda_{liquid}=1.92$ and then increases linearly with increasing temperature : $\beta_{liquid}=7.2\times10^{-4}$ deg^{-1}. Table 2 gives data due to Powell and others [13], who had measured the thermal conductivity and electrical conductivity of solid indium upto a temperature of 393°K; these results agree closely with ours. The maximum discrepancy is 5.2% at 393°K. At lower temperatures the discrepancy is less and at room temperatures our data and those of work [13] agree closely with the

Table 2. Results of measurements of λ and L for gallium and indium in solid and liquid states

Gallium

T, °K	λav, W/cm·deg	$L \cdot 10^3$ W·ohm/deg²	T, °K	λlit W/cm·deg
287.5	0.313 (solid)	—	273	0.328 (sol) [8]
275	0.303 (melting)	2.85	296.5	0.306 (sol) [7]
300	0.305 (melting)	2.64	307	0.302 (liq)
350	0.309 (liquid)	2.28	333	0.315 (liq) [9]
400	0.311 (liquid)	2.24	302.9	0.292–
450	0.317 (liquid)	2.12		0.376 (liq) [12]
500	0.321 (liquid)	2.02		
550	0.324 (liquid)	1.96		
600	0.328 (liquid)	1.92		
650	0.332 (liquid)	1.88		
700	0.337 (extrapolated)	1.86		

Indium

T, °K	λav, W/cm·deg	$L \cdot 10^3$ W·ohm/deg²	T, °K	λlit W/cm·deg
		Solid state		
250	0.87	2.51	250	0.88 [13]
			295	0.80 [14]
300	0.82	2.50	300	0.84 [13]
350	0.78	2.51	350	0.815 [13]
400	0.75	2.49	400	0.79 [13]
		Liquid state		
450	0.382	2.9	156.4	0.37–
				0.50 [12]
500	0.395	2.71		
550	0.407	2.63		
600	0.425	2.58		
650	0.435	2.54		
700	0.450	2.51		
750	0.46	2.48		
800	0.475	2.45		
850	0.488	2.42		
900	0.500	2.38		

results reported in reference [14]. However, in many handbooks [e.g., 15, 16] an obviously erroneous value of thermal conductivity of indium at room temperature is given as 0.25 W/cm . deg. The thermal conductivity of indium above 393°K has not yet been studied. We know of only approximate results [12] relating to the melting point (see Table 2).

The mean value of the resistance of indium at room temperature and at the melting point, for calculation of the thermal conductivity, have been taken from works [11, 13, 14]. It should be noted that the results regarding the thermal conductivity in the solid phase for indium as well as gallium refer to a polycrystalline state. Table 2 also presents the variation of the Lawrence number for Ga and In with temperature, directly measured during experimentation. As can be seen, the Wideman-France law for liquid gallium is valid over a small range of temperature. For liquid indium, this range is somewhat wider. For both metals, the Lawrence number decreases with increasing temperatures, and a deviation from the Wideman-France law is observed. This is true for a majority of the materials investigated [5, 17]. The pattern of the Lawrence number of materials in the liquid state and the probable causes of the deviation from the Wideman-France law have been discussed in reference [17].

References

1. CUTLER, M. *J. Appl. Phys.*, **32**, 1075, 1961.
2. CUTLER, M. and G. T. CHENEY. *J. Appl. Phys.*, **34**, 1714, 1963.
3. KOLRAUSCH. *Ann. Phys.*, **1**, 32, 1960.
4. YURCHAK, R. P. and L. P. FILLIPOV. *Zavodskaya Laboratoriya*, No. 4, 1965.
5. YURCHAK, R. P. and L. P. FILLIPOV. *Teplofizika Vysokikh Temperatur*, **2** (5), 1964.
6. *Spravochnik khimika (Handbook of Chemistry)*, Part 1. Khimiya, Moscow, 1965.
7. PASHAEV, B. P. *Fizika Tverdovo Tela*, **3**, 2, 1961.
8. VARGAFTIK, N. B. *Teplofizicheskie svoistva veshchestv (Thermophysical properties of materials)*. Moscow, 1956.
9. LUMAN, J. and K. BRIGGS. *J. Chem. Phys.*, **26**, 784, 1957.
10. CUSACK, N. E. and P. KENDALL. *Proc. Phys. Soc.*, **75**, 482, 309, 1960.
11. GORYAGA, G. I. and E. P. BELOZEROVA. *Vestrijk MGU*, **1**, 133, 1958. 13.
12. LEON, R. N. *Liquid metals handbook*, 1954.
13. POWELL, R. W. *Phil. Mag.*, **7**, 79, 1962.
14. WHITE, G. K. *Eksperimental'naya tekhnika v fizike nizkikh temperatur (Experimental techniques in low-temperature physics)*. **IIL**, Moscow, 1961.

15. FILYAND, M. A. and E. I. SEMENOVA. *Svoistva redkozemel'nikh elementov (Properties of rare-earth elements).* Moscow, 1953.
16. KEI, J. and G. L. LEBI. *Tablitsi fizicheskikh i khimicheskikh konstant (Tables of physical and chemical constants).* 1962.
17. YURCHAK, R. P. Author's abstract of Ph.D. dissertation, Moscow State University, 1965.

UDC 541.11

ORTHOBARIC DENSITIES AND CRITICAL PARAMETERS OF SERIES OF HIGH-ORDER BROMIDES AND IODIDES OF GROUPS III AND IV ELEMENTS OF THE PERIODIC SYSTEM

L. A. Nisel'son, T. D. Sokolova and *R. K. Nikolayev*

In the literature there are insignificant data on the critical parameters of high-order, highly volatile bromides, and iodides of Groups III and IV of the periodic system of elements. Existing data on the density of these compounds in the liquid state are most incomplete and contradictory, and are presented in the following works : BBr_3 [1-3], BI_3 [4], $AlBr_3$ [5-8], AlI_3 [5-6], $GaBr_3$ and GaI_3 [9], $TiBr_4$ [10-12], TiI_4 [13], $GeBr_4$ [14, 15], GeI_4 [16], $SnBr_4$ [15] and SnI_4 [13]. We have not encountered any data on the density of SiI_4 in the liquid state, whereas data on $SiBr_4$ are presented in an earlier work [17].

In the present work experimental data are presented on the density of liquid and saturated vapor of a series of highly volatile high-order bromides and iodides of Groups III and IV elements, which comprise the basic groups of the periodic system. From the maxima of the orthobaric curves constructed from these data, the critical temperatures are determined, and applying the law of linear diameter, the critical densities of the investigated halides have been determined. An example of such a construction is given in the diagram below, for halides of barium, where the hollow points refer to the orthobaric density of the vapors and the dark points refer to liquids.

The bromides and iodides used in the present investigations were carefully purified by chemical methods and rectification. As shown by analysis, the total contents of associated impurities did not exceed 0.001%, and in some cases 0.0001%.

The density of the liquid was determined in sealed pycnometers (dilatometers), which procedure has been described in detail in our earlier works [18-20]. For the range of temperature from melting point to temperatures remote from critical point, measurements were performed in pycnometers with a relatively high ratio of volume to the diameter of the measuring capillary ($V_{\mathrm{pyc}} \sim 10$ cm^3; $\phi_{\mathrm{cap}} = 2.5$-3 mm). For near-critical regions the instruments used had less favorable ratio of volume to capillary diameter and, consequently, their accuracy was lower but strength higher ($V_{\mathrm{pyc}} \sim 2$-3 cm^3; $\phi = 4$-4.5 mm).

The density of saturated vapors and the critical density were determined by the visual polythermal method in soldered flasks according to the procedure described in work [18] with the subsequent improvements given in work [21]. While determining the density of saturated vapors, the ampoules continued rotating to counteract the undesirable action of the gravitational effect in the critical region to attain equilibrium state more rapidly.

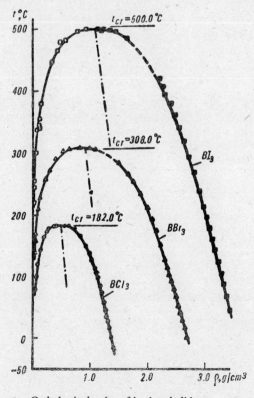

Orthobaric density of borium halides.

Table 1. Density of liquid BCl₃, BBr₃, BI₃ and their saturated vapors

| BCl₃ | | | | BBr₃ | | | | BI₃ | | | |
| Vapor | | Liquid | | Vapor | | Liquid | | Vapor | | Liquid | |
t, °C	ρ, g/cm³	t, °C	ρ, g/cm³	t, °C	ρ, g/cm³	t, °C	ρ, g/cm³	t, °C	ρ, g/cm³	t, °C	ρ, g/cm³
79.0	0.029	—14.5	1.4069	140.0	0.027	0.0	2.6961	218.0	0.011	46.0	3.443
100.0	0.045	0.0	1.3746	157.0	0.040	17.3	2.6473	245.0	0.019	68.2	3.390
120.0	0.072	16.6	1.3381	169.0	0.045	29.0	2.6163	254.0	0.021	88.5	3.335
143.5	0.12	26.5	1.3154	210.0	0.087	43.4	2.5725	300.0	0.041	105.0	3.280
164.0	0.19	35.0	1.2930	227.5	0.12	54.0	2.5418	338.0	0.079	125.0	3.227
174.0	0.25	44.5	1.2729	257.0	0.21	66.9	2.4986	340.0	0.089	144.0	3.177
177.5	0.27	57.5	1.24	271.0	0.28	80.3	2.4605	345.0	0.088	162.0	3.123
181.0	0.35	72.0	1.20	291.0	0.39	92.7	2.4217	354.5	0.10	179.0	3.076
182.0	0.37	85.5	1.16	303.0	0.52	103.7	2.382	378.5	0.14	197.0	3.025
182.0	0.40	97.0	1.13	307.0	0.63	115.8	3.343	447.0	0.32	214.0	2.975
		106.5	1.097	308.0	0.82	128.0	2.304	466.0	0.42	240.0	2.90
		113.0	1.07			153.0	2.22	480.0	0.48	270.5	2.81
		127.5	1.02			175.0	2.14	483.0	0.56	295.0	2.72
		138.5	0.97			193.0	2.07	496.0	0.75	320.0	2.62
		150.0	0.92			212.0	1.99	497.5	0.76	343.0	2.54
		166.5	0.82			235.0	1.86	498.0	0.79	363.0	2.46
		178.0	0.72			255.0	1.74	500.0	0.91	382.0	2.39
		182.0	0.62			267.0	1.66			396.0	2.29
		182.0	0.55			285.0	1.49			410.0	2.25
		182.0	0.54			307.0	1.09			422.0	2.20
						308.0	0.98			488.0	1.62
										498.0	1.42
										499.0	1.19
										500.0	1.14
										500.0	1.21
										500.0	1.33

Table 2. Density of liquid $AlBr_3$, AlI_3 and their saturated vapors

AlBr₃				AlI₂			
Vapor		Liquid		Vapor		Liquid	
t, °C	ρ, g/cm³	t, °C	ρ, g/cm³	t, °C	ρ, g/cm³	t, °C	ρ, g/cm³
280.0	0.022	111.5	2.607	373.5	0.016	211.0	3.158
295.0	0.025	127.5	2.573	420.0	0.025	231.5	3.118
348.5	0.052	140.0	2.544	456.5	0.041	249.0	3.082
367.5	0.063	155.0	2.508	458.0	0.038	268.0	3.039
374.5	0.075	178.5	2.451	493.0	0.055	285.5	3.004
380.5	0.079	202.5	2.395	496.0	0.058	300.5	2.969
389.5	0.082	223.5	2.342	502.0	0.060	333.0	2.901
420.5	0.14	243.5	2.293	508.5	0.076	360.0	2.837
427.5	0.13	260.5	2.250	512.5	0.077	387.0	2.778
432.5	0.15	281.5	2.18	528.0	0.08	410.5	2.725
437.5	0.17	316.5	2.09	555.0	0.11	441.0	2.64
442.0	0.20	340.5	2.02	575.0	0.12	486.0	2.51
465.5	0.30	361.5	1.95	577.0	0.12	521.0	2.40
479.5	0.36	379.5	1.88	607.0	0.17	544.5	2.33
481.0	0.37	406.5	1.78	615.0	0.20	565.5	2.24
488.0	0.39	425.5	1.69	650.0	0.31	582.0	2.17
491.0	0.45	433.5	1.65	655.0	0.30	595.0	2.11
491.5	0.47	490.5	1.11	670.0	0.36	615.0	2.00
493.5	0.58	492.5	1.08	691.5	0.40	624.0	1.95
494.0	0.83	493.5	0.99	694.0	0.54	701.0	1.47
495.0	0.64			700.0	0.89	701.0	1.38
				703.5	0.55	704.5	1.03
				704.5	0.85		
				706.0	0.92		
				711.0	0.76		
				716.5	0.94		

Table 3.   Density of liquid GaBr$_3$, GaI$_3$ and their saturated vapors

GaBr$_3$				GaI$_3$			
Vapor		Liquid		Vapor		Liquid	
t, °C	ρ, g/cm^3	t, °C	ρ, g/cm^3	t, °C	ρ, g/cm^3	t, °C	ρ, g/cm^3
345.0	0.026	136.0	3.082	376.0	0.016	228.0	3.602
387.5	0.065	151.5	3.048	410.0	0.026	250.5	3.556
423.0	0.10	167.5	3.005	428.0	0.035	268.0	3.516
424.5	0.11	195.5	2.936	446.0	0.044	286.0	3.466
448.0	0.13	208.0	2.902	453.0	0.050	304.0	3.427
478.5	0.21	234.0	2.839	459.0	0.053	318.5	3.387
485.5	0.24	260.0	2.778	468.0	0.059	334.0	3.348
493.5	0.27	282.0	2.718	478.0	0.067	348.0	3.309
510.0	0.36	291.0	2.695	495.0	0.088	360.0	3.268
526.5	0.51	327.0	2.58	517.5	0.11	371.5	3.236
530.0	0.53	364.0	2.45	550.0	0.14	384.0	3.204
532.5	0.92	395.0	2.35	550.0	0.13	423.5	3.07
533.5	0.85	417.0	2.27	557.0	0.15	467.0	2.91
533.5	0.90	436.5	2.20	569.0	0.18	499.0	2.78
534.5	0.70	450.5	2.11	584.0	0.23	520.0	2.69
		472.5	2.00	616.0	0.28	539.0	2.60
		485.5	1.91	639.5	0.46	555.0	2.51
				646.5	0.46	578.5	2.37
		523.0	1.47	649.0	0.53	596.0	2.26
		532.0	1.22	650.0	0.47	671.5	1.38
		533.5	1.12				
				668.0	0.64	674.0	1.17
				669.0	0.71	675.0	1.32
				673.0	1.07	677.5	1.59
				674.5	0.91		
				676.0	0.82		
				677.5	0.88		

Table 4. Density of liquid silicon-tetroxide and its saturated vapors

Vapor		Liquid	
t, °C	ρ, g/cm³	t, °C	ρ, g/cm³
355.0	0.036	142.0	3.340
377.5	0.042	159.0	3.288
380.0	0.047	184.0	3.234
443.0	0.067	204.0	3.181
467.0	0.086	224.0	3.130
489.5	0.11	245.0	3.082
492.0	0.12	266.0	3.030
513.0	0.13	283.0	2.983
520.0	0.15	321.0	2.90
524.0	0.15	361.0	2.78
540.0	0.17	393.0	2.70
593.0	0.27	416.5	2.61
597.5	0.30	445.0	2.52
623.5	0.36	465.0	2.45
652.0	0.49	485.0	2.39
655.0	0.49	502.0	2.32
656.5	0.48	517.0	2.26
661.0	0.53	542.0	2.15
662.0	0.94		
666.0	0.61	652.5	1.67
670.0	0.68	668.0	1.01
676.0	0.72	669.5	1.04

Table 5. Density of liquid tetrabromide and tetriodide of titanium and its saturated vapors

| TiBr$_4$ | | | | TiI$_3$ | | | |
| Vapor | | Liquid | | Vapor | | Liquid | |
t, °C	ρ, g/cm³	t, C°	ρ, g/cm³	t, C°	ρ, g/cm³	t, °C	ρ, g/cm³
238.5	0.0097	48.5	2.9397	392.0	0.013	164.4	3.476
282.5	0.022	69.0	2.8944	409.5	0.017	200.6	3.403
287.0	0.021	88.8	2.8476	418.0	0.017	233.0	3.336
312.5	0.033	107.4	2.8006	418.0	0.018	267.4	3.256
338.5	0.048	128.4	2.7556	466.5	0.034	300.5	3.190
370.0	0.076	147.5	2.7125	495.5	0.046	351.5	3.088
403.5	0.12	167.0	2.6671	500.5	0.048	392.5	2.979
410.8	0.12	184.0	2.6262	514.5	0.056	431.5	2.892
						466.5	2.809
421.5	0.14	230.5	2.50	516.0	0.054	499.5	2.720
491.7	0.34	283.5	2.37	555.5	0.090	527.5	2.631
492.0	0.35	330.3	2.23	571.0	0.10		
499.5	0.39	369.0	2.14	580.0	0.11	557.5	2.55
512.0	0.49	395.5	2.04	589.5	0.13	582.5	2.48
520.5	0.64	421.5	1.94	590.5	0.12	607.5	2.39
521.5	0.79	441.0	1.85	616.5	0.18	643.0	2.22
522.0	0.75	454.7	1.81	666.5	0.26	656.5	2.12
522.0	0.76	468.7	1.72	703.0	0.39	692.0	1.95
522.3	0.67	509.5	1.43	719.5	0.41	704.0	1.90
		520.0	1.22	724.5	0.52	714.5	1.84
		522.0	1.14	725.5	0.50	728.0	1.79
		522.3	1.14	732.5	0.55		
		522.5	1.01	732.5	0.61		
				740.0	0.53		
				743.5	0.52		
				756.0	0.81		
				764.0	0.99		

Table 6. Density of liquid tetrabromide and tetriodide of germanium and its saturated vapors

GeBr$_4$				GeI$_4$			
Vapor		Liquid		Vapor		Liquid	
t, °C	ρ, g/cm^3	t, °C	ρ, g/cm^3	t, °C	ρ, g/cm^3	t, °C	ρ, g/cm^3
240.5	0.029	30.6	3.1149	313.5	0.0072	189.0	3.525
257.5	0.040	49.0	3.0673	362.5	0.016	208.0	3.465
276.0	0.054	65.6	3.0200	375.5	0.018	231.0	3.412
322.0	0.09	83.2	2.9711	385.0	0.022	256.0	3.360
323.0	0.10	98.0	2.9225	398.0	0.027	275.0	3.305
356.0	0.16	117.3	2.8753	411.0	0.029	298.0	3.251
364.5	0.18	134.0	2.8309	449.0	0.049	320.0	3.199
383.5	0.23	151.0	2.7835	481.0	0.071	340.0	3.149
393.5	0.28	166.2	2.7403	486.5	0.057		
434.5	0.51	184.0	2.6948	542.0	0.14	358.0	3.12
440.5	0.63	197.5	2.6507	580.0	0.14	403.0	3.00
446.0	0.75	212.0	2.6069	598.0	0.29	440.0	2.91
						473.0	2.82
446.0	0.85	243.0	2.50	614.0	0.19	504.0	2.72
445.0	0.99	267.0	2.42	631.0	0.22	529.0	2.63
		286.5	2.35	657.0	0.37	567.0	2.49
		306.0	2.29	674.5	0.63	602.0	2.38
		323.0	2.22	689.0	0.89	632.0	2.26
		350.0	2.09	692.0	0.69		
		370.5	1.99	694.0	1.04		
		407.0	1.76	702.0	0.87		
		411.0	1.75				
		418.0	1.60				
		435.0	1.49				
		445.0	1.04				

Table 7. Density of liquid tetrabromide and tetriodide of tin and its saturated vapors

| SnBr$_4$ | | | | SnI$_4$ | | | |
| Vapor | | Liquid | | Vapor | | Liquid | |
t, °C	ρ, g/cm^3	t, °C	ρ, g/cm^3	t, °C	ρ, g/cm^3	t, °C	ρ, g/cm^3
277.0	0.040	34.5	3.3308	326.0	0.0088	169.0	3.645
281.5	0.044	52.2	2.2748	358.0	0.015	194.0	3.586
337.0	0.12	70.5	3.2245	378.3	0.0205	217.0	3.527
381.0	0.18	86.5	3.1747	382.0	0.021	239.0	3.471
420.0	0.30	104.0	3.1232	435.0	0.041	263.0	3.416
422.5	0.30	121.0	3.0720	480.0	0.070	285.0	3.359
425.0	0.30	138.5	3.0227	481.0	0.073	307.0	3.308
432.0	0.33	155.0	2.9755	486.0	0.063	327.0	3.253
464.0	0.58	172.5	2.9255	503.0	0.087	348.0	3.199
466.0	0.63	189.0	2.86	509.0	0.11	369.0	3.146
468.5	0.69	225.0	2.76	511.0	0.096	398.0	3.05
471.0	0.96	256.0	2.67	575.0	0.14	438.0	2.94
472.0	0.76	283.0	2.57	589.0	0.23	471.0	2.85
		310.0	2.47	617.0	0.19	498.0	2.75
		332.0	2.38	624.0	0.23	525.5	2.66
		352.0	2.31	641.0	0.37	547.0	2.58
		370.0	2.23	642.0	0.39	566.0	2.52
		386.0	2.15	645.0	0.41	582.0	2.44
		396.0	2.08	669.0	0.53	610.0	2.31
		409.0	2.03	675.0	0.56	633.0	2.19
		420.0	1.95	683.0	0.64	689.0	1.58
		457.0	1.59	693.0	0.79	694.0	1.26
		467.0	1.39	695.0	0.89		
		469.5	1.33	695.0	1.15		
		470.0	1.26	698.0	0.93		
		471.0	1.15				

Results of the experimental determination of the density of liquid and saturated vapor are presented in Tables 1-7. The results of measurement of density which have been undertaken using pycnometers of larger diameter are indicated in Tables 1-7 by double vertical lines. Those results obtained with smaller pycnometers are indicated by dotted vertical lines.

The experimental data on measurements of density at temperatures remote from critical (obtained with larger pycnometers) have been processed by the least-square method and could be represented by interpolation equations of the type

$$\rho_{liq} = a + bt + ct^2, \text{ g/cm}^3$$

Table 8 gives the values of coefficients a, b and c of the above equation for the bromides and iodides which were investigated in the present work.

Table 8. Compiled data on density of halides of groups III and IV elements in liquid state

Compound	Coefficients in equation			Temperature range, °C	Quadratic error in measurements, $\Delta \rho_{quad} \cdot 10^3$	Reference
	a	$-b \cdot 10^3$	$c \cdot 10^4$			
BCl_3	1.3746	2.281	—	—14.5- 45	1.6	—
BBr_3	2.6962	2.7367	—2.618	0.0-130	1.9	—
BI_3	3.5777	2.8055	—	50*-215	3.8	—
$AlCl_3$	1.164	—2.518	—10.35	192.5*-294	4.7	[22]
$AlBr_3$	2.8455	2.0077	—1.086	98.0*-260	1.3	—
AlI_3	3.5667	1.7994	—0.616	191.0*-410	1.8	—
$GaCl_3$	2.2112	1.8668	—1.164	78.0*-240	4.4	[22]
$GaBr_3$	3.4242	2.5004	—	124.5*-290	2.2	—
GaI_3	4.2102	2.6044	—	210.0*-385	8.0	—
$SiCl_4$	1.5205	1.986	1.74	—5.0 - 83	0.3	[17]
$SiBr_4$	2.8348	2.511	1.206	13.5 -180	1.6	[17]
SiI_4	3.6437	2.0289	—1.092	121.5*-283	5.0	—
$TiCl_4$	1.7588	1.591	0.98	20 -155	0.8	[23]
$TiBr_4$	3.0622	2.5088	0.838	38.0*-184	2.8	—
TiI_4	3.725	1.354	—1.342	150.0*-530	8.4	—
$GeCl_4$	1.9191	2.178	1.67	10.0 -110	0.9	[21]
$GeBr_4$	3.1992	2.7285	—0.223	26.1*-210	3.6	—
GeI_4	4.320	5.111	5.042	145.0*-340	15.0	—
$SnCl_4$	2.2789	2.544	0.81	35 -140	1.4	[19]
$SnBr_4$	3.4347	3.0522	0.566	31.0*-170	1.6	—
SnI_4	4.0623	2.4444	—0.0906	144.5*-370	2.8	—

*Melting point.

Table 9.   Compiled data on density of saturated vapors of bromides and iodides of groups III and IV elements

Compound	Coefficients in equation		Temperature range, °C	Quadratic error in measurements, $\Delta \log_{cr}$
	A	B		
BBr$_3$	2.637	1752	140-290	0.057
BI$_3$	2.796	2361	220-480	0.044
AlBr$_3$	2.410	2282	280-442	0.047
AlI$_3$	2.524	2866	374-692	0.054
GaBr$_3$	3.596	3194	345-510	0.037
GaI$_3$	2.804	2989	376-616	0.026
SiBr$_4$	2.612	2006	200-336	0.020
SiI$_4$	1.714	2015	355-600	0.048
TiBr$_4$	2.401	2265	240-420	0.019
TiI$_4$	2.619	3027	390-700	0.038
GeBr$_4$	2.592	2127	240-395	0.035
GeI$_4$	2.295	2609	315-660	0.074
SnBr$_4$	2.744	2271	280-430	0.029
SnI$_4$	2.660	2855	325-680	0.085

Table 10.   Critical parameters of some halides of groups III and IV elements

Compound	Group III			Compound	Group IV		
	t_{cr}, °C	ρ_{cr}, g/cm^3	Reference		t_{cr}, °C	ρ_{cr}, g/cm^3	Reference
BCl$_3$	182	0.49	—	SiCl$_4$	234	0.52	[17]
BBr$_3$	308	0.92	—	SiBr$_4$	390	0.91	[17]
BI$_3$	500	1.10	—	SiI$_4$	671	0.96	—
AlCl$_3$	354	0.505	[22]	TiCl$_4$	365	0.565	[23]
AlBr$_3$	494	0.84	—	TiBr$_4$	522.5	0.94	—
AlI$_3$	710	1.00	—	TiI$_4$	764	1.10	—
GaCl$_3$	421	0.67	[22]	GeCl$_4$	279	0.65	[21]
GaBr$_3$	533.5	1.02	—	GeBr$_4$	445	1.00	—
GaI$_2$	678	1.14	—	GeI$_4$	700	1.16	—
				SnCl$_4$	320	0.75	—
				SnBr$_4$	471	1.05	—
				SnI$_4$	695	1.18	—

In the same table we have also given, for a complete comparison, data on similar chlorides, based on results of other earlier works. Data for borium trichloride based on the results of the present work are given.

The results of measurement of density of saturated vapors upto temperatures 0.9-0.95 T_{cr} are expressed by an equation of the type

$$\log \rho_n = A - \frac{B}{T, °K}, \quad g/cm^3$$

The coefficients A and B of this equation for the materials under investigation are presented in Table 9.

Table 10 presents data on the critical temperatures and densities, as well as comparison data on similar chlorides, based on the results obtained by earlier investigators.

REFERENCES

1. GHIRA. *Z. phys. Chem.*, **12**, 765, 768, 1893.
2. MICHAELIS and E. RICHTER. *Ann.*, **315**, 29, 1901.
3. POHLAND, E. *Z. anorg Chem.*, **201**, 282, 1931.
4. MOISSAN, *Comptes Rend. Acad Sci.*, **112**, 718, 1891.
5. BILTZ, W. and A. VOIGT. *Z. anorg. Chem.*, **126**, 52, 1923.
6. BILTZ, W. and W. KLEMM. *Z. anorg. Chem.*, **152**, 278, 1926.
7. TREADWELL, W. D. and H. STERN. *Helv. Chim. Acta*, **7**, 635, 1924.
8. IZBEKOV, V. and V. PLOTNIKOV. *ZhRKhO*, **43**, 18, 1911.
9. KLEMM, W. and W. TILK. *Z. anorg. und allg. Chem.*, **207**, 161, 1932.
10. BLOCHER, J. M. and J. E. CAMPBELL. *J. Electr. Soc.*, **103** (9), 209, 1956.
11. OLSEN, J. B. and E. P. RYAN. *J. Am. Soc.*, **54**, 2215, 1932.
12. KLEMM, W., TILK, W. and S. V. MULLENHEIM. *Z. anorg. Chem.*, **176**, 1, 1928.
13. KLEMM, W. and W. TILK, *Z. anorg. und allg. Chem.*, **207**, 161, 1932.
14. DENNIS, L. M. and F. E. HANCE. *J. Am. Soc.*, **44**, 299, 1922.
15. YAKSHIN, M. M., V. M. YEZUCHEVSKAYA and V. A. SOLMENKOVA. *Zh. Neorgan. Khimii*, **6** (11), 2425, 1961.
16. DENNIS, L. M. and F. E. HANCE. *J. Am. Soc.*, **44**, 2856, 1922.
17. NISEL'SON, L. A., T. D. SOKOLOVA and I. I. LAPIDUS. *Zh. Neorgan. Khimii*, **12** (6), 1423, 1967.
18. NISEL'SON, L. A. and T. D. SOKOLOVA. *Zh. Neorgan. Khimii*, **7** (12), 2653, 1962.
19. PUGACHEVICH, P. P., L. A. NISEL'SON T. D. SOKOLOVA and N. S. ANUROV. *Zh. Neorgan. Khimii*, **8** (4), 791, 1963.

20.   NISEL'SON, L. A., A. I. PUSTIL'NIK and T. D. SOKOLOVA. *Zh. Neorgan. Khimii,* **9** (5), 1049, 1964.

21.   NISEL'SON, L. A., T. D. SOKOLOVA and P. P. PUGACHEVICH. *Zh. Neorgan. Khimii,* **12** (3), 589, 1967.

22.   NISEL'SON, L. A. and T. D. SOKOLOVA. *Zh. Neorgan. Khimii,* **10** (7), 1516, 1965.

23.   NISEL'SON, L. A. and K. V. TRETYAKOVA. *Zh. Neorgan. Khimii,* **12** (4), 857, 1967.

VI. MIXTURES, SOLUTIONS AND MATERIALS

UDC 541.11

COEFFICIENT OF DIFFUSION OF VAPORS IN GASES UNDER NORMAL PRESSURE

A. N. Berezhnoi

A generalization [1-3] of the experimental data on diffusion of vapors and gases [4-9] is expressed by the equation

$$\frac{D}{D_{\triangle s}} = 1.012 \left(\frac{s_1 - s_2}{R} \right)^{0.141},$$

where D and $D_{\triangle s}$ are the mean diffusion coefficients in the intervals of entropy changes $s_2 - s_1$ and $\triangle s = s^1_1 - s_1$ respectively. (The value of the scale factor of diffusion $D_{\triangle s}$ was, in the majority of cases, determined by interpolation of the experimental data); s_1 is the entropy during initial measurements; s_2 is the entropy at the end of the open tube in which diffusion occurs; and R is the universal gas constant.

The generalization has been contrived basically for Stepan's stationary method. The generalized equation facilitates calculation of the coefficients of vapors in gases from the saturation temperatures of the respective materials and below (within limits of variation of the defining criterion $(s_1 - s_2)$ R). The results of calculations are presented in the table below.

The deviations of the calculated values from the available experimental data do not exceed the errors in the latter. Much of our earlier data [1-3, 21] have been subsequently corrected.

Coefficients of diffusion of vapors in gases under normal pressure

$t,°C$	cal	exp	Deviation, %	$t,°C$	cal	exp	Deviation, %
	$D \cdot 10^2$, cm²/sec				$D \cdot 10^2$, cm²/sec		
1. Ethyl alcohol-air				—40.0	5.51	—	—
				—30.0	6.04	—	—
—60.0	4.66	—	—	—20.0	6.61	—	—
—50.0	5.57	—	—	—10.0	7.11	—	—
—40.0	6.45	—	—	0.0	7.68	7.77[5]	—1.1
—30.0	7.36	—	—	0.0	7.68	7.45[4]	3.1
—20.0	8.25	—	—	0.0	7.68	7.57[4]	1.4
—10.0	9.17	—	—	0.0	7.68	7.94[15]	—3.2
0.0	10.05	10.16[4]	—1.1	10.0	8.28	8.10[6]	2.2
0.0	10.05	10.20[5]	—1.5	10.0	8.28	8.34[6]	—0.6
10.0	10.82	—	—	19.9	8.82	8.77[4]	0.6
20.0	11.62	—	—	20.0	8.83	9.00[6]	—2.0
30.0	12.58	—	—	30.0	9.41	9.20[6]	2.3
40.4	13.59	13.57[4]	0.1	40.0	9.94	9.90[6]	0.4
40.4	13.59	13.72[4]	—0.9	42.0	10.00	10.20[5]	—2.0
49.4	14.38	14.13[4]	1.8	45.0	10.19	10.11[4]	0.8
50.0	14.40	—	—	50.0	10.44	10.75[6]	—2.8
60.0	15.43	15.10*	2.1	60.0	11.05	11.15*	—0.9
66.9	15.91	14.75[4]	7.1	70.0	11.55	11.70[6]	—1.2
67.0	15.92	15.34[17]	3.6	80.0	12.09	12.30*	—1.6
70.0	16.30	15.90*	2.5	**4. Toluene-air**			
78.4	16.96	16.56*	2.3				
2. Methyl alcohol-air				—60.0	3.53	—	—
				—50.0	4.12	—	—
—60.0	7.70	—	—	—40.0	4.70	—	—
—50.0	8.66	—	—	—30.0	5.28	—	—
—40.0	9.60	—	—	—20.0	5.86	—	—
—30.0	10.58	—	—	—10.0	6.44	—	—
—20.0	11.57	—	—	0.0	7.03	7.09[6,7]	—0.6
—10.0	12.49	—	—	10.0	7.59	—	—
0.0	13.42	13.25[4]	1.3	20.0	8.12	8.00[6]	1.3
10.0	14.34	—	—	25.0	8.42	8.44[7]	—0.3
20.0	15.33	—	—	25.9	8.47	8.60[8]	—1.5
25.6	15.88	16.20[4]	—2.0	30.0	8.71	—	—
30.0	16.27	—	—	39.4	9.30	9.20[8]	1.1
40.0	17.25	—	—	40.0	9.32	—	—
49.6	18.07	18.09[4]	—0.1	50.0	9.93	—	—
50.0	18.08	—	—	59.0	10.41	10.40[8]	0.1
60.0	19.10	—	—	60.0	10.46	—	—
64.6	19.52	—	—	70.0	11.11	—	—
3. Benzene-air				80.0	11.69	—	—
				90.0	12.24	—	—
—60.0	4.42	—	—	100.0	12.79	—	—
—50.0	4.96	—	—	110.6	13.39	—	—

Table—*Continued*

$t,°C$	$D \cdot 10^2$, cm²/sec		Deviation, %	$t,°C$	$D \cdot 10^2$, cm²/sec		Deviation, %
	cal	exp			cal	exp	
	5. n-Hexane-air			−10.0	4.56	—	—
				0.0	4.97	5.05[7]	−1.6
−60.0	3.64	—	—	10.0	5.34	—	—
−50.0	4.26	—	—	20.0	5.76	—	—
−40.0	4.77	—	—	25.0	5.98	6.02[7]	−0.7
−30.0	5.16	—	—	30.0	6.22	—	—
−20.0	5.62	—	—	40.0	6.71	—	—
−10.0	6.08	—	—	50.0	7.18	—	—
0.0	6.61	6.55[7]	0.9	60.0	7.69	—	—
10.0	7.09	—	—	70.0	8.15	—	—
20.0	7.55	7.55[6]	0.0	80.0	8.62	—	—
30.0	8.09	7.93[6]	2.0	90.0	8.99	—	—
40.0	8.68	—	—	100.0	9.54	—	—
50.0	9.02	—	—	110.0	9.97	—	—
60.0	9.47	—	—	120.0	10.39	—	—
68.7	9.98	—	—	124.7	10.60	—	—
	6. n-Heptane-air				**8. Cyclohexane-air**		
−60.0	3.06	—	—	−60.0	3.58	—	—
−50.0	3.59	—	—	−50.0	4.05	—	—
−40.0	4.13	—	—	−40.0	4.53	—	—
−30.0	4.66	—	—	−30.0	5.01	—	—
−20.0	5.20	—	—	−20.0	5.50	—	—
−10.0	5.86	—	—	−10.0	6.00	—	—
0.0	6.29	6.40[7]	−1.6	0.0	6.46	—	—
10.0	6.78	6.78[6]	0.0	10.0	6.96	6.96[6]	0.0
20.0	7.38	7.36[6]	0.3	20.0	7.45	7.45[6]	0.0
30.0	7.91	7.97[6]	−0.8	30.0	7.93	7.81[6]	1.5
40.0	8.42	8.36[6]	0.7	40.0	8.35	8.29[6]	0.7
50.0	9.01	8.90*	1.2	45.0	8.62	8.60[9]	0.3
60.0	9.53	9.30*	2.5	50.0	8.88	—	—
70.0	10.07	9.80*	2.8	60.0	9.33	—	—
80.0	10.54	10.20*	3.3	70.0	9.77	—	—
90.0	11.04	10.55*	4.8	80.0	10.18	—	—
98.4	11.41	10.80*	5.8	80.7	10.29	—	—
	7. n-Octane-air				**9. Methylcyclohexane-air**		
−60.0	2.17	—	—	−60.0	2.84	—	—
−50.0	2.63	—	—	−50.0	3.25	—	—
−40.0	3.10	—	—	−40.0	3.67	—	—
−30.0	3.55	—	—	−30.0	4.10	—	—
−20.0	4.00	—	—	−20.0	4.51	—	—

Table—*Continued*

$t,°C$	$D \cdot 10^2$, cm²/sec cal	exp	Deviation, %	$t,°C$	$D \cdot 10^2$, cm²/sec cal	exp	Deviation, %
—10.0	4.94	—	—	10.0	13.20	—	—
0.0	5.33	—	—	20.0	14.13	14.13[6]	0.0
10.0	5.72	5.71[6]	0.1	30.0	14.97	—	—
20.0	6.15	6.15[6]	0.0	40.0	15.92	—	—
30.0	6.59	6.60[6]	—0.1	50.0	16.78	—	—
40.0	7.03	7.06[6]	—0.4	60.0	17.66	—	—
50.0	7.39	—	—	70.0	18.36	—	—
60.0	7.89	—	—	76.5	19.10	—	—
70.0	6.29	—	—				
80.0	8.70	—	—	12.	Carbon disulfide-air		
90.0	8.98	—	—				
100.9	9.57	—	—	—60.0	5.90	—	—
				—50.0	6.39	—	—
10.	Acetic acid-air			—40.0	6.90	—	—
				—30.0	7.37	—	—
—60.0	5.90	—	—	—20.0	7.85	—	—
—50.0	6.70	—	—	—10.0	8.36	—	—
—40.0	7.47	—	—	0.0	8.87	8.92[10]	—0.6
—30.0	8.28	—	—	10.0	9.39	—	—
—20.0	9.05	—	—	19.9	9.82	10.15[4]	—3.6
—10.0	9.82	—	—	20.0	9.83	—	—
0.0	10.64	10.64[4]	0.0	30.0	10.22	—	—
10.0	11.41	—	—	32.8	10.38	11.20[4]	—7.2
20.0	12.15	—	—	40.0	10.70	—	—
30.0	12.97	—	—	46.2	11.02	—	—
40.0	13.79	—	—				
50.0	14.77	—	—	13.	o-Xylene-air		
60.0	15.74	—	—				
70.0	16.65	—	—	—60.0	2.46	—	—
80.0	17.65	—	—	—50.0	3.09	—	—
90.0	18.55	—	—	—40.0	3.71	—	—
100.0	19.44	—	—	—30.0	4.34	—	—
110.0	20.30	—	—	—20.0	4.99	—	—
117.9	20.95	—	—	—10.0	5.50	—	—
				0.0	6.20	6.20[11]	0.0
11.	Carbon tetrachloride-air			10.0	6.80	—	—
				20.0	7.42	—	—
—60.0	6.90	—	—	30.0	8.06	—	—
—50.0	7.79	—	—	40.0	8.70	—	—
—40.0	8.67	—	—	50.0	9.30	—	—
—30.0	9.56	—	—	60.0	9.93	—	—
—20.0	10.46	—	—	70.0	10.58	—	—
—10.0	11.31	—	—	80.0	11.14	—	—
0.0	12.28	—	—	90.0	11.69	—	—

Table—*Contiuued*

$t,°C$	$D \cdot 10^2,$ cm²/sec cal	exp	Deviation, %	$t,°C$	$D \cdot 10^2,$ cm²/sec cal	exp	Deviation, %
100.0	12.35	—	—	50.0	8.44	—	—
110.0	12.97	—	—	60.0	8.92	—	—
120.0	13.56	—	—	70.0	9.46	—	—
130.0	14.16	—	—	80.0	10.02	—	—
140.0	14.82	—	—	90.0	10.58	—	—
144.4	15.08	—	—	100.0	11.12	—	—
				110.0	11.66	—	—
14. m-Xylene-air				120.0	12.20	—	—
				130.0	12.80	—	—
—60.0	2.45	—	—	138.4	13.25	—	—
—50.0	3.02	—	—				
—40.0	3.59	—	—	16. n-Propylbenzene-air			
—30.0	4.17	—	—				
—20.0	4.79	—	—	—60.0	2.78	—	—
—10.0	5.34	—	—	—50.0	3.12	—	—
0.0	5.90	5.90[11]	0.0	—40.0	3.43	—	—
10.0	6.47	—	—	—30.0	3.79	—	—
20.0	7.08	—	—	—20.0	4.15	—	—
30.0	7.61	—	—	—10.0	4.47	—	—
40.0	8.20	—	—	0.0	4.81	4.81[11]	0.0
50.0	8.79	—	—	10.0	5.17	—	—
60.0	9.40	—	—	20.0	5.48	—	—
70.0	9.97	—	—	30.0	5.79	—	—
80.0	10.56	—	—	40.0	6.14	—	—
90.0	11.12	—	—	50.0	6.50	—	—
100.0	11.66	—	—	60.0	6.81	—	—
110.0	12.25	—	—	70.0	7.19	—	—
120.0	12.80	—	—	80.0	7.51	—	—
130.0	13.42	—	—	90.0	7.83	—	—
139.1	13.94	—	—	100.0	8.15	—	—
				110.0	8.50	—	—
15. p-Xylene-air				120.0	8.85	—	—
				130.0	9.16	—	—
—60.0	2.31	—	—	140.0	9.51	—	—
—50.0	2.85	—	—	150.0	9.87	—	—
—40.0	3.42	—	—	159.2	10.18	—	—
—30.0	3.98	—	—				
—20.0	4.57	—	—	17. n-Hexane-nitrogen			
—10.0	5.11	—	—				
0.0	5.60	5.60[11]	0.0	—60.0	2.77	—	—
10.0	6.19	—	—	—50.0	3.28	—	—
20.0	6.74	—	—	—40.0	4.28	—	—
30.0	7.23	—	—	—30.0	5.29	—	—
40.0	7.80	—	—	—20.0	5.80	—	—

Table—*Continued*

$t,°C$	$D \cdot 10^2$, cm²/sec		Deviation, %	$t,°C$	$D \cdot 10^2$, cm²/sec		Deviation, %
	cal	exp			cal	exp	
−10.0	6.30	—	—	30.0	7.16	7.10[12]	0.8
0.0	6.84	—	—	30.1	7.19	7.26[13]	−1.0
10.0	7.34	—	—	40.0	7.68	—	—
15.5	7.63	7.57[12]	0.8	50.0	8.21	—	—
15.6	7.64	7.53[12]	1.4	60.0	8.73	—	—
20.0	7.84	—	—	70.0	9.32	—	—
30.0	8.39	—	—	80.0	9.81	—	—
40.0	8.88	—	—	90.0	10.40	—	—
50.0	9.36	—	—	100.0	10.90	—	—
60.0	9.82	—	—	110.0	11.40	—	—
68.7	10.27	—	—	120.0	11.96	—	—
				124.7	12.18	—	—

18. n-Heptane-nitrogen

20. Isoctane-nitrogen

$t,°C$	cal	exp	Dev	$t,°C$	cal	exp	Dev
−60.0	3.00	—	—				
−50.0	3.50	—	—	−60.0	2.90	—	—
−40.0	4.00	—	—	−50.0	3.38	—	—
−30.0	4.51	—	—	−40.0	3.87	—	—
−20.0	5.00	—	—	−30.0	4.36	—	—
−10.0	5.53	—	—	−20.0	4.84	—	—
0.0	6.00	—	—	−10.0	5.34	—	—
10.0	6.53	—	—	0.0	5.87	—	—
20.0	7.02	—	—	10.0	6.30	—	—
30.0	7.55	7.43[14]	1.5	20.0	6.82	—	—
30.3	7.60	7.40[13]	2.6	30.0	7.29	7.05[12]	3.5
40.0	8.07	—	—	30.1	7.30	7.13[13]	2.3
50.0	8.61	—	—	40.0	7.76	—	—
60.0	9.09	—	—	50.0	8.27	—	—
70.0	9.60	—	—	60.0	8.74	—	—
80.0	10.08	—	—	70.0	9.19	—	—
90.0	10.55	—	—	80.0	9.64	—	—
98.4	11.03	—	—	90.0	10.13	—	—
				99.2	10.59	—	—

19. n-Octane-nitrogen

21. Cyclohexane-nitrogen

$t,°C$	cal	exp	Dev	$t,°C$	cal	exp	Dev
−60.0	2.35	—	—				
−50.0	2.88	—	—	−60.0	3.69	—	—
−40.0	3.40	—	—	−50.0	4.20	—	—
−30.0	3.93	—	—	−40.0	4.70	—	—
−20.0	4.49	—	—	−30.0	5.19	—	—
−10.0	5.02	—	—	−20.0	5.68	—	—
0.0	5.56	—	—	−10.0	6.17	—	—
10.0	6.09	—	—	0.0	6.64	—	—
20.0	6.63	—	—	10.0	7.13	—	—

Table—*Continued*

t,°C	$D \cdot 10^2$, cm²/sec cal	exp	Deviation, %	t,°C	$D \cdot 10^2$, cm²/sec cal	exp	Deviation, %
15.5	7.38	7.46[12]	—1.1	40.0	10.86	—	—
20.0	7.64	7.60[12]	0.5	50.0	11.50	—	—
30.0	8.13	—	—	60.0	12.10	—	—
40.0	8.56	—	—	70.0	12.78	—	—
50.0	9.12	—	—	80.0	13.31	—	—
60.0	9.58	—	—	80.1	13.32	—	—
70.0	10.03	—	—				
80.0	10.54	—	—	24.	Carbon tetrachloride-nitrogen		
81.0	10.60	—	—				
				—60.0	4.30	—	—
22.	Methylcyclohexane-nitrogen			—50.0	4.82	—	—
				—40.0	5.35	—	—
—60.0	3.58	—	—	—30.0	5.86	—	—
—50.0	4.13	—	—	—20.0	6.39	—	—
—40.0	4.68	—	—	—10.0	6.89	—	—
—30.0	5.23	—	—	0.0	7.41	7.37[15]	0.6
—20.0	5.81	—	—	10.0	7.89	—	—
—10.0	6.38	—	—	20.0	8.46	—	—
0.0	6.97	—	—	30.0	9.02	—	—
10.0	7.47	—	—	40.0	9.54	—	—
12.8	7.63	7.58[12]	0.7	50.0	10.05	—	—
20.0	8.02	—	—	60.0	10.52	—	—
30.0	8.61	—	—	70.0	11.03	—	—
40.0	9.18	—	—	76.8	11.40	—	—
50.0	9.68	—	—				
60.0	10.29	—	—	25.	n-Octane-oxygen		
70.0	10.82	—	—				
80.0	11.35	—	—	—60.0	2.25	—	—
90.0	11.92	—	—	—50.0	2.78	—	—
100.0	12.50	—	—	—40.0	3.34	—	—
				—20.0	3.86	—	—
23.	Benzene-nitrogen			—20.0	4.40	—	—
				—10.0	4.95	—	—
—60.0	4.64	—	—	0.0	5.48	—	—
—50.0	5.28	—	—	10.0	6.03	—	—
—40.0	5.90	—	—	20.0	6.54	—	—
—30.0	6.52	—	—	30.0	7.08	—	—
—20.0	7.15	—	—	30.1	7.09	7.05[12]	0.4
—10.0	7.74	—	—	40.0	7.61	—	—
0.0	8.36	8.23[15]	1.6	50.0	8.16	—	—
10.0	9.01	—	—	60.0	8.73	—	—
20.0	9.64	—	—	70.0	9.24	—	—
30.0	10.25	—	—	80.0	9.78	—	—
38.3	10.74	10.22[16]	4.7	90.0	10.32	—	—

Table—*Continued*

$t,°C$	$D . 10^2$, cm²/sec		Deviation, %	$t,°C$	$D . 10^2$, cm²/sec		Deviation, %
	cal	exp			cal	exp	
100.0	10.83	—	—	**28. Methylcyclohexane-oxygen**			
110.0	11.31	—	—				
120.0	11.86	—	—	—60.0	3.55	—	—
124.7	12.10	—	—	—50.0	4.06	—	—
				—40.0	4.60	—	—
26. Isoctane-oxygen				—30.0	5.14	—	—
				—20.0	5.66	—	—
—60.0	3.01	—	—	—10.0	6.22	—	—
—50.0	3.46	—	—	0.0	6.73	—	—
—40.0	3.90	—	—	10.0	7.21	—	—
—30.0	4.37	—	—	14.0	7.42	7.42[12]	0.0
—20.0	4.80	—	—	20.0	7.74	—	—
—10.0	5.23	—	—	30.0	8.31	—	—
0.0	5.71	—	—	40.0	8.86	—	—
10.0	6.15	—	—	50.0	9.41	—	—
20.0	6.64	—	—	60.0	9.93	—	—
30.0	7.02	—	—	70.0	10.45	—	—
30.1	7.03	6.88[13]	2.1	80.0	10.96	—	—
40.0	7.48	—	—	90.0	11.45	—	—
50.0	7.99	—	—	100.0	11.96	—	—
60.0	8.44	—	—	100.9	12.02	—	—
70.0	8.88	—	—				
80.0	9.31	—	—	**29. Ethanol-hydrogen**			
90.0	9.73	—	—				
99.2	10.10	—	—	—60.0	19.75	—	—
				—50.0	20.03	—	—
27. Cyclohexane-oxygen				—40.0	23.60	—	—
				—30.0	27.20	—	—
—60.0	3.70	—	—	—20.0	30.50	—	—
—50.0	4.19	—	—	—10.0	33.90	—	—
—40.0	4.68	—	—	0.0	37.60	37.53[10]	0.2
—30.0	5.18	—	—	0.0	37.60	38.06[4]	—1.2
—20.0	5.68	—	—	0.0	37.60	37.70[17]	—0.2
—10.0	6.15	—	—	10.0	40.16	—	—
0.0	6.63	—	—	20.0	44.10	—	—
10.0	7.18	—	—	30.0	47.50	—	—
15.0	7.40	7.44[12]	—0.5	40.0	50.95	—	—
20.0	7.61	—	—	40.4	51.02	50.30[4]	1.2
30.0	8.10	—	—	49.4	54.48	54.10[4]	0.7
40.0	8.63	—	—	50.0	54.65	—	—
50.0	9.09	—	—	60.0	58.22	57.50*	1.3
60.0	9.55	—	—	66.9	60.90	54.30[4]	10.7
70.0	10.07	—	—	67.0	60.18	58.60[17]	2.7
80.0	10.56	—	—	70.0	60.95	61.50*	—1.0
81.4	10.65	—	—	78.4	64.33	63.06*	1.9

Table—*Continued*

$t,^\circ C$	$D \cdot 10^2$, cm²/sec cal	exp	Deviation, %	$t,^\circ C$	$D \cdot 10^2$, cm²/sec cal	exp	Deviation, %
	30. Methanol-hydrogen			−50.0	27.39	—	—
				−40.0	31.10	—	—
−60.0	22.15	—	—	−30.0	34.83	—	—
−50.0	29.30	—	—	−20.0	38.58	—	—
−40.0	33.52	—	—	−10.0	42.30	—	—
−30.0	37.63	—	—	0.0	46.32	—	—
−20.0	41.72	—	—	10.0	50.00	—	—
−10.0	45.90	—	—	20.0	53.27	—	—
0.0	50.33	50.59[10]	−0.5	28.0	56.94	57.10[13]	−0.3
0.0	50.33	50.00[4]	0.7	30.0	57.65	—	—
10.0	54.02	—	—	40.0	60.44	—	—
20.0	57.86	—	—	50.0	64.27	—	—
25.6	60.55	60.15[4]	0.6	60.0	68.44	—	—
30.0	62.29	—	—	70.0	72.87	—	—
40.0	66.56	—	—	80.0	76.60	—	—
50.0	71.09	—	—	90.0	80.28	—	—
60.0	75.04	—	—	100.0	83.88	—	—
64.6	77.26	—	—	110.0	87.35	—	—
				110.6	87.60	—	—
	31. Benzene-hydrogen						
−60.0	16.09	—	—		**33. n-Hexane-hydrogen**		
−50.0	18.30	—	—				
−40.0	20.50	—	—	−60.0	14.50	—	—
−30.0	22.70	—	—	−50.0	16.35	—	—
−20.0	24.51	—	—	−40.0	18.30	—	—
−10.0	27.22	—	—	−30.0	20.29	—	—
0.0	29.46	29.48[5]	−0.1	−20.0	22.28	—	—
0.0	29.46	29.40[4]	0.2	−10.0	24.15	—	—
0.0	29.46	31.77[4]	−7.5	0.0	25.97	—	—
10.0	31.61	—	—	10.0	27.95	—	—
19.9	33.73	34.06[4]	−1.0	15.6	29.19	29.00[12]	0.3
20.0	33.73	—	—	15.7	29.20	28.80[12]	1.3
30.0	36.06	—	—	20.0	30.08	—	—
38.3	37.95	40.36[16]	−6.1	30.0	32.21	—	—
40.0	38.37	—	—	40.0	34.08	—	—
45.0	39.61	39.93[4]	−0.8	50.0	35.92	—	—
50.0	40.77	—	—	60.0	37.70	—	—
60.0	42.80	—	—	68.7	39.40	—	—
70.0	44.83	—	—				
80.0	47.12	—	—		**34. n-Heptane-hydrogen**		
80.2	47.20	—	—				
	32. Toluene-hydrogen			−60.0	11.20	—	—
				−50.0	13.10	—	—
−60.0	23.57	—	—	−40.0	15.52	—	—

Table—*Continued*

$t,°C$	$D \cdot 10^2$, cm²/sec cal	exp	Deviation, %	$t,°C$	$D \cdot 10^2$, cm²/sec cal	exp	Deviation, %
—30.0	16.80	—	—	—40.0	16.70	—	—
—20.0	18.73	—	—	—30.0	18.54	—	—
—10.0	20.07	—	—	—20.0	20.45	—	—
0.0	22.57	—	—	—10.0	22.30	—	—
10.0	24.33	—	—	0.0	24.16	—	—
20.0	26.30	—	—	10.0	25.95	—	—
30.0	28.18	28.60[14]	—1.5	20.0	27.88	—	—
30.1	28.20	28.30[13]	—0.3	30.0	29.70	28.80[13]	3.1
40.0	30.08	—	—	30.0	29.70	29.20[12]	1.6
50.0	32.16	—	—	30.1	29.72	29.20[13]	1.6
60.0	34.01	—	—	40.0	31.62	—	—
70.0	35.74	—	—	50.0	33.50	—	—
80.0	37.61	—	—	60.0	35.37	—	—
90.0	39.38	—	—	70.0	37.16	—	—
98.4	41.00	—	—	80.0	39.03	—	—
				90.0	40.89	—	—
				99.2	42.67	—	—

35. n-Octane-hydrogen

37. Cyclohexane-hydrogen

$t,°C$	cal	exp	%	$t,°C$	cal	exp	%
—60.0	9.30	—	—				
—50.0	11.34	—	—	—60.0	15.80	—	—
—40.0	13.35	—	—	—50.0	17.95	—	—
—30.0	15.30	—	—	—40.0	20.12	—	—
—20.0	17.30	—	—	—30.0	22.27	—	—
—10.0	19.38	—	—	—20.0	24.59	—	—
0.0	21.40	—	—	—10.0	26.71	—	—
10.0	23.40	—	—	0.0	28.61	—	—
20.0	25.45	—	—	10.0	30.86	—	—
29.7	27.38	27.10[12]	1.0	15.5	31.93	31.90[12, 16]	0.1
30.0	27.47	—	—	20.0	33.04	—	—
30.2	27.50	27.70[12,13]	—0.7	30.0	35.18	—	—
40.0	29.08	—	—	40.0	37.31	—	—
50.0	31.00	—	—	50.0	39.52	—	—
60.0	33.50	—	—	60.0	41.64	—	—
70.0	35.55	—	—	70.0	43.75	—	—
80.0	37.50	—	—	80.0	45.91	—	—
90.0	39.45	—	—	80.7	46.10	—	—
100.0	41.50	—	—				
110.0	43.63	—	—				
120.0	45.48	—	—	38. Methylcyclohexane-hydrogen			
125.7	46.70	—	—				
				—60.0	15.80	—	—
36. Isoctane-hydrogen				—50.0	17.95	—	—
				—40.0	20.12	—	—
—60.0	12.88	—	—	—30.0	22.27	—	—
—50.0	14.80	—	—				

Table—*Continued*

$t,°C$	$D \cdot 10^2$, cm²/sec cal	exp	Deviation, %	$t,°C$	$D \cdot 10^2$, cm²/sec cal	exp	Deviation, %
—20.0	24.45	—	—	—20.0	22.75	—	—
—10.0	26.72	—	—	—10.0	25.02	—	—
0.0	28.89	—	—	0.0	27.30	27.30[4]	0.0
10.0	30.77	—	—	10.0	29.66	—	—
15.0	31.93	31.80[12]	0.2	20.0	32.95	—	—
20.0	32.94	—	—	30.0	34.18	—	—
30.0	35.01	—	—	40.0	36.45	—	—
40.0	37.23	—	—	50.0	38.78	—	—
50.0	39.45	—	—	60.0	41.07	—	—
60.0	41.60	—	—	70.0	43.19	—	—
70.0	43.76	—	—	77.1	44.90	—	—
80.0	45.89	—	—				
90.0	48.05	—	—				

41. Carbon disulfide-hydrogen

$t,°C$	cal	exp	Deviation, %
100.0	50.15	—	—
100.4	50.25	—	—

39. Acetic acid-hydrogen

$t,°C$	cal	exp	Deviation, %	$t,°C$	cal	exp	Deviation, %
				—60.0	23.06	—	—
				—50.0	25.35	—	—
—60.0	21.00	—	—	—40.0	27.53	—	—
—50.0	24.45	—	—	—30.0	29.76	—	—
—40.0	28.01	—	—	—20.0	32.20	—	—
—30.0	31.46	—	—	—10.0	34.59	—	—
—20.0	34.95	—	—	0.0	36.28	36.89[4]	—1.8
—10.0	38.44	—	—	10.0	38.52	—	—
0.0	41.96	41.63[4]	1.0	20.0	41.20	42.55[4]	—3.2
10.0	45.45	—	—	30.0	43.29	—	—
20.0	49.03	—	—	32.8	43.80	46.26[4]	—5.8
30.0	52.61	—	—	40.0	45.27	—	—
40.0	56.16	—	—	46.2	46.85	—	—
50.0	59.65	—	—				
60.0	63.14	—	—				

42. Water-hydrogen

$t,°C$	cal	exp	Deviation, %	$t,°C$	cal	exp	Deviation, %
70.0	66.64	—	—				
80.0	70.10	—	—	—60.0	43.70	—	—
90.0	73.64	—	—	—50.0	49.00	—	—
100.0	77.10	—	—	—40.0	54.10	—	—
110.0	80.63	—	—	—30.0	59.42	—	—
117.9	83.40	—	—	—20.0	64.65	—	—
				—10.0	69.89	—	—

40. Ethyl acetate-hydrogen

$t,°C$	cal	exp	Deviation, %	$t,°C$	cal	exp	Deviation, %
				0.0	75.16	75.16[4]	0.0
				10.0	80.10	—	—
				20.0	85.37	—	—
				30.0	90.25	—	—
—60.0	13.73	—	—	40.0	95.26	—	—
—50.0	15.97	—	—	49.5	100.74	100.00[4]	0.7
—40.0	18.22	—	—	50.0	101.04	—	—
—30.0	20.46	—	—	60.0	107.03	—	—

Table—*Continued*

t,°C	$D \cdot 10^2$, cm²/scc cal	exp	Deviation, %	t,°C	$D \cdot 10^2$, cm²/sce cal	exp	Deviation, %
70.0	112.72	—	—	70.0	26.30	—	—
80.0	118.80	—	—	80.0	27.68	—	—
90.0	124.90	—	—	90.0	29.06	—	—
100.0	130.87	—	—	100.0	30.51	—	—
				110.0	31.80	—	—
43. Toluene—16.5% Ar+83.5% H₂				110.6	31.84	—	—
—60.0	11.24	—	—	**45. Toluene—51.4% Ar+48.6% H₂**			
—50.0	13.22	—	—				
—40.0	15.23	—	—	—60.0	6.08	—	—
—30.0	17.23	—	—	—50.0	7.09	—	—
—20.0	19.25	—	—	—40.0	8.10	—	—
—10.0	21.36	—	—	—30.0	9.09	—	—
0.0	23.11	—	—	—20.0	10.09	—	—
10.0	25.20	—	—	—10.0	11.10	—	—
20.0	27.23	—	—	0.0	12.11	—	—
28.0	28.72	28.60[18]	0.4	10.0	13.21	—	—
30.0	29.06	—	—	20.0	14.07	—	—
40.0	31.19	—	—	28.1	14.87	14.80[18]	0.2
50.0	33.20	—	—	30.0	15.03	—	—
60.0	35.18	—	—	40.0	15.96	—	—
70.0	37.20	—	—	50.0	16.91	—	—
80.0	39.12	—	—	60.0	18.02	—	—
90.0	41.00	—	—	70.0	19.24	—	—
100.0	43.13	—	—	80.0	20.22	—	—
110.0	45.12	—	—	90.0	21.18	—	—
110.6	45.25	—	—	100.0	22.15	—	—
				110.0	23.04	—	—
44. Toluene—31% Ar+69% H₂				110.6	23.09	—	—
—60.0	8.22	—	—	**46. Toluene-argon**			
—50.0	9.60	—	—				
—40.0	10.98	—	—	—60.0	3.69	—	—
—30.0	12.37	—	—	—50.0	4.27	—	—
—20.0	13.75	—	—	—40.0	4.84	—	—
—10.0	15.16	—	—	—30.0	5.42	—	—
0.0	16.54	—	—	—20.0	5.98	—	—
10.0	17.92	—	—	—10.0	6.57	—	—
20.0	19.40	—	—	0.0	7.18	—	—
28.0	20.46	20.40[18]	0.3	10.0	7.83	—	—
30.0	20.72	—	—	20.0	8.26	—	—
40.0	22.03	—	—	28.1	8.73	8.70[18]	0.8
50.0	23.51	—	—	30.0	8.85	—	—
60.0	24.86	—	—	40.0	9.42	—	—

Table—*Continued*

t,°C	$D \cdot 10^2$, cm²/sec cal	exp	Deviation, %	t,°C	$D \cdot 10^2$, cm²/sec cal	exp	Deviation, %
50.0	9.98	—	—	50.0	6.88	—	—
60.0	10.62	—	—	60.0	7.35	—	—
70.0	11.33	—	—	70.0	7.76	—	—
80.0	11.91	—	—	80.0	8.21	—	—
90.0	12.49	—	—	90.0	8.66	—	—
100.0	13.04	—	—	100.0	9.10	—	—
110.0	13.54	—	—	110.0	9.56	—	—
110.6	13.60	—	—	120.0	10.00	—	—
				124.7	10.20	—	—

47.   n-Heptane-argon

49.   Isoctane-argon

t,°C	cal	exp	Dev %	t,°C	cal	exp	Dev %
—60.0	2.60	—	—	—60.0	2.56	—	—
—50.0	3.06	—	—	—50.0	2.96	—	—
—40.0	3.51	—	—	—40.0	3.37	—	—
—30.0	3.96	—	—	—30.0	3.78	—	—
—20.0	4.43	—	—	—20.0	4.17	—	—
—10.0	4.90	—	—	—10.0	4.60	—	—
0.0	5.38	—	—	0.0	5.00	—	—
10.0	5.79	—	—	10.0	5.39	—	—
20.0	6.25	—	—	20.0	5.75	—	—
30.0	6.69	—	—	30.0	6.14	6.05[12]	1.5
30.2	6.70	6.58[13]	1.9	30.0	6.14	6.18[12]	—0.6
40.0	7.16	—	—	30.2	6.14	5.99[13]	2.4
50.0	7.68	7.60*	1.1	40.0	6.57	—	—
60.0	8.13	8.05*	1.1	50.0	7.05	—	—
70.0	8.57	8.55*	0.2	60.0	7.43	—	—
80.0	9.00	8.90*	1.1	70.0	7.84	—	—
90.0	9.42	9.30*	1.2	80.0	8.22	—	—
98.4	9.84	9.65*	1.8	90.0	8.56	—	—
				90.2	8.98	—	—

48.   n-Octane-argon

50.   n-Heptane-helium

t,°C	cal	exp	Dev %	t,°C	cal	exp	Dev %
—60.0	1.90	—	—				
—50.0	2.36	—	—	—60.0	10.46	—	—
—40.0	2.80	—	—	—50.0	12.29	—	—
—30.0	3.25	—	—	—40.0	14.16	—	—
—20.0	3.71	—	—	—30.0	16.04	—	—
—10.0	4.15	—	—	—20.0	17.86	—	—
0.0	4.60	—	—	—10.0	19.60	—	—
10.0	5.06	—	—	0.0	21.35	—	—
20.0	5.52	—	—	10.0	23.28	—	—
30.0	5.94	—	—	20.0	24.96	—	—
30.2	5.95	5.87[13]	1.3	30.0	26.75	—	—
40.0	6.39	—	—				

Table—*Continued*

$t,°C$	$D \cdot 10^2$, cm²/sec		Deviation, %	$t,°C$	$D \cdot 10^2$, cm²/sec		Deviation, %
	cal	exp			cal	exp	
30.2	26.80	26.50[13]	—	30.0	25.65	—	—
40.0	28.60	—	0.4	30.2	25.70	25.30[13]	1.5
50.0	30.44	—	—	40.0	27.32	—	—
60.0	32.30	—	—	50.0	28.91	—	—
70.0	34.15	—	—	60.0	30.52	—	—
80.0	35.95	—	—	70.0	32.14	—	—
90.0	37.79	—	—	80.0	33.25	—	—
98.4	39.34	—	—	90.0	35.35	—	—
				99.2	36.83	—	—

51. n-Octane-helium

53. Water-helium

$t,°C$	cal	exp	Deviation, %	$t,°C$	cal	exp	Deviation, %
—60.0	7.67	—	—				
—50.0	9.60	—	—	—60.0	33.48	—	—
—40.0	11.53	—	—	—50.0	39.39	—	—
—30.0	13.44	—	—	—40.0	45.24	—	—
—20.0	15.38	—	—	—30.0	51.13	—	—
—10.0	17.30	—	—	—20.0	57.00	—	—
0.0	19.22	—	—	—10.0	62.88	—	—
10.0	21.12	—	—	0.0	68.70	—	—
20.0	23.05	—	—	10.0	74.42	—	—
30.0	24.94	—	—	20.0	80.49	—	—
30.2	24.99	24.80[13]	0.7	30.0	86.30	—	—
40.0	26.86	—	—	34.0	88.70	90.20[19]	—1.5
50.0	28.29	—	—	40.0	92.11	—	—
60.0	30.70	—	—	50.0	98.10	—	—
70.0	32.63	—	—	55.3	101.10	101.10[19]	0.0
80.0	34.55	—	—	60.0	104.90	—	—
90.0	36.49	—	—	70.0	110.02	—	—
100.0	38.42	—	—	79.3	115.40	112.10[19]	2.8
110.0	40.36	—	—	80.0	116.00	—	—
120.0	42.29	—	—	90.0	121.95	—	—
124.7	43.20	—	—	100.0	127.22	—	—

52. Isoctane-helium

54. n-Heptane-deuterium (heavy hydrogen)

$t,°C$	cal	exp	Deviation	$t,°C$	cal	exp	Deviation
—60.0	11.16	—	—				
—50.0	12.75	—	—	—60.0	8.58	—	—
—40.0	14.39	—	—	—50.0	10.05	—	—
—30.0	15.99	—	—	—40.0	11.54	—	—
—20.0	17.60	—	—	—30.0	13.05	—	—
—10.0	19.18	—	—	—20.0	14.52	—	—
0.0	20.80	—	—	—10.0	16.04	—	—
10.0	22.42	—	—	0.0	17.51	—	—
20.0	24.05	—	—	10.0	19.01	—	—

Table—*Continued*

t,°C	$D \cdot 10^2$, cm²/sec cal	exp	Deviation, %	t,°C	$D \cdot 10^2$, cm²/sec cal	exp	Deviation, %
20.0	20.47	—	—	10.0	18.58	—	—
30.0	21.96	—	—	20.0	19.97	—	—
30.2	22.02	21.80[13]	0.9	30.0	21.35	—	—
40.0	23.52	—	—	30.2	21.40	21.20[13]	1.0
50.0	25.00	—	—	40.0	22.77	—	—
60.0	26.47	—	—	50.0	24.18	—	—
70.0	27.95	—	—	60.0	25.58	—	—
80.0	29.43	—	—	70.0	26.95	—	—
90.0	30.91	—	—	80.0	28.34	—	—
98.4	32.15	—	—	90.0	29.73	—	—
				99.2	31.00	—	—

55. n-Octane-deuterium

57. Ethanol-carbon dioxide

t,°C	cal	exp	Dev.	t,°C	cal	exp	Dev.
—60.0	6.96	—	—				
—50.0	8.52	—	—	—60.0	3.22	—	—
—40.0	10.09	—	—	—50.0	3.81	—	—
—30.0	11.62	—	—	—40.0	4.40	—	—
—20.0	13.20	—	—	—30.0	4.99	—	—
—10.0	14.78	—	—	—20.0	5.57	—	—
0.0	16.37	—	—	—10.0	6.15	—	—
10.0	17.93	—	—	0.0	6.74	6.85[4]	—1.5
20.0	19.51	—	—	10.0	7.34	—	—
30.0	21.06	—	—	20.0	7.92	—	—
30.2	21.09	20.80[13]	1.4	30.0	8.50	—	—
40.0	22.65	—	—	40.0	9.09	—	—
50.0	24.23	—	—	40.4	9.12	8.98[4]	1.8
60.0	25.79	—	—	49.4	9.65	9.86[4]	—2.0
70.0	27.35	—	—	50.0	9.69	—	—
80.0	28.87	—	—	60.0	10.27	—	—
90.0	30.46	—	—	70.0	10.85	—	—
100.0	32.00	—	—	78.4	11.35	—	—
110.0	33.58	—	—				
120.0	35.13	—	—				
124.7	35.81	—	—				

58. Methanol-carbon dioxide

t,°C	cal	exp	Dev.
—60.0	5.29	—	—
—50.0	5.88	—	—
—40.0	6.47	—	—

56. Isoctane-deuterium

t,°C	cal	exp	Dev.	t,°C	cal	exp	Dev.
				—30.0	7.06	—	—
				—20.0	7.65	—	—
—60.0	8.86	—	—	—10.0	8.24	—	—
—50.0	10.28	—	—	0.0	8.84	8.80[4]	0.4
—40.0	11.62	—	—	10.0	9.44	—	—
—30.0	13.00	—	—	20.0	10.03	—	—
—20.0	14.40	—	—	25.6	10.37	10.46[4]	—0.9
—10.0	15.80	—	—				
0.0	17.20	—	—				

Table—*Continued*

$t,°C$	$D \cdot 10^2,$ cm^2/sec cal	exp	Deviation, %	$t,°C$	$D \cdot 10^2,$ cm^2/sec cal	exp	Deviation, %
30.0	10.63	—	—	60.0	10.68	—	—
40.0	11.23	—	—	70.0	11.28	—	—
49.6	11.79	—	—	80.0	11.87	—	—
50.0	11.83	—	—	90.0	12.47	—	—
60.0	12.40	—	—	100.0	13.07	—	—
64.6	12.67	—	—	110.0	13.66	—	—
				117.9	14.13	—	—

59.   Benzene-carbon dioxide

61.   Ethylacetate-carbon dioxide

$t,°C$	cal	exp	Deviation %	$t,°C$	cal	exp	Deviation %
−60.0	2.84	—	—				
−50.0	3.24	—	—	−60.0	2.41	—	—
−40.0	3.63	—	—	−50.0	2.82	—	—
−30.0	4.03	—	—	−40.0	3.22	—	—
−20.0	4.42	—	—	−30.0	3.63	—	—
−10.0	4.82	—	—	−20.0	4.03	—	—
0.0	5.22	5.27[4]	−1.0	−10.0	4.43	—	—
10.0	5.61	—	—	0.0	4.83	4.87[4]	−1.1
20.0	6.01	6.09[4]	−1.4	10.0	5.25	—	—
30.0	6.41	—	—	20.0	5.64	—	—
40.0	6.81	—	—	30.0	6.06	—	—
45.0	7.00	7.15[4]	−2.0	40.0	6.47	—	—
50.0	7.20	—	—	50.0	6.86	—	—
60.0	7.59	—	—	60.0	7.27	—	—
70.0	7.99	—	—	70.0	7.64	—	—
80.0	8.39	—	—	77.1	7.97	—	—
80.1	8.40	—	—				

60.   Acetic acid-carbon dioxide

62.   Carbon disulfide-carbon dioxide

$t,°C$	cal	exp	Deviation %	$t,°C$	cal	exp	Deviation %
−60.0	3.53	—	—	−60.0	4.32	—	—
−50.0	4.12	—	—	−50.0	4.65	—	—
−40.0	4.71	—	—	−40.0	4.98	—	—
−30.0	5.31	—	—	−30.0	5.31	—	—
−20.0	5.90	—	—	−20.0	5.63	—	—
−10.0	6.49	—	—	−10.0	5.96	—	—
0.0	7.10	7.16[4]	−0.8	0.0	6.29	6.30[4]	−0.2
10.0	7.69	—	—	10.0	6.61	—	—
20.0	8.30	—	—	20.0	6.94	—	—
30.0	8.90	—	—	30.0	7.27	—	—
40.0	9.50	—	—	40.0	7.58	—	—
50.0	10.09	—	—	46.2	7.93	—	—

*The values of diffusion coefficients marked with asterisks (*) have been obtained by interpolation of experimental results of [4-7, 10, 13, 20].

REFERENCES

1. USMANOV, A. G. and A. N. BEREZHNOI. *ZhFKh,* **34**, 908, 1960.
2. USMANOV, A. G. and A. N. BEREZHNOI. *ZhFKh,* **37**, 179, 1963.
3. BEREZHNOI, A. N. and A. G. USMANOV. *Trudy Kazanskovo Khim. Tekhn. Instituta.* **35**, 201, 1965.
4. WINKELMANN, A. *Ann. Physik,* **22**, 1, 1884; **22**, 152, 1884; **22**, 201, 1884; **23**, 203, 1884; **26**, 105, 1885; **32**, 445, 1888; **36**, 931, 1889.
5. LE BLANC, M. and G. WUPPERMANN. *Z. phys. Chem.,* **91**, 143, 1916.
6. IRISOV, A. S. *Isparyaemost' topliv dlya porshnevikh dvigatelei i metodi eyo issledovaniya.* GTTI, 1955.
7. MACK, E. *J. Am. Chem. Soc.,* **47** (10), 2468, 1925.
8. GILLILAND, E. K. *Ind. and Eng. Chem.,* **26**, 681, 1934.
9. GORYUNOVA, N. A. and E. V. KUVSHINSKY. *ZhTF,* **28**, 1421, 1948.
10. STEFAN, J. *Sitzüngsber. Akad. Wiss. Wien,* Abt. 2, **63**, 63, 1871, **65**, 323, 1872; **68**, 385, 1873; **83**, 943, 1881; **98**, 1418, 1889; *Ann. Physik,* **17**, 550, 1882; **41**, 725, 1890.
11. *Tekhnicheskaya entsiklopediya. Spravochnik fizicheskikh i tekhnologicheskikh velichin (Technical encyclopedia. Handbook of physical and technological quantities),* Vol. **7**. OGIZ, 1931.
12. CUMMINGS, G. A. and A. R. UBBELOHDE. *J. Chem. Soc.,* (12), 3751, 1953; (7), 2524, 1955.
13. CLARKE, J. K. and A. R. UBBELOHDE. *J. Chem. Soc.,* (5), 2050, 1957.
14. CUMMINGS, G. A., E. MCLAUGHLIN and A. R. UBBELOHOLE. *J. Chem. Soc.,* (4), 1141, 1955.
15. BOSE, N. K. and R. N. CHAKRABORTY *Trans. Ind. Inst. Chem. Eng.,* **8**, 67, 1955.
16. HUDSON, G. H., J. C. MCCOUBREY and A. R. UBBELOHDE. *Trans. Farad. Soc.,* **56** (8), 1144, 1960.
17. TRAUTZ, M. and W. MÜLLER, *Ann. Physik,* **22**, 333, 1935.
18. FAIRBANKS, D. F. and C. R. WILKE. *Ind. and Eng. Chem.,* **42**, 471, 1950.
19. SCHWERTZ, F. A. and J. E. BROW. *J. Chem. Phys.,* **19**, 640, 1951.
20. GVERDTSITELLI, I. G., A. G. KARAMYANN and N. E. MENABDE. *Soobsheniya AN Gruz. SSR,* **26** (4), 409, 1961.
21. VARGAFTIK, N. B. *Spravochnik no teplofizicheskim svoistvam gazov i zhidkostei (Handbook of thermophysical properties of gases and liquids).* Fizmatgiz, Moscow, 1963.

UDC 541.11

MEASUREMENT OF THE MOLAL VOLUMES OF GASEOUS MIXTURES AT HIGH PRESSURES

D. S. Tsiklis, L. R. Linshits and *I. B. Rodkina*

The objective of the present work is measurement of the molal volumes of technologically important gaseous mixtures at high pressures by Barnett's method [1]. We shall describe the operational principle of this method in description of the experimental apparatus, which is schematically displayed in Fig. 1.

As shown in Fig. 1, the high-pressure containers (7, 8) are placed in a thermostat (3) and are connected by a constant-volume valve (6). An electromagnetic mixer is placed inside the container (7), enabling preparation of gaseous mixtures.

The inlet and outlet gas pipes and the pipe line leading to the pressure-measuring system are connected to the cap of the container (7). The pressure-measuring system consists of a membrane-type zero instrument (5), piston-type manometer (1), hydraulic press (15) and tube manometer (2). The cap of the container (8) is connected by a soldered Kovar glass joint to the volumetric unit of the apparatus which consists of calibrated bulbs (12) of different volumes, mercury pump (11) and mercury manometer (13).

Containers (7, 8), having volumes of 200 and 60 cm^3 respectively, are constructed of nonmagnetic steel EI437B. The construction of container (7) is shown in Fig. 2. The containers are closed by seals with gaskets containing noncompensated area of the first type [2]. The mandrel of the electromagnetic mixer rotates inside the cap of container (7) while its solinoid is wound on the cap. The gas is compressed to the required experimental pressure by a mercury pressure adjusting device (Fig. 1, 14).

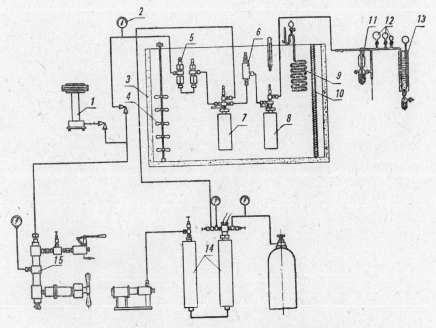

Fig. 1. Schematic arrangement of the experimental apparatus for determination of the molal volumes of gases.

The gas pressure in the apparatus is measured by the piston manometer MP-600 with class 0.05 accuracy. Since the piston manometer system is filled with castor oil, to separate gas and oil we utilized a mercury-membrane zero instrument (see Fig. 3).

Between the surfaces of the small table (6) and the nipple (4) is pressed a stainless steel membrane (5) of 0.1 mm thickness, and holes of 0.4 mm diameter are drilled in both the table (6) and the nipple (4). These components form the two surfaces supporting the membrane, protecting it from rupture even when the limiting "pressure drops" of the order of several hundred atmospheres are created on one side of the membrane.

Mercury is poured over the membrane and inside the channel in the nipple. When the membrane is displaced, the mercury level in the channel changes, causing either formation or rupture of the electrical connection between the mercury and the platinum contact (3), which is registered by an instrument. The platinum contact (3) is introduced into the zero instrument through an insulated body (2) and stuffing box (1). A pyrophyllite sleeve is adjusted on the body (2); this is glued in the tapered hole by epoxy-resin. Such an electrical lead can endure high temperature. In addition to separating oil from gas, the zero instrument enables determination of pressure balance on the two sides of the membrane. The

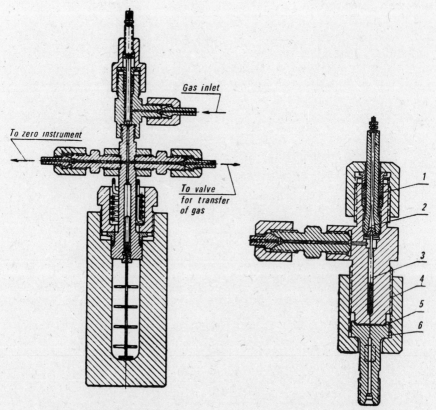

Fig. 2.   Construction of high
pressure container.

Fig. 3.   Construction of membrane-
type zero instrument.

sensitivity of the membrane is such that with a disbalance of 0.02 atmospheres, neither formation nor rupture of the electrical contact occurs.

The thermostat is constructed of stainless steel and is thermally insulated by a layer of perlite sand.   Two blade stirrers (4) are positioned and a starting heater is located inside the thermostat (see Fig. 1).   The thermostat is also adjusted with separate heaters for rough and fine setting of temperature (not shown in Fig. 1).   Fine control of temperature is achieved by a thermoregulator (Fig. 1, 9) filled with olive oil.   The temperature is measured by a mercury thermometer with a minimum count of 0.1 deg.

Our experimental procedure was as follows.   The gas under investigation was fed at the required pressure to the container (7).   After a steady temperature had been established, the gas pressure was measured by the piston manometer.   Following this, the valve (6) was opened and the gas from container (7) was released into the container (8) slowly, preventing temperature fluctuation during the throttling of the gas.   The valve (6) was then closed and gas from the container was released into the atmosphere. The container (8) was again evacuated and the gas-transfer procedure was repeated. These gas-release operations (from container 7) were performed as long as it was possible to measure the pressure accurately.

In one of the randomly selected operations of transferring gas from container (7) to container (8), the gas from container (8) was transferred to the volumetric unit of the apparatus where its quantity was measured, enabling calculation of molal volumes of the gas at all measured pressures in the following manner.

Denoting the ratio of the total volume of both containers (7, 8) to the volume of container (7) by N,

$$N = \frac{V_1 + V_2}{V_1}. \tag{1}$$

The number of moles of the gas in container (7) at maximum pressure during the experiment is denoted by n_0, and the number of moles of the residual gas in container (7) following the first, second,......, and mth transfer will be given respectively by

$$n_0\left(\frac{1}{N}\right), \quad n_0\left(\frac{1}{N}\right)^2, \ldots\ldots\ldots, n_0\left(\frac{1}{N}\right)^m. \tag{2}$$

Hence the number of moles of the residual gas in container (7) following any given transfer of gases can be expressed in terms of n_0, and the number of moles of the gas transferred from container (8) (denoted by n_2) into the volumetric unit of the apparatus can be expressed (after the first transfer) as follows :

$$n_2 = n_0 - n_0\left(\frac{1}{N}\right). \tag{3}$$

Following the mth gas transfer, it can easily be shown that

$$n_2 = n_0\left(\frac{1}{N^{m-1}} - \frac{1}{N^m}\right). \tag{4}$$

If the value of N is known, from equation (4) n_0 can be determined, as well as the number of moles of the gas in container (7) following any known number of transfers. Thus, if the volume of container (7) is known, it would be possible to calculate the magnitude of the molal volume of the gas at each experimentally measured pressure.

The value of the constant N was determined by graphically plotting the ratio of the pressure prior to the gas transfer against that following the gas transfer as a function of the pressure proper. The segment intercepted by the straight line (in cases of hydrogen and helium) on the ordinate numerically equals the value of the constant [3]. In our experimentation, helium was used for the determination of the constant.

The volume of container (7) was determined by its calibration with respect to nitrogen, whose molal volumes are accurately known [4].

The variation in volume of container (7) with pressure was calculated by the following equation [5] :

$$\triangle V = \frac{V_1 P}{E(r_2^2 - r_1^2)} [3(1-2\mu)r_1^2 + 2(1+\mu)r_2^2], \qquad (5)$$

where $\triangle V$ is the change in the volume of the container; V_1 is the volume of the container at atmospheric pressure; r_1 and r_2 are the internal and external radii of the container; E is Young's modulus for the container material; and μ is Poisson's coefficient.

Under a pressure of 600 atm, the change in the volume of the container was 0.1%.

The change in the volume of the container due to heating was calculated from the well-known expression

$$V_t = V_0 (1 + \beta t), \qquad (6)$$

where V_0 is the initial volume of the container; V_t is the volume at the given temperature; β is the volumetric coefficient of thermal expansion for the steel EI437B, equal to 3.81×10^{-5} deg^{-1}; and t is the temperature in °C.

As a check on the accuracy of the method of our investigation, molal volumes of nitrogen were measured at 320°K. The deviation of the results obtained from those available in the literature [4] averaged only 0.2%.

The relative error in the determination of molal volume, calculated by the law of distribution of errors [6], is 0.3%. Considering the possibility of averaging the data, this error could be further reduced.

On the experimental apparatus described above we measured the molal volumes of a nitrogen-hydrogen mixture (1 : 3) containing 5.2 moles of methane and 9.2 moles of argon at respective temperatures of 50, 100 and 150°C and at different pressures upto 560 atm. The nitrogen-hydrogen mixture was obtained by decomposition of ammonia over ferrous catalyzers at 600°C. The products of decomposition were subjected to purification from ammonia, hydrogen sulfide and moisture. The methane contained 1% nitrogen. Argon contained oxygen as impurity (0.005%). These data coincide within permissible experimental error limits with the data obtained for a pure nitrogen-hydrogen mixture [7, 8].

Molal volumes were determined for the nitrogen-hydrogen mixture containing 5-60 mole % ammonia at respective temperatures of 75, 100, 150, 200 and 250°C and under pressures of 400-600 atm. Since the experimental apparatus is designed solely for investigation of homogeneous gas systems, we calculated the composition of the mixture with respect to temperature and pressure in order to ensure a homogeneous mixture in each case. The experimental results are presented in the table below and in Figs. 4-8. The table presents the values of molal volumes of the mixtures under study, as obtained by interpolation from the diagrams having coordinates pV-p and pV-N in terms of integer pressures and compositions.

Molal volumes of nitrogen-hydrogen-methane-argon mixture containing different amounts of ammonia, cm³

p, atm	Molal volume (cm³) for NH_3 contents of, mole %							
	5	10	15	20	30	40	50	60
100	298.1	293.8	289.3	284.2	—	—	—	—
200	156.2	153.0	149.1	144.9	—	—	—	—
300	109.6	107.1	103.9	100.2	—	—	—	—
400	86.8	84.6	81.8	78.8	—	—	—	—
500	73.0	71.5	69.3	66.6	—	—	—	—
600	—	—	—	—	—	—	—	—

$$t = 100°C$$

100	318.7	316.5	314.2	311.6	—	—	—	—
200	166.6	164.7	162.5	159.2	—	—	—	—
300	116.6	115.0	112.9	109.7	—	—	—	—
400	91.8	90.6	88.8	86.0	—	—	—	—
500	77.2	76.0	74.5	72.2	—	—	—	—
600	—	—	—	—	—	—	—	—

$$t = 150°C$$

100	358.4	357.2	355.1	352.2	345.5	335.0	320.0	302.5
200	186.6	185.8	184.0	181.5	175.0	166.2	154.2	142.0
300	130.3	129.3	127.6	125.6	119.7	112.3	102.5	92.8
400	102.8	101.6	100.0	98.0	93.1	87.2	79.1	70.9
500	86.4	85.0	83.5	81.7	77.6	72.8	66.3	59.1
600	76.2	74.6	73.0	71.3	67.5	63.1	58.0	52.0

Table—*Continued*

p, atm	Molal volume (cm³) for NH₃ contents of, mole %							
	5	10	15	20	30	40	50	60
				$t=200°C$					
100	401.9	399.1	396.3	393.5	388.2	382.0	370.7	358.5
200	209.4	207.4	205.4	203.4	198.7	192.7	184.4	173.6
300	145.7	144.0	142.4	140.6	136.4	130.9	123.6	114.7
400	113.8	112.5	111.1	109.6	106.2	102.0	95.7	86.8
500	95.0	93.6	92.3	91.0	88.3	85.2	79.7	71.2
600	82.3	81.8	80.0	78.7	76.4	73.0	68.5	61.6
				$t=250°C$					
100	439.0	438.0	436.2	434.0	427.0	—	—	—
200	228.5	227.7	227.0	226.0	222.2	—	—	—
300	158.7	158.0	157.0	155.5	153.0	—	—	—
400	123.5	123.2	122.5	121.0	116.0	—	—	—
500	103.0	102.5	101.5	100.0	96.0	—	—	—

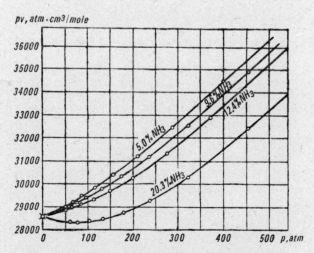

Fig. 4. Relationship between values of pv and p for the
mixture with ammonia at 75°C.

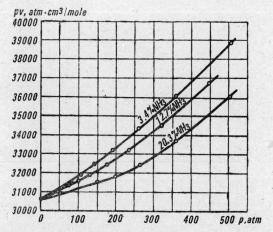

Fig. 5. Relationship between values of pv and p for the mixture with ammonia at 100°C.

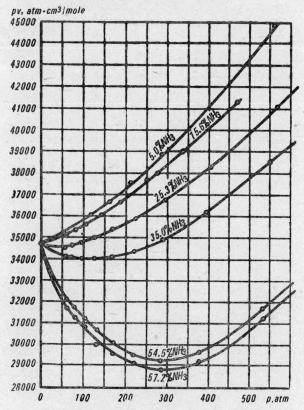

Fig. 6. Relationship between values of pv and p for the mixture with ammonia at 150°C.

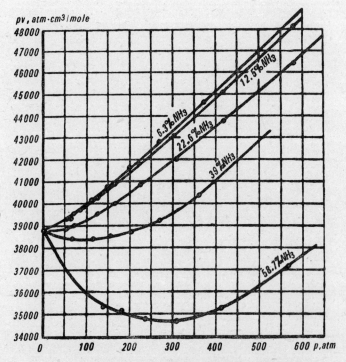

Fig. 7. Relationship between the values of *pv* and *p* for the mixture with ammonia at 200°C.

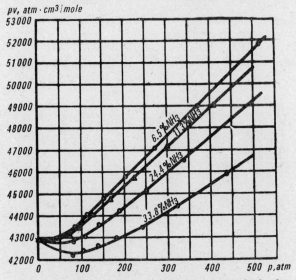

Fig. 8. Relationship between the values of *pv* and *p* for the mixture with ammonia at 250°C.

The maximum contribution to the error in the measurement of molal volume of a gas is due to the error in volume measurements. With the apparatus described above, the molal volumes of a gas can be measured without requiring determination of the actual volume of the container (7) and without any transfer of gas to the volumetric system. For this purpose it is necessary to measure the pressures during the transfer of the gas upto the atmospheric pressure.

Representing the equation of state (as suggested by I. R. Krichevsky) with the second virial coefficient, in terms of notations adopted earlier,

$$P_m \mathcal{N}^m = \frac{n_0 R T}{V_1} + \frac{n_0^2}{V_1^2} \cdot \frac{R T B(T)}{\mathcal{N}^m}, \tag{7}$$

If the experimental results are plotted in a graph possessing coordinates $P_m \mathcal{N}^m$ and $1/\mathcal{N}^m$, the points must lie on a straight line intersecting the ordinate in a segment equal to $n_0 R T/V_1$, where the value of V_1/n_0 would represent the molal volume of the gas at the maximum pressure attained during the experiment and $V_1/n_0 \left(\dfrac{1}{\mathcal{N}} \right)^m$ would represent the molal volume of the gas at the pressure of the mth transfer. The accuracy of the data thus obtained would completely depend upon the accuracy of measurements of pressure near the atmospheric pressure. This method also enables determination of the second virial coefficient.

REFERENCES

1. BARNETT, E. S. *J. Appl. Mech.*, **3** (4), A-136, 1936.
2. TSIKLIS, D. S. *Tekhnika fiziko-khimicheskikh issledovanii pri vysokikh devleniyakh* (*Technology of physicochemical investigations at high pressures*). Khimiya, Moscow, 1965.
3. TSIKLIS, D. S., L. R. LINSHITS and I. B. RODKINA. *ZhFKh*, **40**, 2823, 1966.
4. DIN, F. *Thermodynamic Functions of Gases*, 3, 149, 1961.
5. BILEVICH, A. V., L. F. VERESHCHAGIN and YA. A. KALASHNIKOV. *PTE*, No. 3, 146, 1961.
6. NALIMOV, V. V. *Primineniye maternaticheskoi statistiki pri analize veshchestv* (*Application of mathematical statistics in the analysis of substances*). Fizmatgiz, Moscow, 1960.
7. BARTLETT, E. P. and H. L. SUPPLES. *J. Am. Chem. Soc.*, **50**, 1275, 1928.
8. MICHELS, A., S. R. DE GROOT and R. I. LUNBEK. *Appl. Sci. Res.*, **A1**, 378, 1949.

UDC 541.11

DENSITY OF AQUEOUS SOLUTIONS OF CERTAIN STRONG ELECTROLYTES UNDER PRESSURES UPTO 1200 BAR

A. L. Seifer, V. N. Razumikhin, N. A. Nevolina and *V. A. Borzunov*

Precise measurement of isothermal compressibility of highly electrolytic solutions is essential for estimating the electrostriction effect and for a clear understanding of the dependence of ion hydration on pressure. In the present work the densities of aqueous solutions of potassium chloride, sodium chloride and ammonium chloride were determined at 20 and 45°C respectively by the method of hydrostatic suspension [1, 2]. These temperatures were selected on the basis of the well-established fact that the skeleton structure of water at 20°C under conditions of low pressure intensively disintegrates if temperature is increased to 45°C.

Measurements were undertaken in the pressure range of 1-1200 bar. The solutions investigated were of concentrations at approximately 0.25, 0.5 and 1.0 mole/liter. Selection of these concentration values was based on the objective of solutions characterized by contact between the nearest hydrated spheres of ions, at 1.0 mole/liter. Such contact is possible, at 0.5 mole/liter, or completely impossible, at 0.25 mole/liter.

For preparation of the solutions under investigation, double-distilled water and chemically pure salts were used. The estimated error in the measured density at the maximum value of pressure during the experiment was two to five units of the fourth decimal place (0.02-0.05%), determined by class 0.5 manometer and by accurately maintaining constant temperatures (0.05-0.1°C).

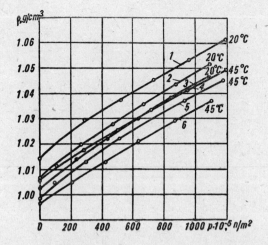

Fig. 1. Isotherms of density of solutions NH_4Cl in water at corresponding temperature and concentration, mole/liter.
1—0.996; *2*—0.517; *3*—0.262; *4*—0.996; *5*—0.517; *6*—0.262.

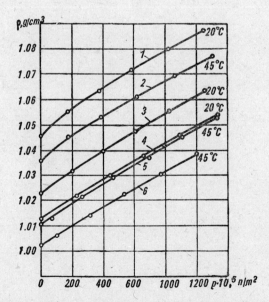

Fig. 2. Isotherms of density of solution of KCl in water at corresponding temperature and concentration, mole/liter.
1—1.037; *2*—1.037; *3*—0.524; *4*—0.264; *5*—0.524; *6*—0.264.

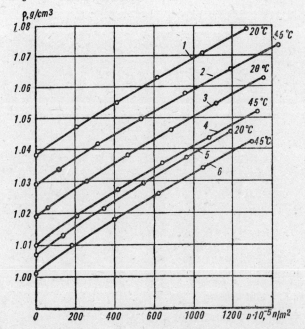

Fig. 3. Isotherms of density of solutions of NaCl in water at the corresponding temperature and concentration, mole/liter.
1—1.006; *2*—1.006; *3*—0.507; *4*—0.507; *5*—0.219; *6*—0.219.

Table 1. Density and relative volume decrements of solutions of NH_4Cl at corresponding temperature, pressure and concentration

Concentration of solution, mole/liter	t, °C	$p \cdot 10^{-5}$, n/m²	ρ, g/cm³	$\triangle v/v$ (1 bar)
		1	1.0145	
		200	1.0247	0.0099
		400	1.0331	0.0180
	20	600	1.0402	0.0247
		800	1.0473	0.0313
		1000	1.0541	0.0375
		1100	1.0573	0.0405
0.996				
		1	1.0064	
		200	1.0142	0.0076
		400	1.0217	0.0149
	45	600	1.0290	0.0219
		800	1.0361	0.0286
		1000	1.0425	0.0345
		1100	1.0457	0.0375

Table 1—*Continued*

Concentration of solution, mole/liter	t, °C	$p \cdot 10^{-5}$, n/m²	ρ, g/cm³	$\triangle\, v/v$ (1 bar)
		1	1.0067	
		200	1.0158	0.0089
		400	1.0243	0.0171
	20	600	1.0326	0.0250
		800	1.0405	0.0324
		1000	1.0478	0.0392
		1100	1.0515	0.0425
0.517				
		1	0.9986	
		200	1.0081	0.0093
		400	1.0171	0.0181
	45	600	1.0252	0.0259
		800	1.0323	0.0326
		1000	1.0391	0.0389
		1100	1.0422	0.0418
		1	1.0025	
		200	1.0117	0.0091
		400	1.0203	0.0174
	20	600	1.0285	0.0252
		800	1.0361	0.0324
		1000	1.0432	0.0390
		1100	1.0467	0.0422
0.262				
		1	0.9946	
		200	1.0045	0.0098
		400	1.0120	0.0171
	45	600	1.0193	0.0242
		800	1.0265	0.0310
		1000	1.0337	0.0378
		1100	1.0366	0.0405

Table 2.   Density and relative volume decrements of solutions of KCl at corresponding temperature, pressure and concentration

Concentration of solution, mole/liter	t, °C	$p \cdot 10^{-5}$ n/m²	ρ, g/cm³	$\Delta v/v$ (1 bar)
		1	1.0460	
		200	1.0570	0.0103
		400	1.0625	0.0180
	20	600	1.0726	0.0247
		800	1.0798	0.0313
		1000	1.0866	0.0373
1.037				
		1	1.0358	
		200	1.0461	0.0097
		400	1.0541	0.0173
	45	600	1.0613	0.0240
		800	1.0681	0.0301
		1000	1.0745	0.0359
		1100	1.0777	0.0388
		1	1.0227	
		200	1.0321	0.0090
	20	400	1.0403	0.0169
		600	1.0480	0.0240
		800	1.0552	0.0307
		1000	1.0623	0.0372
0.524				
		1	1.0129	
		200	1.0208	0.0077
		400	1.0286	0.0152
	45	600	1.0360	0.0222
		800	1.0431	0.0289
		1000	1.0498	0.0351
		1100	1.0532	0.0382

Table 2—*Continued*

Concentration of solution, mole/liter	t, °C	$p \cdot 10^{-5}$, n/m²	ρ, g/cm³	$\triangle v/v$ (1 bar)
		1	1.0106	
		200	1.0191	0.0083
		400	1.0270	0.0174
	20	600	1.0348	0.0234
		800	1.0422	0.0303
		1000	1.0493	0.0369
		1100	1.0526	0.0398
0.264				
		1	1.0024	
		200	1.0098	0.0073
	45	400	1.0175	0.0148
		600	1.0247	0.0217
		800	1.0316	0.0283
		1000	1.0386	0.0346

Table 3. Density and relative volume decrements of solutions of NaCl at corresponding temperature, pressure and concentration

Concentration of solution, mole/liter	t, °C	$p \cdot 10^{-5}$ n/m²	ρ, g/cm³	$\triangle v/v$ (1 bar)
		1	1.0386	
		200	1.0472	0.0082
		400	1.0551	0.0156
	20	600	1.0625	0.0224
		800	1.0695	0.0288
		1000	1.0766	0.0352
		1100	1.0793	0.0377
1.006				
		1	1.0291	
		200	1.0372	0.0078
		400	1.0450	0.0152
	45	600	1.0521	0.0218
		800	1.0591	0.0283
		1000	1.0656	0.0342
		1100	1.0688	0.0372

Table 3—*Continued*

Concentration of solution, mole/liter	t, °C	$p \cdot 10^{-5}$, n/m²	ρ, g/cm³	$\Delta v/v$ (1 bar)
		1	1.0188	
		200	1.0276	0.0085
		400	1.0357	0.0163
	20	600	1.0433	0.0234
		800	1.0506	0.0302
		1000	1.0575	0.0365
		1100	1.0608	0.0396
0.507				
		1	1.0098	
		200	1.0190	0.0089
		400	1.0268	0.0165
	45	600	1.0341	0.0234
		800	1.0410	0.0298
		1000	1.0477	0.0361
		1100	1.0508	0.0390
		1	1.0087	
		200	1.0155	0.0099
	20	400	1.0236	0.0145
		600	1.0312	0.0218
		900	1.0388	0.0290
		1000	1.0460	0.0356
0.219				
		1	1.0011	
		200	1.0098	0.0086
		400	1.0178	0.0164
	45	600	1.0255	0.0237
		800	1.0325	0.0304
		1000	1.0391	0.0365
		1100	1.0423	0.0396

Figs. 1-3 show the isotherms with density-pressure coordinates for the corresponding aqueous solutions, and Tables 1-3 present the values of density and the relative volume decrements,

$$\frac{\Delta v}{v \, (1 \text{ bar})} = 1 - \frac{\rho}{\rho \, (1 \text{ bar})}$$

for rounded values of pressure.

The existing data in the literature on the density of aqueous solutions of ammonium, potassium, and sodium chlorides cover only 9-210 bar pressure; hence, we could not compare our data with those of other authors.

REFERENCES

1. BORZUNOV, V. A. and V. N. RAZUMUKHIN. *Trudy VNIIFTRI,* No. 75, 135, 134, 1964.
2. RAZUMUKHIN, V. N. *Trudy VNIIFTRI,* No. 46, 106, 96, 1960.

UDC 541.11

THERMAL CONDUCTIVITY OF SOME ORIENTED PLASTICS UNDER COMPRESSION AND AT TEMPERATURES OF 180-200°K

R. I. Zhukova, M. G. Kaganer and *N. B. Markelova*

Data on thermal conductivity of anisotropic materials under conditions of compression are essential in thermal design and calculations for insulating elements of load-carrying structures.

The thermal conductivity of certain oriented structural plastics under compressive stresses upto 20-30 mn/m² was determined by the present authors on an apparatus described in reference [1]. At the upper end of the specimen, having a cylindrical shape with a diameter of 20-25 mm, a temperature of 285°K was maintained, and at the lower end it was maintained at 90-92°K. The heat flowing along the specimen was determined by measuring the amount of liquid oxygen evaporated from the chamber (liquid oxygen was used to cool the lower end of the specimen). The specimen was loaded by a suitable lever system.

Experiments were performed under conditions of prolonged, continuous loading, since the thermal conductivity of the specimen in a compressed state increases with time, approaching a certain constant value. This phenomenon is explained by the pliability of the material under investigation. The duration of the experiment at one and the same temperature varied from three to twelve days. Experimental error did not exceed 10%, on an average.

It has been established that compressive stresses of the order of 20 mn/m² will induce increased thermal conductivity by about 50% in the direction perpendicular to the axis of the fibers. However, the thermal conductivity in the direction parallel to the axis of the fibers increases to a lesser extent (by 10-15%). The fact that the coefficient of thermal conductivity increases in the compressed state may be explained by the following factors : (1) decrease in the thermal resistance in the contacts between the fibers of the filler material, due to a decrease in the volume of the bubbles existing in the bounding material, (2) increase in the coefficient of thermal conductivity of the gas and (3) reduction in the thickness of the bounding material.

The experimental data obtained on the thermal conductivity in the direction perpendicular to the fibers for textolite, glass-textolite, and some of the glass plastics of epoxy-resin base are presented in the table below.

Coefficient of thermal conductivity of various materials as a function of specific loads

Material	Process	ρ, kg/m³	Specific load, mn/m²	λ, W/m . deg
Textolite PTK	Loading	1400	1.5	0.18
			4.8	0.21
			9.5	0.23
			15.2	0.24
			20.0	0.26
	Unloading		6.4	0.23
Glass-textolite KAST	Loading	1700	1.9	0.20
			5.7	0.23
			11.4	0.24
			22.9	0.28
Glass-plastic AG-4S, unistressed	Loading	1800	1.2	0.29
			5.1	0.32
			15.9	0.37
			20.4	0.41
High-strength glass-plastic on epoxy-resin base, unidirectional	Loading	1950	1.2	0.18
			9.4	0.23
			12.9	0.25
			14.8	0.26
			15.4	0.26
			23.0	0.26
Glass-plastic SVAM, uniform strength	Loading	2000	9.6	0.19
			18.7	0.25
	Unloading		9.6	0.23
			1.3	0.14

Laminated plastics having the following two compositions were investigated : (1) unidirectional plastics, prepared by compressing the strips containing parallel and unidirectionally oriented fibers, and (2) uniform-strength plastics, prepared by impregnation of cloth or plywood, having a crossed structure. For the two experiments the data obtained on thermal conductivity during unloading from a load corresponding to about 20 mn/m² are given in the table above. The variation in the value of thermal conductivity at the same load during both loading and unloading is explained by the occurrence of residual deformations in the layer of the bonding material.

REFERENCES

1. KAGANER, M. G. and R. I. JHUKOVA. *IFZh,* **11** (3), 1966.